APPLIED POLICE
AND FIRE PHOTOGRAPHY

APPLIED POLICE AND FIRE PHOTOGRAPHY

Second Edition

By

RAYMOND P. SILJANDER

Former Police Officer
Loss Control Specialist

and

DARIN D. FREDRICKSON

Police Officer
Phoenix Police Department
Phoenix, Arizona

With Forewords by

John D. Douthit
Mel Hardy

and

Dennis A. Garrett

CHARLES C THOMAS • PUBLISHER, LTD.
Springfield • Illinois • U.S.A.

Published and Distributed Throughout the World by

CHARLES C THOMAS • PUBLISHER, LTD.
2600 South First Street
Springfield, Illinois 62794-9265

© *1997 by* CHARLES C THOMAS • PUBLISHER, LTD.

ISBN 0-398-06687-6

Library of Congress Catalog Card Number: 96-36244

First Edition, 1976
Second Edition, 1997

With THOMAS BOOKS *careful attention is given to all details of manufacturing
and design. It is the Publisher's desire to present books that are satisfactory as to their
physical qualities and artistic possibilities and appropriate for their particular use.*
THOMAS BOOKS *will be true to those laws of quality that assure a good name
and good will.*

Printed in the United States of America
SC-R-3

Library of Congress Cataloging-in-Publication Data

Siljander, Raymond P.
    Applied police and fire photography / by Raymond P. Siljander and
Darin D. Fredrickson ; with forewords by John D. Douthit, Mel Hardy,
and Dennis A. Garrett. — 2nd ed.
        p.   cm.
    Includes bibliographical references and index.
    ISBN 0-398-06687-6 (cloth : alk. paper)
    1. Legal photography. 2. Criminal investigation. 3. Fire
investigation. I. Fredrickson, Darin D. II. Title.
TR822.S53   1997
363.2'5 — dc20   96-36244
                                                                CIP

*This book is dedicated to
the many police officers and
firemen who have so diligently
served their fellowman.*

FOREWORD TO THE SECOND EDITION

Photography is one of the cornerstones of contemporary police investigation and the technology continues to expand to meet demand. Criminal investigators, forensic scientists, attorneys, and other members of the criminal justice system rely on the accurate representation of specific factors in any investigation. These factors might include the conditions at a crime scene, the analysis and identification of evidence, the observations of a surveillance team, or a simple photo line-up.

Whatever the need, the photographic specialist has an increasing array of technological tools available to record vital information. Today, sophisticated cameras, a variety of film types, computer enhancements, and video techniques are all used in the investigation, reconstruction, and prosecution of criminal acts. The updated information in this revision will benefit everyone involved in this process.

DENNIS A. GARRETT
Chief of Police
Phoenix Police Department
Phoenix, Arizona

FOREWORD TO THE FIRST EDITION

Photography, especially that employed in law enforcement, is very highly diversified in methods, techniques, and the equipment used. Equipment varies from the most simplified and inexpensive to a wide selection of expensive, sophisticated pieces.

The technician is aware of his responsibility to photograph in a true, complete and accurate manner, whether the evidence involves a crime or accident scene, or human remains. A number of persons including the criminalist in the laboratory, the investigator, the prosecuting and defense attorneys and the court will rely on his results.

This text has been prepared to aid the experienced as well as the novice forensic photographer in this endeavor.

JOHN D. DOUTHIT
Identification Officer
Minnesota Department of Public Safety

FOREWORD TO THE FIRST EDITION

Each year there are an enormous number of fires in the United States and throughout the world, resulting in billions of dollars in losses and, more importantly, in an increasing number of injuries and deaths. Most of these fires are of accidental origin, but, in an alarming number, the figures and investigation into the causes show that, in too many cases, the fire was intentional. When this is found to be the case, it is then that the investigator is called upon to determine who set the fire and why, and to continue the investigation to a satisfactory conclusion.

There is no one type of person that commits the crime of arson, and the motives are many. Age is no determining factor, and the reasons or motives are many: hate and revenge, pyromania, fraud for insurance, covering up other crimes, or an arsonist trying to attract attention to himself.

The job of the investigator is not an easy one, and as many have stated, the crime of arson is one of the hardest to prove. For this reason it is necessary that every available tool and agency of science and technology be utilized at some point. Laboratories and photography play an important role in a successful investigation.

Most investigators take photographs at the scene and in many cases someone else may be called in to take photographs in preparation for a court case. In either case, both the photographer and the investigator must have an understanding, not only of photography, but also the reasons for a certain photograph. Nothing can depict the scene as well as a photograph; it is a visual aid for educating a jury. For these reasons it is necessary that the investigator have a knowledge of photography so he will be able to determine what he wants to illustrate and explain later what the photograph does depict. Photographs are permanent records of the scene and are most essential.

Photographs will enable other assisting investigators to better understand the scene as first viewed, many times observing overlooked items that appear on the photographs. Many times the same faces appear among the spectators, such as that of a pyromaniac who enjoys watching his work. The photographs will also serve well in court to illustrate a number of key points and will be of great aid to attorneys as they prepare the case.

Having known the author for some time, having been involved with him on a number of fire situations, and having further examined the manuscript and illustrations of this book, it is apparent to me that this text will prove invaluable as a learning aid and reference book. It should be of great assistance to the novice and the experienced veteran in the fire and arson field whether he be a fireman or an investigator.

MEL HARDY
Assistant State Fire Marshal
Minnesota Department of Public Safety

INTRODUCTION TO THE SECOND EDITION

This Second Edition of APPLIED POLICE AND FIRE PHO-
TOGRAPHY represents a major emendation of an excellent book.
Some old material has been deleted with the addition of a great deal of
new material. Notable changes include a tremendously expanded chapter on surveillance photography with the inclusion of video. A great deal
of new material is provided on photographic film. The chapter on flash
photography is expanded, as is the section on camera types to include
newer features such as automatic exposure control, auto focus, and
automatic film advance. The chapter on identification photography,
although still brief, was expanded and is exciting. It begins with a brief
overview of the history of civil and criminal identification and goes on to
illustrate how the basic format of the traditional identification photo, the
so-called *mug shot*, has remained the same over the years. That is
apparent when comparing a modern identification photograph with the
identification photo taken of the infamous Alphonse Capone in 1929.
The regrettable weakness of identification photography is well illustrated by the startling difference apparent when examining photos of the
same individual taken 22 years apart. Indeed, one does not look like the
other. Some chapters have been combined so that unrelated but relevant
information can be presented each in light of the other, and the order of
some chapters has been changed to improve the sequential flow of
information.

INTRODUCTION TO THE FIRST EDITION

When an offense has been committed, the information and evidence sometimes left behind by the perpetrator can be very delicate and perishable in nature. It is essential, therefore, that the scene be quickly secured and thus protected from damage by unauthorized persons. Similarly, it is of utmost importance that the scene and any information and evidence contained therein be photographed as soon as it is possible or practical. It is also important that the photographing take place prior to a detailed examination of the scene.

When photographing a crime, fire or traffic accident scene, it is not essential that the photographic equipment be expensive or of professional quality. For general field applications, almost any moderately priced camera will usually suffice; however, inferior quality equipment will not accomplish the task. What is important, however, is that the person using the equipment *know it well.* The owner's manual that accompanies the purchase of a new camera should be studied until the person is familiar and proficient in its use. It should not be necessary to dwell upon this point, as it stands to reason that any tool, to be used to its greatest advantage, must be used properly.

The individual concerned with forensic photography should understand that the purpose of evidential photographs is to document an act or a condition, or to clarify some specific point in a matter that is under investigation. Therefore, each photograph has a specific purpose. Generally, in order to ensure thoroughness, a scene is photographed in a somewhat systematic manner. Be sure always to utilize the camera to *document* things rather than attempt to create photographs that offer little more than a pleasing artistic quality. Leave the latter to the press photographers, for the forensic photographer must seek evidence, not a creative work of art.

The investigative photographer will also be called upon to photograph under adverse conditions: in attics and basements, burned buildings, in the rain, snow and cold or at night. All these things, although a bit undesirable on the surface, lend themselves to a general feeling of satisfaction and accomplishment when a day's work has been completed.

On the opposite extreme of field photography are the more specialized photographs which are taken in a laboratory setting. This area of photography ranges from general copy work to some very technical applications involving infrared and ultraviolet materials, photographing minute specimens through a microscope, etc. While these laboratory applications of forensic photography exist under controlled conditions which are generally more desirable than those encountered in the field, they are no more or less important than field photography.

Over a half century ago, Charles C. Scott, in his book, *Photographic Evidence*, made the statement that "Photographic evidence is not treated adequately in law schools; hence, the embryo lawyer rarely is impressed with the importance of photography. The active attorney, however, soon discovers that a knowledge of the principles of photography is necessary for the general practitioner. Indeed, whether he realizes it or not, the modern lawyer would be as handicapped should he be deprived of the use of photographs as evidence as would the physician were he forced to practice without his clinical camera and X-ray apparatus. Photography, therefore, is not merely one of those subjects every lawyer should understand but probably does not; it is an essential medium for the presentation of evidence that all lawyers should master."*

What Scott has stated applies just as strongly to law enforcement and fire personnel, for it is with the evidence compiled by these people, much of it photographic in nature, that the prosecutor will try a case. If the officer or investigator responsible for taking photographs, whether it be at the scene or in the lab, is found to be lacking insofar as photographic knowledge and ability are concerned, it is doubtful that the photographs will serve their intended purpose to the degree they could if taken by someone reasonably knowledgeable in photography. It was stated that an attorney, to be effective, must possess a good understanding of photographic evidence. Police and fire personnel, however, must not only understand photographic evidence, they must be capable of producing it.

This book does not attempt to illustrate how every individual piece of evidence must be photographed, since each case, just as the evidence,

---

*Scott, Charles C., *Photographic Evidence*, Kansas City, Vernon Law Book Company, 1942, p. v.

will differ. This book will, however, provide the reader with the necessary information to make him or her capable of photographing the various types of evidence. The reader will become aware that there are certain photographic techniques that have proven, over a period of time, to be effective when dealing with certain types of evidence. This is not to infer, however, that the methods discussed here are the only methods which will work well. One should always be open to new ideas and techniques if growth in this field is to be realized.

Finally, this book, which deals with investigative photography, discusses techniques which lend themselves to both field and laboratory applications. The reader is carefully led through the basic principles of photography and gradually into the more advanced applications involving the use of such things as infrared and ultraviolet materials, close-up lenses and a number of special accessories. Whether the reader is an amateur with little or no previous photographic experience, an advanced photographer, a policeman or a fireman, this book was written and is intended to serve as a learning tool and a reference manual.

RAYMOND P. SILJANDER

ACKNOWLEDGMENTS TO
THE SECOND EDITION

The authors would like to acknowledge and thank those people who have generously contributed to the second edition of this book. Special thanks is extended to: Lance Juusola, Commercial Photographer, Mound, Minnesota; Kevin De Nomie, Criminalist, Phoenix Police Department; Jack Jordan, Photographer, Phoenix Fire Department; Bill Navarro, Navarro Film Services, Phoenix, Arizona.

R.P.S.
D.D.F.

CONTENTS

APPLIED POLICE AND
FIRE PHOTOGRAPHY

Chapter 1

CAMERAS AND LENSES

How a Camera Works

Certain basic principles are applicable to *all* cameras, whether they are still or motion picture, a $10 box camera or an expensive professional quality view camera.

To better understand how a present-day camera works, it is helpful to examine the functions of a pin-hole camera. Figure 1-1 shows light rays reflecting off of a subject. Notice that the light rays striking any given point will reflect in many directions. Also note that the light rays striking the film are in confusion and will do nothing more than expose the film without producing any kind of image. If, however, the film was to be placed at the rear of a box with a very small hole in the front of the box, the light reflecting from the subject and traveling to the film could be controlled and an image of the subject would result (see Figure 1-2).

The image formed by a pin-hole camera is always in focus and in no way limited by depth of field. It should not be difficult to understand, however, why the necessary exposure time will be very long since the hole size must be very small for a sharp image to result. If the size of the hole were increased in an effort to shorten the exposure time, the sharpness of the image would decrease remarkably because the light being reflected from any given point on the subject would not strike just one fine point on the film, but a larger portion of the film (see Figure 1-3). The only way the size of the hole can be increased to let in more light and yet maintain the sharpness of the image is to place a lens in the opening to control the light.

If one were to take a common magnifying glass and a piece of white paper, position the magnifying glass between a light bulb and the paper, and then vary the distance between the lens and the paper, at some given point an image of the light bulb would appear on the paper (Figure 1-4). The lens is projecting an image of the light bulb onto the paper. If the lens and the piece of paper were enclosed in a light-tight box and then a

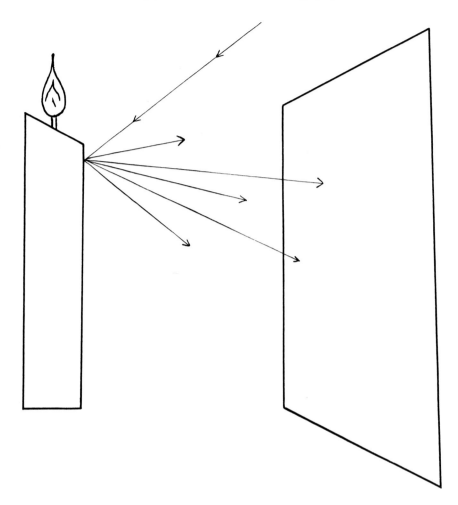

Figure 1-1. Light rays reflecting from any given point upon a subject will reflect in many directions. If no means of controlling the light rays is provided for, they will strike the film in a confusion and do nothing more than fog it without having created any kind of an image of the original subject matter.

piece of photographic film was substituted for the paper, the result would be a simple box camera. The only lack would be a shutter mechanism by which to control the time duration of the light entering the camera.

Based on the above example, observe that a camera is basically a light-tight box which utilizes some means of holding a piece of photographic film in position while a lens projects an image onto the film. The image that is recorded on the film is a latent image, as it is not visible

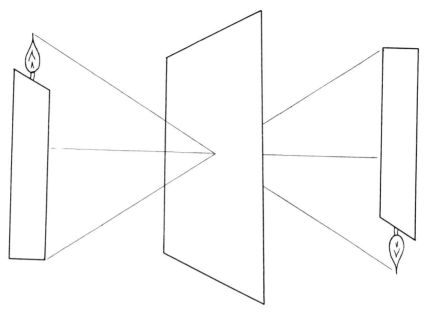

Figure 1-2. If the subject matter and the photographic film are separated by a barrier containing a small hole, the light rays reflecting from the subject will be controlled and produce an image of the subject on the film.

until after it has undergone the necessary chemical process. Again, the only other detail that is necessary in order to make our simple box camera complete is a means of controlling the amount of light that will be permitted to reach and subsequently expose the film in the camera. This is accomplished, as has already been stated, by means of a shutter mechanism. The shutter controls the duration of time that the light is permitted to expose the film, while the size of the lens opening will control how much light may pass during that given period of time.

By further examining Figure 1-4, notice why the image the lens projects is reversed. The image is reversed both left to right and top to bottom. Since this is a phenomenon that always occurs with lenses (Figure 1-5), the image in a camera is always recorded in reverse and upside down. The image, however, is turned around in the printing process so that the final image is the way the original scene was observed and photographed. In short, when an object is photographed, it is reversed in the camera and then righted when the image is projected with a slide projector or an enlarger. The final result is an image that is top side up and correct as far as left and right are concerned.

It has been previously stated that when the film in the camera is

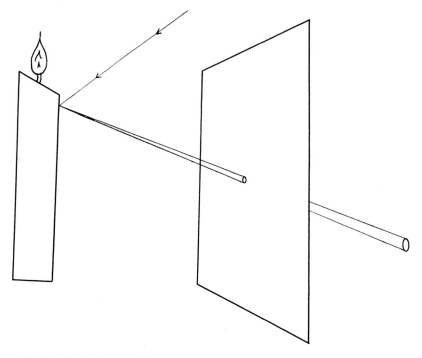

Figure 1-3. If the hole of a pin-hole camera is enlarged to allow a greater passage of light, the sharpness of the resulting image will suffer greatly.

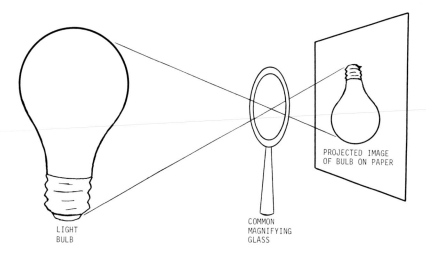

PROJECTED IMAGE
OF BULB ON PAPER

LIGHT
BULB

COMMON
MAGNIFYING
GLASS

Figure 1-4. If a magnifying glass is positioned between a light bulb and a sheet of white paper, and then moved back and forth to achieve proper focus, a reversed image of the light bulb will appear on the paper.

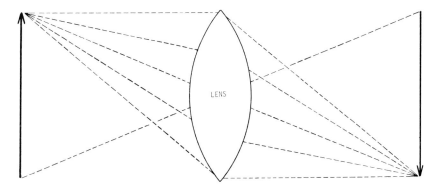

Figure 1-5. This figure illustrates why a lens projects a reversed image.

exposed, the shutter mechanism causes an opening to appear for a predetermined period of time, permitting light to pass through the lens to the film. In addition to the time duration of the lens opening, the amount of light that may pass is also controlled by the size of the opening. Figure 1-6 shows three diaphragm or f/settings. Assuming that the opening of each is for the same time duration, it is not difficult to reason that the largest opening will pass the greatest amount of light, whereas the smallest opening will pass the least amount of light. The opening which lies somewhere between the largest and smallest will naturally pass an amount of light somewhere between that permitted to pass by the other two openings, one larger and one smaller. Try equating this to a window shade that is open only a few inches, then part way and finally all the way.

The size of the lens opening is designated by a number. The number indicates the diameter of the lens opening in relation to the focal length of the lens. Figure 1-7 shows a 101mm lens and the lever with which one can control the diaphragm to select the desired opening size. Note that on the lens mount there is a series of numbers ranging from f4.5 to f32. The numbers designate the size of the opening that will be obtained by aligning that number and the indicator lever. As already stated, the number for the lens opening is determined by the size of the opening in relation to the focal length of the lens. If a lens is set at f8, for example, the opening of the lens will be 1/8th the focal length of that particular lens. If set at f11, the diameter of the opening will be 1/17th the focal length of the lens. This is illustrated in Figure 1-8.

It should be understood now that the number of the lens opening is determined, not by the actual diameter of the opening but by the

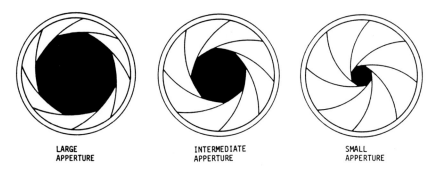

LARGE
APPERTURE

INTERMEDIATE
APPERTURE

SMALL
APPERTURE

Figure 1-6. Illustrated are three lens openings, each larger than the previous. Assuming that each is open for the same time duration, the largest opening will pass the greatest amount of light while the smallest will pass the least amount of light.

Figure 1-7. On the lower portion of the lens mount are a series of numbers ranging from f4.5 to f32. The lever is set at f8 which means that in this particular instance the size of the lens opening will be one-eighth the focal length of the lens.

diameter in relation to the focal length of the lens. When a 1000mm lens is set at f16, the diameter of the opening will be about 62.5mm. When a 50mm lens is set at f16, the diameter of the opening will only be about 3.1mm. Although the diameter of the opening on the 50mm lens is

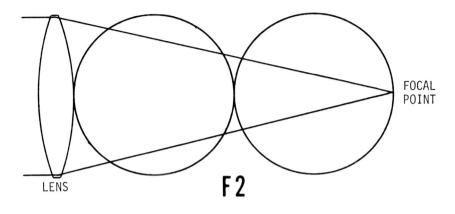

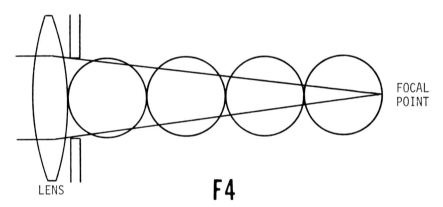

Figure 1-8. The f-setting of any lens is determined by the diameter of the lens opening against the focal length of the lens.

physically considerably smaller than that on the 1000mm lens, they both pass the same amount of light to the film when set at the same f/setting. While it is true that the 1000mm lens has an opening that is physically considerably larger than the 50mm lens when set at the same f/number, they are both the same size in relation to the focal length of that particular lens. With a long focal-length lens, light must travel much farther in order to reach the film plane. Because light intensity falls off as it travels, the long lens must have a larger diameter in order to offer the same light value as shorter lenses when set at the same f/setting. This is a fact governed by physical laws. To illustrate how rapidly light intensity falls off, consider that if one were to measure the intensity of the light given off from a light bulb at a distance of 10 feet and again at 20 feet, one would find that the intensity at 20 feet is not half of what it was at ten feet, but only one-fourth.

Focal Length of Lenses

Photographic lenses are categorized according to their focal length and the maximum diameter of the aperture of the lens. The focal length of a lens is the distance between the lens and the point at which parallel rays of light passing through the lens will converge and meet (see Figure 1-9). If a lens has a focal length of 10 inches, for example, the lens will project a sharp image of a distant object at a point 10 inches behind the lens. If the object is very near rather than distant, the point of focus will be farther from the lens than 10 inches.

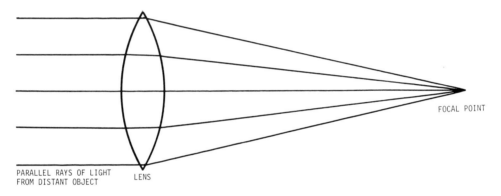

FOCAL POINT

PARALLEL RAYS OF LIGHT
FROM DISTANT OBJECT   LENS

Figure 1-9. The focal length of a lens is the distance between the lens and the point at which parallel rays of light passing through the lens will converge and meet.

Focal length has a very direct effect on the size of the image produced; the longer the focal length of a lens, the larger will be the image size. It is exactly this principle upon which telephoto lenses work. If a subject to be photographed is a great distance from the camera, a long focal length lens will be needed in order to secure an image of sufficient size to reveal the desired detail.

It was stated that when a lens is focused at infinity for a very distant object, the distance between the lens and the point of focus is equal to the focal length of the lens. It was also stated that as an object moves progressively closer to the camera, the distance between the lens and the point of perfect focus increases. In other words, when photographing a distant object, the lens is positioned at a distance from the film which is equal to its focal length. When focusing a camera on an object that is closer, the distance between the lens and the film is increased so that a sharp image can be produced. It is true that there are some highly expensive lenses available that not only increase the distance between the lens and film when focusing is taking place, but have a number of optical elements that are actually being repositioned in their spacing. This is done in an effort to maintain the highest degree of aberration correction possible throughout the full range of focus. While this is being done, however, the basic principle is still that of moving the lens to and from the film plane.

It was stated at the beginning of this chapter that lenses are categorized according to their focal length and the maximum diameter of the lens (see Figure 1-10). If you have a lens that has a focal length of 50mm and the largest f/setting is f1.4, you have what would be referred to as a 50mm f1.4 lens. If you have a telephoto lens of 500mm, and the largest f/setting or aperture of the lens is f6.3, you have a 500 millimeter f6.3 lens.

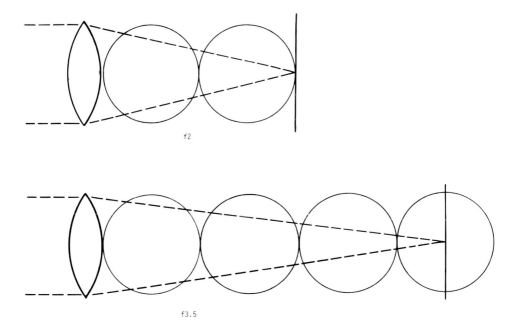

Figure 1-10. Lenses are classified by both their focal length and their diameter in relation to the focal length.

Curvature of the Lens and Focal Length

Various physical factors or conditions control the focal length of a lens. The lens has a noticeably curved surface; some lenses have a curved surface on only one side while others are curved on both sides.

Notice in Figure 1-11, that a plano (single) convex lens has a focal length which is approximately twice the radius of curvature, whereas the double convex lens has a focal length which is approximately equal to the radius of curvature.

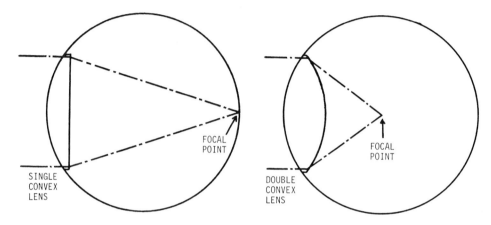

Figure 1-11. A plano (single) convex lens has a focal length which is approximately twice the radius of curvature, while the double convex lens has a focal length which is approximately equal to the radius of curvature. Although the refractive index of the optical glass used in a lens will have an effect upon the exact focal length, this general rule will be found to apply.

Color Correction of Lenses

Figure 1-12 illustrates a simple lens. Note how a simple lens breaks up light into its various colors and focuses them all at different points. This happens because a lens tends to exhibit the characteristics of a prism.

Figure 1-13 illustrates how the introduction of a second element to a simple achromatic lens has caused the red and blue colors to focus at the same point. The colors between the red and blue do not focus at *exactly* the same point, but they are much closer nonetheless. By correcting a lens in this manner, sharp images are possible. The second element is often of a different type of glass from the first and has a different refraction index and is ground to a different shape. When a lens is being color-corrected by the addition of a second element, it is at the same time being corrected for spherical aberration.

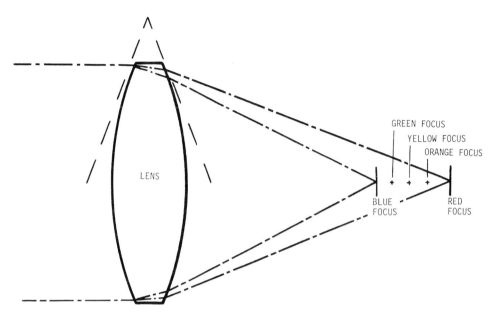

Figure 1-12. Because a simple lens tends to exhibit the characteristics of a prism, such lenses also tend to break up light into the various colors and focus them each at a different point.

Spherical aberration is a condition whereby the lens fails to focus a subject on the film plane because of the radius of the curvature of the lens. The lens exhibiting this aberration has a tendency to focus the rays of light passing through the center portion of the lens at one point while the rays of light passing through the outer portions of the lens are focused at yet another point. This condition is illustrated in Figure 1-14.

Many photographic lenses have one-half dozen or more elements that have been introduced in an effort to cancel the many aberrations that are often present. This is especially true of lenses designed to perform special tasks such as extremely fast (wide aperture) lenses and extreme wide-angle lenses.

The lenses in good cameras almost always consist of at least three elements, while only the cheapest of cameras have lenses consisting of only one element. In the area of extreme telephoto lenses, however, very good lenses with only two elements (achromatic) can be obtained.

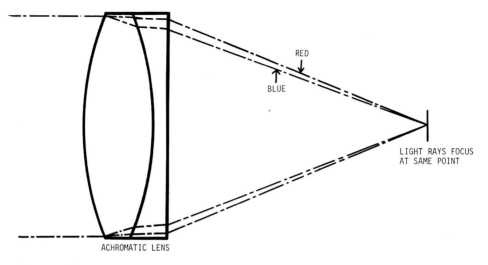

Figure 1-13. The introduction of a second element to a simple lens creates an *achromatic lens.* Such lenses bring the red and blue colors to focus at the same point.
F01:13

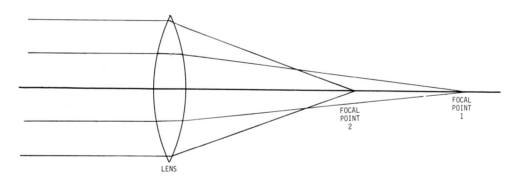

Figure 1-14. *Spherical aberration* is the tendency of a lens to focus the rays of light passing through the center portion of the lens at one point while the rays of light passing through the outer portions of the lens are focused at yet another point. A lens which has been corrected for chromatic aberration is also corrected for spherical aberration.

Depth of Field

Generally speaking, depth of field is the distance in front of and beyond a given subject that will remain in *acceptable* focus when the subject is in *perfect* focus. When focusing at a given point, everything at that point is considered to be in perfect focus, while objects in front of and behind that point become progressively less sharp as they become more distant from the point of perfect focus. As a general rule, there is about one-third the depth of field in front of the point of perfect focus in proportion to the rear. It can also be said that depth of field will increase about twice as fast beyond the subject as ahead when the lens is stopped down.

It can be presumed from the last statement that the size of the lens opening also has a very direct effect on depth of field. A lens opening of f8, for example, will not offer as great a range of acceptable focus as will the same lens when set at f16. This is why, if the subject matter to be recorded on film is not basically all the same distance from the camera position and cannot be so arranged, the use of a small lens opening is desirable. By using a small lens opening, a greater depth of field is achieved, and more subject matter will be within the range of acceptable focus (see Figure 1-15). If the situation is such that it is desirable to have only a certain item in perfect focus and distracting items would better be left out of the picture, a very large lens opening may be selected (see Figure 1-16). This offers a very limited depth of field and only the object focused upon will be sharp while everything else will be blurred. This technique is referred to as selective focusing. Figures 1-17A and 17B illustrate the effect that aperture settings have upon depth of field. Figure 1-18 illustrates how one should focus when a wide range of sharpness is desired.

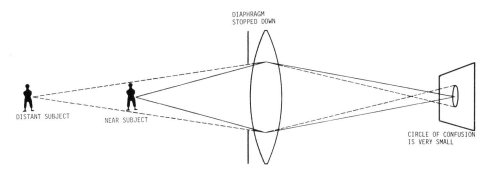

Figure 1-15. Stopping a lens down (smaller opening) causes a smaller circle of confusion and thus greater depth of field.

A very common misconception is that the shorter the focal length of a lens, the greater the depth of field it will offer. In other words, some photographers claim that wide angle lenses offer greater depth of field

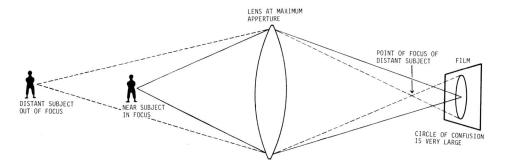

Figure 1-16. A large lens opening causes a very large circle of confusion and only the object focused upon will be in sharp focus.

than do normal and telephoto lenses. This is not true from a technical standpoint, but the reason for this generalization or belief is understandable and perhaps can even be said to carry some truth when viewed from a *practical* rather than a technical standpoint.

To begin with, consider the fact that depth of field and image size have a direct effect on each other. In other words, depth of field is determined by the f/setting and the reproduction ratio (image size). As an example, consider photographing a man using first a wide-angle lens, then a normal lens and finally a telephoto lens. Consider that in all three photographs the same f/setting will be used, and also that the photographer will vary the camera-to-subject distance in each photograph so that the same image size of the subject will be achieved in all cases. When using the wide-angle lens, the camera will be very close to the subject so that his feet touch the bottom of the frame and his head touches the top of the frame. When photographing with the normal lens, the camera will be moved back, thus increasing the camera-to-subject distance, so once again the subject will touch both the top and bottom of the frame. Finally, when photographing the subject using the telephoto lens, the camera will be moved way back to achieve a very long camera-to-subject distance so that again the subject will touch both the top and bottom of the frame. Remember, the photographer has used the same f/setting with all lenses and has maintained the same image size with each lens. With these factors, the depth of field in all three photographs will be the same. The reason a wide-angle lens is said to offer a greater depth of field than do normal and telephoto lenses is because, when using a wide-angle lens from a given position, the image size achieved is

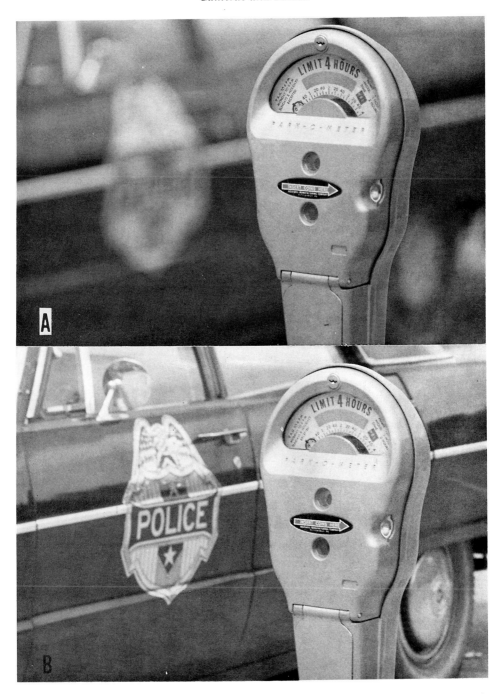

Figure 1-17. (A) This parking meter was photographed with an f-setting of f2.8. Note that only the meter is in sharp focus. (B) This is the same meter as in 1-17A. In this photo the lens was set at f16. The patrol car is about ten feet beyond the meter.

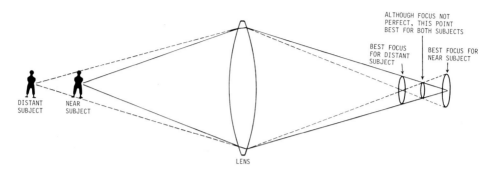

Figure 1-18. When two objects, one closer to the camera than the other, need to be in sharp focus, the lens should be focused at a point between the two objects and the lens stopped down to the smallest practical opening.

much smaller than if a normal or telephoto lens had been used from that same position.

Fixed Focus, Range Focus and Continuous Focus Cameras

To fully understand and appreciate how fixed focus and range focusing cameras operate, it is first necessary to examine the depth of field and the factors affecting it, because depth of field plays a very important role in the function of fixed focus and range focus cameras.

Cameras with *fixed* focus lenses, cameras that are often advertised as having a lens that does not require focusing, generally have lenses of a fairly short focal length and they generally have a rather small lens opening; both factors working together offer great depth of field. These lenses, however, just as any other lens, will have one point of perfect focus and everything else will be in varying degrees of sharpness as they become progressively farther from the point of perfect focus.

Cameras which feature *zone* focusing operate in basically the same manner as do fixed focus lenses, except that the point of perfect focus can be set at two or three different points or distances. The distances generally offered are close range for head and shoulder shots such as portraits, an intermediate range for such things as group pictures and finally a setting for distant objects such as scenes and landscapes. With such a camera, sharper photographs can be realized because depth of field is relied upon to a much lesser degree than with a camera having a fixed focus lens. Because depth of field is not so essential, faster lenses

(lenses with a larger maximum opening) and somewhat longer focal length lenses are possible. Both will be found to contribute significantly to the quality of the resultant photographs.

Continuous focusing lenses do not restrict to one point of perfect focus or even three points, but the photographer may focus at any point between minimum focus and infinity. With such cameras one can generally utilize the aperture setting to control depth of field, or eliminate it almost entirely and still be assured that the subject image will be in sharp focus.

While discussing depth of field, let us examine the depth of field scales that are very often printed on the camera lens barrel. This is especially true of lenses designed to be used with 35mm single lens reflex (SLR) cameras. In Figure 1-19 the f/setting numbers on the lens barrel are engraved in different colors. The lines that comprise the depth of field scale are in corresponding colors. Since the illustration is in black and white, consider that the outermost markings are of a color corresponding to f16. The second set of markings from the outermost corresponds in color to f11. The third corresponds to f8, etc. The small dot is the infrared auxiliary focusing mark. By utilizing the depth of field scale, it is possible to focus on a subject, adjust the shutter speed and the f/setting for proper exposure and then determine what the full range of acceptable focus will be by referring to the scale on the lens barrel.

In Figure 1-19 the normal (50mm) lens has been set at f16 and focused on a subject that is 10 feet from the camera. While studying the depth of field scale, note that the range of acceptable focus is from just under 7 feet (A) to approximately 30 feet (B). The point of perfect focus is at 10 feet (C). The scales on 35mm SLR camera lenses are more often than not given in both the metric and inch system. Exercise care not to confuse the two scales; this is easily done when referring to them at a glance or under low light level conditions.

A continuous focusing lens can be used as a fixed focus lens if one is out doors and not certain at what distance an object or subject may be when it becomes desirable to make an exposure instantly in order to capture an act on film. This is called *focusing hyperfocally,* and is done by adjusting the exposure using as small a lens opening as conditions will permit. Remember, the larger the number, the smaller the lens opening. When the f/setting has been set, align the infinity mark (D) on the focusing ring with the depth of field marking that corresponds to the f/setting being used. In this illustration, the lens is set at f16. By

Figure 1-19. This normal (50mm) lens from a 35mm camera has been set at f16 and focused at ten feet. By studying the depth of field scale, it will be noted that the range of acceptable focus is just under seven feet (A) to about thirty feet (B). The point of perfect focus (C) is ten feet.

studying the depth of field scale, note that everything from about 7 feet (A) to about 30 feet (B) will be in acceptable focus with about 10 feet (C) being the point of perfect focus.

With a lens set in this fashion, if it is necessary to make a grab shot and there is no time for focusing, any action taking place at some point between 7 and 30 feet will yield an image in acceptable focus. The focus will not be perfect, however, unless the action is taking place at about 10 feet from the camera. As one moves away from the point of perfect focus toward the outer extremes of the depth of field range, the image will become progressively less sharp. At some given point the image will go from acceptable to unacceptable sharpness. It is just within those points that the range of acceptable sharpness, that is, depth of field, is figured.

Film Formats

In the field of photography there are a number of film formats and sizes from which to choose. Of the many sizes, only a few are very popular in the area of police and fire photography. The most common formats are the 35mm, which is 24 × 36mm, 2¼-inch square, and the 4 × 5-inch format. Some of the less popular formats are the 2¼ × 2¾-inch, 2¼ × 3¼-inch and 3¼ × 4¼-inch.

In more recent times, pocket cameras have become more popular. The most common film sizes for such cameras are 9.5mm, which has an image format of 8 × 11mm; and 16mm film, which offers an image format of 10 × 14mm in some cameras and as large as 12 × 17mm in others. Pocket cameras, however, have very little application in police photography. On the other extreme, there are view cameras with film formats of 5 × 7 inches and greater, but these, just as the pocket cameras, are of limited value in the field of police and fire photography. This then puts one back to the 35mm, 2¼-inch square, and 4 × 5-inch formats. Of these three, the 35mm SLR cameras dominate.

Film Grain

The most obvious advantage of a large over a small format negative is the great detail and seemingly grainless pictures one can obtain from them, since the large format negatives need not undergo the great degree of enlargement that is necessary with a smaller negative in order to achieve a print of the same size. Consider that when making an 8 × 10-inch print from a 35mm negative there is an enlargement of about 8 diameters. To obtain an 8 × 10-inch print from a 4 × 5-inch negative an enlargement of only 2 diameters is necessary. This does make a difference.

The main reason it is desirable to keep the degree of enlargement to a minimum is the fact that films have a structure that is somewhat grainy due to silver particles in the film's emulsion which tend to cluster together when the film is processed. If the degree of enlargement is very great, the graininess sometimes becomes noticeable and in some cases can become objectionable. If one anticipates greatly enlarging a negative, it is advisable to select a film that is very fine grained. It will, however, be found that films with very fine grain characteristics are also slow films (low ISO rating). Likewise, the faster a film (high ISO) the grainier it will tend to be.

Film Size and the Normal Lens

Another factor that has a very direct effect on the fact that large format cameras offer much finer detail than do smaller format cameras is the longer focal length of the camera's normal lens. The larger the format of the camera, the longer will be the focal length of the normal lens; consequently, the larger will be the image size thus produced.

The focal length of the normal lens of a camera is approximately equal to the diagonal of the negative format. By using a camera so equipped, the scene photographed with the camera will offer an image that is pretty much in the same perspective as one would normally observe it. The angle of acceptance for a normal lens is generally about 45°. Consider, for example, the negative format of a 35mm camera which measures 24 × 36mm and has a diagonal which measures roughly 45mm. The normal lens of a 35mm camera is considered to be between 45mm and 55mm. The diagonal of a 2¼-inch square negative is about 80mm. The normal lens of such a camera is in some cases 75mm and in other cases 80mm, with 80mm being the most common (see Figure 1-20).

Since the size of the format of a camera determines what the focal length of the normal lens will be, what may be classified as a normal lens on one camera may fall into the classification of a wide-angle or tele-photo lens on another camera.

Focal Length, Negative Format and Angle of Acceptance

The angle of acceptance of a given lens on a camera is determined by the focal length of the lens and the negative format (study Figure 1-21). If a lens of a given focal length is placed onto a camera with a very large negative format, and a second lens of the same focal length is placed onto a camera with a very small negative format, the lens on the large format camera will have a greater angle of acceptance or field of view than will the same lens when on the small format camera. The image size remains the same, however. The angle of acceptance is not governed only by the size of the image a lens can produce, but rather it is a condition whereby the negative only makes use of a certain portion of the image projected by the lens. Any excess image a lens projects is generally eliminated by the use of light baffles in the lens barrel or camera (see Figure 1-22).

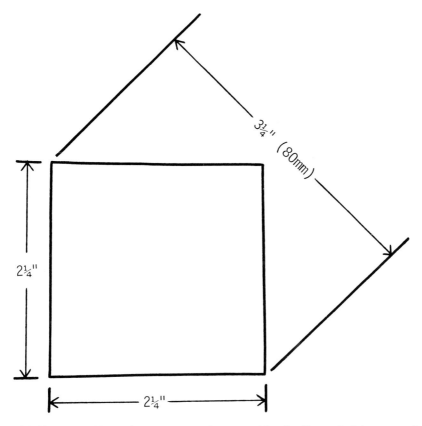

Figure 1-20. The normal lens of any camera is determined by the diagonal of that camera's film format. The diagonal of the 2¹/₄ × 2¹/₄ inch square format is about 80mm, which is the focal length of the normal lens of a camera of that format size.

Magnifying Power of Telephoto Lenses

The magnifying power of a telephoto lens for any camera is generally determined by dividing the focal length of the normal lens into the focal length of the telephoto lens. This is because the power of the telephoto lens is figured against the normal lens. If you are using a 135mm lens on a 35mm camera, you are using a 2.7 power telephoto lens, since the normal lens of a 35mm camera is generally accepted as being about 50mm. (135mm ÷ 50mm = 2.7). Incidentally, any lens that has a focal length longer than that of the normal lens of the camera on which it is being used is considered to be a telephoto lens. If an 85mm lens, which is a mild telephoto when used on a 35mm camera, was placed on a 4 ×

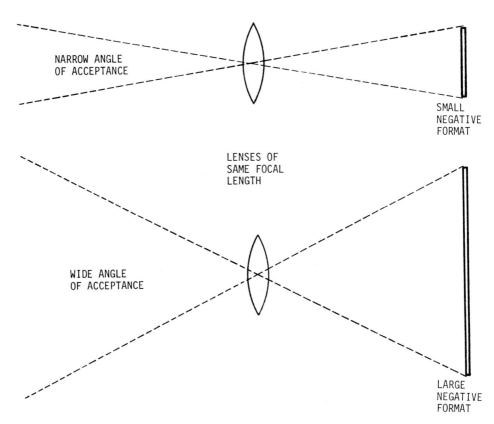

Figure 1-21. The angle of acceptance of a lens is determined by both the focal length of the lens and the negative format of the camera upon which the lens is being used.

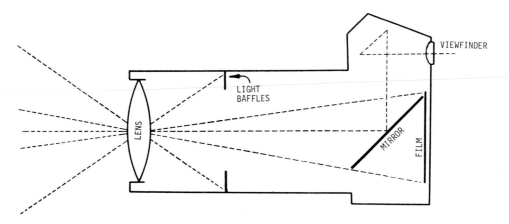

Figure 1-22. Any excess image a lens projects is generally eliminated by the use of light baffles in the lens barrel or camera.

5-inch format camera, it would fall into the category of a wide-angle lens since its focal length is shorter than the normal lens of such a camera. Whether a lens is considered to be a wide-angle, normal or telephoto is governed by the format of the camera upon which it is used.

Specific Camera Types

Having examined some of the basic principles and functions upon which cameras operate, it is appropriate at this time to examine some of the various camera types which are available to the police and fire photographer.

The reader should understand that this discussion of camera types is not all-inclusive but is intended primarily to provide the reader with a general introduction to some of the more common camera types. The reader should further understand that there are many manufacturers of each camera type, the majority of them providing good cameras. Should the reader develop an interest in any of the camera types discussed, he or she would do well to gather and compare the promotional literature of some of the various makes and models. It is also advisable to take a look at a consumer's report concerning a particular camera in question. This is important because, although the cameras of a given type operate upon the same basic principle, they will differ insofar as their individual characteristics, such as the location of controls, whether the camera features a built-in light metering system, the extent of the aperture and shutter speed range, and so forth. Furthermore, each specific camera model will generally exhibit certain minor shortcomings although not necessarily in mechanical construction or quality. Often a camera's shortcoming will consist of nothing more than the placement of various controls and the camera's overall ease of operation. Consumer's reports will generally point these things out.

In the following discussion of camera types, the cameras are not presented in the order of their desirability. That is not possible since each camera possesses its own virtues and qualities. This being the case, it is reasonable to say that a camera's desirability will depend largely upon the needs of the photographer, the amount of money available for a camera and the circumstances under which that particular camera will be used. Finally, there is a wide price range among the specific camera types discussed, an aspect which is not touched upon in this discussion.

Press Cameras

For many years, press cameras were widely used by both the news media and law enforcement agencies. However, it has been many years since such cameras have been used by either to any significant degree. Both have gone almost exclusively to small format cameras. Of these, the most commonly used are the 2¼-inch square and 35mm format cameras, the latter being dominant. The police, although much slower to make the change, largely for reasons of budget and policy, did make the transition.

Press cameras, because of their large format, can produce negatives which are capable of extremely large blowups of high quality. These cameras accept either a cut film holder, a film pack or a roll film adapter. Also available is a Polaroid Adapter® which makes it possible to utilize Polaroid films with any 4 × 5-inch format camera.

Press cameras are of extremely rugged construction, and are very versatile. Most press cameras possess a double extension bellows system which makes it possible to take life-size close-ups (1:1) without the use of accessory items.

The press camera is equipped with a viewfinder and is designed to be used at eye level. This is a desirable feature on a camera to be used in the investigative field, since overall views of a scene should generally be made from a person's normal eye level. The camera also features a ground glass for critical framing and focusing when engaged in close-up work. These cameras, while they are very useful and capable of high-quality photography, are unfortunately rather large, bulky and slow to use when compared to the smaller format cameras presently available. Furthermore, the large negatives of the press camera are not as important or necessary today as they were some years ago because of the higher quality of the films now available.

If one presently has a press camera or is contemplating the purchase of one, this discussion should not be discouraging, since press cameras are, as already stated, very high quality. Many of the problems encountered by their size and bulk can be overcome by working with the camera and becoming accustomed to it. Many photographers who have been using such cameras for years are very reluctant to give them up in favor of a smaller format camera.

Illustrated in Figure 1-23 is the Speed Graphic®, the most common press camera. The Speed Graphic is available in three format sizes which are $2\frac{1}{4} \times 3\frac{1}{4}$ inch, $3\frac{1}{4} \times 4\frac{1}{4}$ inch and 4×5 inch. A less expensive model of the Speed Graphic is the Crown Graphic®; the most notable difference between the two is the lack of a focal plane shutter on the Crown Graphic. The Speed Graphic has both a focal plane and a between-the-lens shutter.

Figure 1-23. **Speed Graphic Press Camera.** These cameras are available in three format sizes, are very versatile and produce photographs of very high quality. Because of their bulk, however, they are being replaced in favor of smaller format cameras by both the news media and investigative agencies.

Twin Lens Reflex Cameras

Figure 1-24 illustrates a twin lens reflex (TLR) camera. These cameras have a $2\frac{1}{4}$-inch square format and are capable of taking excellent photographs. Such cameras are not as suitable for close-up work as SLR cameras since one may experience some problems with parallax because the subject matter is viewed through one lens while the film will be exposed by a second lens which lies directly below the viewfinder lens (see Figure 1-25). Another drawback of a TLR, although not a serious one, is the fact that these cameras are equipped with a waist-level viewfinder; the general overall views of a crime, fire or accident scene should normally be taken from eye level. TLR's have also proven to be a bit awkward in photographing evidence such as foot and tire impressions, where the camera must be positioned so as to point directly toward the ground. Critical framing and focusing in such cases is somewhat troublesome unless the photographer has become very accustomed to the camera. Also characteristic of TLR systems is an image on the ground glass (focusing screen) that is reversed. Unless the camera user becomes accustomed to this, it can be confusing.

Figure 1-24. **Twin Lens Reflex (TLR).** These cameras utilize a 2¼ inch square format and are capable of excellent results.

Many of the shortcomings characteristic of most TLR systems are not necessarily true of the Mamiya cameras which feature, among other things, lens interchangeability and an automatic parallax adjustment when close-up work is done.

It would serve well to point out again, however, that the role of the

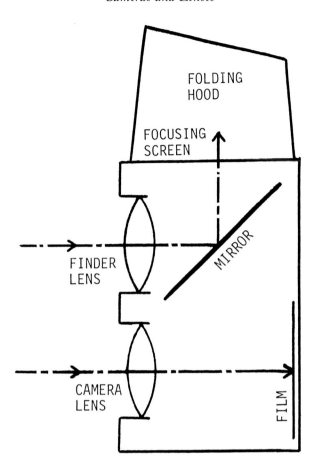

Figure 1-25. With a TLR camera, the upper lens is only for viewing purposes, while the lower lens exposes the film.

camera at the scene is basically general, and for such applications a TLR system should present no serious drawbacks.

35mm Rangefinder Camera

Figure 1-26 illustrates a 35mm rangefinder camera. With a rangefinder camera, the photographer views and frames the subject matter through a small window which is positioned above the camera's lens (see Figure 1-27).

The lenses of 35mm rangefinder cameras are generally fairly fast, anywhere from f1.7 to f2.8, and the viewfinder affords a much brighter image with which to compose the subject matter than does a single lens reflex camera.

Figure 1-26. **A 35mm rangefinder camera.**

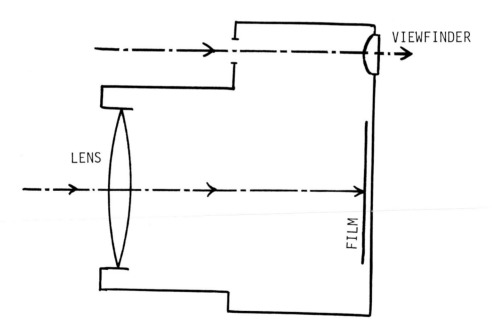

Figure 1-27. With a rangefinder camera the photographer views the subject matter through a viewfinder which is positioned above the camera's lens.

Rangefinder cameras are capable of offering very good results, but they are somewhat limited in that there will often be problems of parallax and framing when using close-up attachments, and telephoto work is not practical because there is no way to ensure proper framing. The photographer cannot focus by actually viewing the subject matter through the camera's lens. Rather, some such cameras are equipped with a rangefinder which indicates when proper focus has been achieved, while less expensive models will require the photographer to estimate the distance and set the footing scale accordingly.

While a rangefinder camera is good for general crime, fire and accident scene work, its desirability for specialized applications is limited.

35mm SLR Cameras

Figure 1-28 illustrates a 35mm SLR camera. *Single Lens Reflex* indicates that the photographer, when looking into the viewfinder, is actually looking through the camera's one lens which will expose the film when an exposure is made (refer to Figure 1-29).

Figure 1-28. **A 35mm Single Lens Reflex (SLR) camera.**

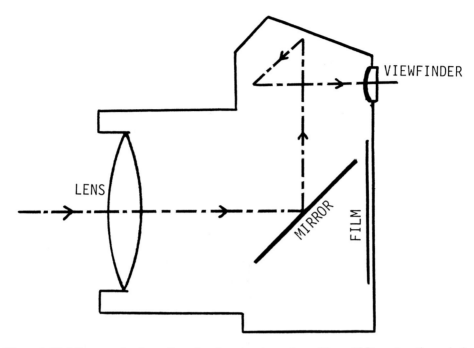

Figure 1-29. Mirrors and prisms allow the photographer using a 35mm SLR to view through the camera's lens exactly what will be exposed upon the film. Such a feature makes these cameras ideal for close-up and telephoto work.

Because the photographer views through the camera's lens exactly what will appear on the film, SLR cameras are very suitable for use with telephoto lenses, wide-angle lenses and also for close-up work, since there is never a problem of focus, parallax or framing. When examining the array of accessories available for most brands of SLR cameras, it is no wonder that the SLR systems are today perhaps the most versatile of any camera system made.

Thirty-five millimeter SLR systems are very convenient; they are capable of as many as thirty-six exposures on one roll of film, they are compact and light, they generally have very fast lenses and sequence shots are possible because one sweep of the film advance lever advances the film and cocks the shutter, making the camera ready for the next exposure. Also, a large negative format is no longer necessary for high-quality prints because of significant advances in film quality. These factors have had a tendency in recent years to make the 35mm camera systems more and more attractive to investigative agencies.

2¼ Inch SLR Cameras

The Hasselblad 500C/M® is an SLR camera with a 2¼ inch square format. Cameras of this type are manufactured by a number of companies and utilize the same film as do the 2¼ inch TLR cameras discussed earlier. These cameras generally accept either twelve or twenty-four exposure rolls of film. Finally, these cameras are extremely versatile due to their reflex viewing, the lens interchangeability and the wide variety of accessories available to them. These are good cameras for investigative photography (see Figure 1-30).

Figure 1-30. **A 2¼ inch square format SLR.** Cameras of this type are manufactured by a number of companies and utilize the same film as do the 2¼ inch TLR cameras that were discussed. These cameras are ideal for investigative photography because of their reflex viewing. (Courtesy of Paillard, Inc.)

Polaroid Cameras

For many years Polaroid has been used a great deal by law enforcement and investigative personnel. No doubt the most notable reason is the fact that with Polaroid products one has the benefit of instant results, thus eliminating the possibility of leaving the scene with a roll of film that has been improperly exposed or which for any number of other reasons may be no good. With Polaroid products there is no problem insofar with the processing of the film, nor are there problems insofar as the chain of custody of the film is concerned.

Polaroid products are discussed in greater detail in Chapter 14.

Subminiature Cameras

Figure 1-31 shows a Minolta 16II® subminiature camera. This camera, which is fairly representative of subminiature cameras in general, accepts a special film cartridge containing 16mm film, has a wide range of f/settings and shutter speeds and accepts auxiliary close-up lenses.

Figure 1-31. **Minolta 16II Subminiature Camera.** The pen lying beside the camera indicates its compactness.

While the results that can be achieved by the use of a subminiature camera will in no case equal those possible with a good full frame 35mm camera or larger format, it is such cameras that enable investigators, especially undercover agents, to secure photographic evidence under unique conditions that would otherwise prevent the use of a larger and more conspicuous camera or when conditions prohibit working from a distance with telephoto lenses. Many such cameras have, in addition to a full shutter speed and aperture range, an internal light meter; several are fully automatic. The price range of these cameras will vary from just under fifty dollars to several hundred dollars.

As has been stated, such cameras will be found useful under certain unique situations. For general crime, fire or accident scene photography these cameras will be of limited value.

Motion Picture and Closed Circuit Television Equipment

An important photographic tool that should not be overlooked or slighted by those in the investigative fields is the motion picture camera and video cameras. The advantages offered by such equipment are many.

In the area of surveillance, for example, a photographic record made at the scene of a demonstration may well serve to disprove charges of brutality directed at law enforcement personnel when they are forced to make arrests. The presence of a camera will also sometimes serve as a deterrent to those who may have a tendency to turn a peaceful demonstration into a riot. In such cases, the presence of a camera can serve to protect not only law enforcement personnel but the demonstrators as well. Many crimes occurring in the streets can be photographically documented. Consider, for example, the sales of contraband; photographic documentation of such activity can be good evidence. In the area of traffic control, the arrest of an individual for driving while under the influence of an alcoholic beverage will very often stand better in court if a short motion picture film or section of video tape is made of the subject performing various balance tests while in his intoxicated condition. If the individual later decides to plead not guilty, he may well be encouraged to reconsider his decision when faced with such evidence. At any rate, such evidence will generally serve to disprove his claim of innocence. To the investigator, the filming of an interrogation process and the suspect's signed statement can serve to guard against later claims of duress or coercion. Finally, motion picture films or video tapes are very effective for inservice training films for both law enforcement and fire personnel. Many such films can be rented or purchased. It is also feasible to film lectures conducted by outside speakers. Video cameras are discussed and illustrated in greater detail in Chapter 16.

Digital Cameras

Digital cameras are relatively new for the recording of "still" photographs. And, although their use in the investigative fields is relatively limited at this time, at least in comparison to conventional cameras, they will likely be used to greater degrees in the not too distant future. Hence, it would be an omission to not at least acknowledge their existence and some of the possibilities they offer.

Digital cameras operate much like a conventional camera inasmuch as a lens focuses an image onto a recording medium with the intensity and duration being controlled by the lens opening and shutter speed. But unlike the conventional camera that records the image onto a film coated with a light sensitive material (emulsion) that must later undergo chemical development, the digital camera records the image electronically as is the case with a camcorder. The resultant information is then downloaded to a computer to be viewed, stored, printed, or transmitted via modem.

Just as with conventional cameras, the specific features of each camera will differ somewhat and it is necessary to evaluate each relative to the intended use of the instrument. With some cameras, once the allotted number of exposures has been made, it is necessary to download the information into a computer before additional exposures can be made. That may or may not be a problem depending on intended use. With others a removable storage media enables one to continue making exposures in the field by removing and replacing a fully exposed media with a fresh one. Also, the effective ISO rating will vary by camera. Some cameras feature lens interchangeability while others do not. And the aperture and shutter speed range will also vary from one camera model to another as will the maximum number of exposures possible with one set of batteries. The number of exposures that can be made in a given period of time also will vary by camera and model.

Some cameras enable one to choose between high or low resolution, but the number of exposures possible will be affected accordingly. High resolution means less exposures before downloading or replacement of storage media is required. Needs will suggest the appropriate choice.

With time, one can anticipate that the sophistication and possibilities offered by digital cameras will increase. To realize that such is true one need only acknowledge the rapidity with which the field of computers is advancing. Will digital cameras eventually replace the conventional camera as it has been known? Only time will tell!

Autofocus Cameras and Lenses

Over the years, camera manufacturers have made cameras increasingly user friendly. There was a time when a technically correct photograph required the photographer to manually focus the camera and calculate the exposure. Additionally, if flash was required that too had to be properly calculated. That all took time and required a degree of expertise.

Today there are numerous high quality camera models on the market that automatically focus the image and calculate exposure whether it be for existing light or flash photography. The result is that a technically correct photograph can be obtained most of the time under *normal* circumstances without having to make several critical calculations. Such cameras are available in a wide price range with some being very basic for the amateur anticipating vacation, to highly sophisticated models made for professional use.

Under discussion here are *autofocus systems* which make proper focusing quick and easy. However, to realize the greatest benefit from such a feature, the user should understand its basic function and how to deal with situations that can interfere with an autofocus system's ability to function properly. Although this discussion should serve to remove the mystery from autofocus systems, the reader should understand that any time an unfamiliar camera is to be used, the owner's manual should be carefully studied. And it is desirable to then shoot a *test roll* of film to ensure that the various features of the camera are understood and being utilized properly.

In this discussion we will briefly examine *infrared* focus detection which is active, *phase-detection* autofocus which is passive, *multi-beam* auto focus which evaluates a wide area of the scene and focuses accordingly, and *continuous* auto focus which maintains focus on moving subjects.

First, *infrared focus detection* is referred to as an *active* system because it emits an infrared beam that is reflected from the subject back to a sensing unit in the camera so that its distance can be measured and the camera automatically focused accordingly. Such systems will work in total darkness.

Second, *phase-detection autofocus* is referred to as being *passive* because instead of emitting an infrared beam with which to gauge the camera-to-subject distance, it focuses by using existing light reflected from the subject. Such systems tend not to work well in subdued light or in total darkness. To overcome that limitation some camera models featuring built-in flash will automatically fire a series of low-power light bursts which enables the camera to focus. That feature will make focusing possible even in total darkness.

Third, *Multi-beam autofocus* takes a reading off a large area of the scene and chooses a setting accordingly so as to allow for subjects at varying distances from the camera. Generally a point towards the front of the scene will end up being the point of perfect focus.

Fourth, *Continuous autofocus* seeks and determines focus on a continuing basis so as to enable one to track and photograph moving subjects. Some systems feature *predictive auto-focus* and will measure the time space between focus readings so as to predict where the subject will be when an exposure is made and prefocus to that point. Such calculations are naturally made very rapidly.

When looking through the viewfinder of a camera featuring autofocus, whether it be a rangefinder camera or single-lens reflex, one will see marks in the center of the viewfinder that indicate the area upon which focus is being calculated. If the *primary focal point*, the subject to be focused upon, is not in the center of the frame, many cameras allow one to place the focus indicators on the subject and then lock the focus by depressing the shutter release button part way. Once the focus has been locked proper framing of the overall scene may be accomplished and then the picture taken by depressing the shutter release button the rest of the way.

When there is more than one point of importance in the scene, with some being further from the camera than the others, it is generally desirable to focus at a mid-range point between them. Because depth of field tends to be greater beyond a subject than in front, it is suggested that the distance between the nearest and furthest point of importance be divided into thirds and focus made at a point *one-third* the distance beyond the nearest subject. For example, if there were 30 feet between the nearest and furthest point of importance, one would focus on a point ten feet beyond the nearest point of importance. Depth of field will then, often, compensate for the fact that not everything in the scene will be in perfect focus. Some textbooks suggest focusing at a point 2/5th beyond the nearest subject of interest, but the authors feel it is *easier to visualize* a point at 1/3rd the distance. And, in reality, the points at 1/3rd and 2/5th the distance are very close one to the other.

Active infrared autofocusing systems do not tend to have a problem focusing on many difficult subjects such as those of low contrast. Passive phase-detection autofocus systems, however, tend to be confused by some types of surfaces. When such is the case and the camera is not able to achieve proper focus, a possible solution is to lock focus on a nonconfusing surface that is approximately the same distance from the camera. Then reframe the picture and make the exposure. As with so many things, experimentation and experience will prove to be the best teacher.

Automatic Exposure Control

It was stated that automatic exposure control is a useful feature for the investigative photographer. When considering that feature, one must be aware of *aperture-priority* versus *shutter-priority.*

Aperture-priority enables the photographer to set the desired aperture (lens opening) and the shutter speed will be automatically set according to the light conditions so that a proper exposure results. *Shutter-priority* enables the photographer to set the desired shutter speed and the aperture will be automatically set according to the lighting conditions.

Many automatic cameras are designed and programmed to adjust both the shutter speed and aperture giving optimum results. They seek to always provide the best relationship between aperture and shutter speed and avoid excessively slow shutter speeds that may result in a blurred image, or maximum aperture resulting in limited depth-of-field.

Many fully automatic cameras feature a *manual override* giving the photographer full control by being able to deactivate the automatic exposure control system and select all aperture and shutter speed settings according to the conditions and desired result.

When automatic exposure control is desired when using nonautomatic long telephoto lenses during a surveillance operation, aperture-priority is the choice. Again, aperture-priority lets the photographer select the desired aperture and the shutter speed will adjust itself. Most high-powered telephoto lenses are not automatic, so the shutter-priority feature would not work.

Automatic Film Advance and Motor Drives

It was stated earlier that there has been a strong trend to manufacture sophisticated cameras that are increasingly user friendly. Today, as in the past, many cameras require the photographer to manually advance the film following each exposure, and to manually rewind the film after a roll of film has been exposed. However, over the years there has been a trend to make cameras that will automatically advance the film after each exposure is made, and then rewind it automatically after the last exposure. Today such cameras in the 35mm format are very common, if not in the majority.

Features such as automatic film advance, automatic rewind, automatic exposure control, auto focus, and automatic flash computation serve to greatly simplify camera operation and maximize the success rate for those who must use cameras in their work but are not as well versed in photography as they would like to be.

Many 35mm cameras will automatically advance the film to the proper point to begin taking pictures once the film cassette has been inserted into the film chamber and the film leader pulled out to a designated starting point and the camera back closed. Then, when the last picture has been taken, the camera will automatically rewind the film. Most automatic cameras also have a feature by which one may cause the film to rewind before the entire film has been exposed.

When using 35mm still cameras and telephoto lenses during surveillance operations, automatic film advance along with the feature of automatic exposure control is a very useful feature. Not having to calculate exposure and manually advance the film leaves the photographer better able to concentrate on the subject's activity and select exposures accordingly.

Automatic film rewind is beneficial in a couple of ways. First, while the film is automatically rewinding the photographer can be getting the next roll of film ready for insertion into the camera thus losing less time. Second, when manually rewinding film it is possible to do it too fast. That can result in the film passing over material in the camera and/or cassette and building up a static charge thus exposing the film resulting in little dark spots on the negative that will be painfully evident in the resultant photograph. Automatic rewinding typically takes about 18 seconds for a 36 exposure roll of film, a speed that is slow enough to preclude this problem.

When considering 35mm format cameras, *automatic film advance* is not to be confused with what is referred to as *motor drive*. Automatic film advance simply advances the film after each picture is taken, enabling the photographer to take pictures more easily and quickly, perhaps 1–2 exposures per second. And with automatic film advance only one picture will be taken each time the shutter release button is depressed. *Motor drive,* however, will begin taking pictures in rapid succession when the shutter release button is depressed and held down. Motor drive speeds vary by manufacture, but 5–6 frames per second is common. Of course, when using a camera equipped with a motor drive one may take individual pictures.

Camera Support

Tripods

For general crime, fire and accident scene photography, a tripod is not usually needed. There are, however, several applications of photography in the investigative field that will often require the use of a tripod to produce quality photographs. A few of the photographic applications referred to here are telephotography, photomacrography, copy work, close-up photography, time exposures and painting with light.

There are a number of different types and makes of tripods on the market from which to choose, and, although the many various tripods will differ in size, weight and specific features, they all function in basically the same manner and are not difficult to use. Perhaps the most important consideration when selecting a tripod is the task it will perform. If the tripod will be used primarily in the studio in conjunction with a press or view camera, consider a rather heavy, solid tripod. Tripods such as these are generally made of hardwood. If, however, the tripod will be used and carried in the field, weight and bulk will be important considerations. Determine what will be the heaviest camera to be used with the tripod, then get the lightest tripod that will effectively support it.

When selecting a tripod, there are other important considerations such as maximum height to which the tripod can be extended, whether or not it has a tilt-head, the finish and so forth. The tilt-head that was mentioned is very useful since it allows the photographer to level the camera when the tripod is on uneven ground without having to change the position and length of the tripod legs. Also worth noting is whether the tripod has a center post elevator that will make precise adjustments in the camera height easier. A center post also extends the maximum height of a tripod.

The Tilt-all® type tripods shown in chapter 15 are very popular among professional photographers because they are quite versatile, sturdy and lightweight. These tripods, although very effective for press cameras as large as a 4 × 5 inch format, are perhaps a bit light for use with a 5 × 7 inch view camera. In spite of this there are photographers using this tripod with a 5 × 7 inch format cameras. Many photographers feel that for what they may lose in the way of solid support, they gain in having a versatile lightweight tripod to carry with them in the field.

If no tripod is available for an exposure requiring support of the camera, other solid objects such as automobiles or lampposts may be used.

Cable Releases

A cable release is an essential accessory to the tripod. As Figure 1-32 illustrates, a cable release is simply a flexible type of cable that permits the photographer to release the camera's shutter mechanism without touching the camera and causing vibrations that the tripod was intended to prevent. To better understand the necessity for such a tool, place a camera with a long telephoto lens, or a camera with a bellows extension for close-up work, upon a tripod. After focusing the image, tap lightly upon the camera and observe in the viewfinder or on the ground glass the vibrations the light tap caused.

Cable releases are available in a wide variety of lengths, ranging from about 6 inches to several feet (refer again to Chapter 15). Note that the cable release is held in an "S" position, and that the cable is long enough to prevent vibrations or movement when the exposure is made.

Some cable releases are equipped with a feature that permits the photographer to depress the plunger on the release, thus activating the camera's shutter, and then lock it in that position. If the camera has a shutter setting for "bulb" but not for "time," a cable release with this feature should definitely be necessary.

Care of Photographic Equipment

Much of the care of photographic equipment amounts to little more than good judgment. That holds true whether considering conventional cameras or video equipment. Keep them dry, clean, avoid temperature extremes, and do not subject them to physical abuse such as dropping, striking or excessive vibrations.

Good care of photographic/video equipment begins with understand-

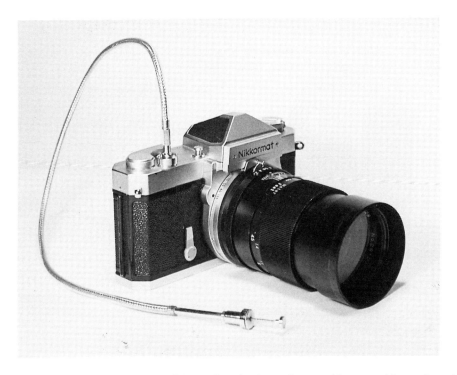

Figure 1-32. A cable release is a useful item for releasing a shutter without touching and moving the camera.

ing their proper use and limitations. And the owners manual of virtually all equipment provides instructions on proper care. When examining their suggestions one begins to see redundancy; they all have about the same things to suggest. The following list of suggestions is by no means complete, but does provide ideas and is applicable to almost all equipment. The reader should adopt them in whatever form will best ensure long-term reliability of the equipment.

1. Keep autofocus windows clean if the camera has that feature.
2. Never touch a shutter curtain; they are easily damaged.
3. Never touch the lens. Remove dust using a blower or brush intended for that purpose.
4. After brushing or blowing dust away, dust that could scratch the lens surface, use a lens cleaning tissue or cotton cloth with a drop of lens cleaning solution applied. Never apply the cleaning solution directly to the lens as it may run into components and cause damage. Never use a Kleenex® or similar product to clean a lens as they will cause scratches.

5. Do not touch the mirror of a single-lens-reflex camera. It is a *front-surface* mirror meaning the silver is on the front surface and is easily damaged.
6. When taking the equipment from one temperature extreme to another place the equipment in a plastic bag or case while the temperature equalizes. That helps to prevent harmful condensation.
7. Keep the camera/equipment in a case when not in use to prevent dust accumulation and protect it from physical damage.
8. Store in a dry place that is not excessively hot or cold.
9. Never leave a camera's mechanical shutter or self-timer cocked if the camera is to be stored overnight or longer.
10. Attach a body cap if the body is to be stored without a lens.
11. Keep the lens cap on the lens when not in use. Helpful also is to keep a *UV* or *skylight* filter on the lens to protect it from physical damage.
12. Do not lubricate anything unless the owner's manual specifically instructs one to do so.
13. Do not use accessory items not intended for the equipment in question. Use only accessories made by the manufacturer or an after-market manufacturer whose accessory has been designed for the equipment with which it will be used.
14. With video equipment disconnect all power sources before cleaning.
15. Some electronic equipment, such as with video, can generate heat. Do nothing to interfere with ventilation intended by the manufacturer.
16. Maintain power sources as recommended by the manufacturer.
17. Never lay equipment where it may be knocked to the floor and be damaged.
18. Submit the equipment to a competent repair shop when repairs are necessary. Unless trained, do not attempt to repair equipment one's self.

Chapter 2

FILM AND FILTERS

FILM TYPES AND CHARACTERISTICS

Introduction

There are numerous types of film available to the photographer. The most appropriate film to use depends upon the desired result and conditions under which photographing is to occur. A basic understanding of film types and characteristics will enable one to make a selection consistent with their needs. Generally, the investigative photographer will find that a limited number of film types will fill almost all their needs. One type of film may satisfy their accident, crime or fire scene photography while one or two other types may satisfy their surveillance photography needs. In this respect a bit of experimentation coupled with experience and talking with other photographers will be the best teacher.

Color Temperature of Light Sources

Color film is not all created equal. Some color films are intended to record proper colors under sunlight (5400°K), some under 3200°K Tungsten, and others under 3400°K Photolamps. When each is used under the lighting source for which it was intended proper colors are realized. When used with a light source different than that for which it was intended, the proper filter must be employed for correct colors to be realized. Conversion filters are discussed in the second half of this chapter.

Film Speed
(ISO Rating)

Before discussing the three basic film types available, it would be helpful to examine what is referred to as film speed. Photographic film carries an emulsion which is the light sensitive substance that responds to light and makes recording an image possible. Film emulsion, whether for black-and-white or color, varies in its diverse characteristics, one of which is the degree to which it is sensitive to light. Throughout this book the reader will note that at times film is referred to as being fast, medium, or slow. A film that is highly sensitive to light and therefore requires very little light to be properly exposed is referred to as being a *fast film*. It is also referred to as being a *high-speed* film. Film that is less sensitive to light and therefore requires a much greater amount of light to be properly exposed is referred to as being a *slow film*. And, of course, there is a variety of film types with speeds falling somewhere between the two extremes that are referred to as being *medium-speed* films. Each speed and type of film features its own characteristics offering both advantages and limitations.

For years photographic film has been assigned a numerical rating that indicates its speed or, if you prefer, its sensitivity to light. The rating was indicated by an *ASA* and *DIN* number. ASA was American (*American Standards Association*) while *DIN* was German. For example, Kodak Tri-X film was ASA 400 and DIN 27. One was equal to the other. Several years ago it was decided to discontinue the ASA rating system and assign film an *ISO* rating (*International Standards Organization*), a rating that combined ASA and DIN. Hence, a film that formerly had an ASA rating of 400 and a DIN number of 27 now carries an ISO rating of $400/27°$. Nothing significant has changed except the designation; we no longer say film has a given ASA rating, but rather, we say it has a given ISO rating.

DX–Coded Film

Film types vary insofar as their sensitivity to light is concerned. Film that is fast, in other words very sensitive to light, naturally does not require as much light to be properly exposed as does a film that is slow (not as sensitive to light). Cameras with an internal light meter must know what film is being used or they cannot compute proper exposure.

If one previously used a high speed film and later inserted a roll of slow film but forgot to change the film speed indicator on the camera, under exposure would result.

There was a time when cameras with an internal light meter required one to set the ISO rating on the camera so that its meter would *know* what speed film was being used and provide exposure information accordingly. Today, cameras commonly have a feature that automatically reads *DX-coded film* and sets the light metering system accordingly. Hence, the photographer need only insert the film in the camera with no manual setting relative to film speed being required. The DX-code range a camera will respond to depends upon the specific camera. The Minolta Maxxum camera, for example, accepts DX-coded film in the range of ISO 25 to ISO 5000. If non-DX-coded film is inserted into the camera, the light metering system is programed to assume the film has a speed of ISO 100, with this latter feature being common.

Film Types

The multitude of 35mm film types available may seem overwhelming to the beginning photographer until considering that they all fit into three basic categories. They are:

1) Color Print Film
2) Color Slide Film (chrome)
3) Black-and-white negative film

Color print film, like the other types, is available in a variety of speeds. Color print film can be recognized by the suffix of its name *color.* The names *Kodacolor* and *Fujicolor,* for example, lets one know it is a color film for making negatives from which prints will be made. Also, on the box it will say *Color Print Film.* This film type, at this time, is most commonly available in a speed range of ISO 25 to ISO 3200. The speed of the film, on the high end, can be increased by push-processing although color film generally does not respond as well to push-processing as does black-and-white. Further, some film development labs can't, or won't, push-process color film.

Push-processing, also called *force-processing,* is simply *overdevelopment* to compensate for *underexposure.* That is discussed under the heading *Push-Processing.*

Black-and-white film, like color negative film, results in a negative that must be printed for viewing. On the box it will say *Black-and-White Print Film.* Film of this type is most commonly available in a speed range of ISO 25 to ISO 3200. The range extends much further on the high end if the film is push-processed. With negative film, whether black-and-white or color, the more light it receives the darker (*more dense*) it gets.

Color slide film, also referred to as *reversal* film or simply as *chrome,* is also available in a wide variety of speeds. This film type can be recognized by the suffix of its name *chrome.* For example, the names *Kodachrome, Ektachrome,* and *Fujichrome,* lets one know it is a color slide film for making *transparencies* suitable for projection or direct viewing. Also, on the box it will say *film for color slides.* While color print film results in a negative image that must be printed for a positive image to be realized, slide film results in a *positive* image. Hence, no printing is necessary.

Color slide film is, at this time, most commonly available in a speed range of ISO 25 to ISO 1600. Color slide film can also be push-processed to increase the effective ISO rating but, as with negative films, there is a resultant loss of image quality relative to contrast and grain.

With slide film, the more light it gets the lighter it gets. That is why exposure on the shy side is better than too much; too much exposure results in a very thin washed out image with a notable loss of detail.

Film Characteristics

It was stated that the three basic categories of film are available in a wide range of speeds, the speed of a film referring to its sensitivity to light. But, the speed of a film also affects four other characteristics. They are:

1) Grain
2) Sharpness
3) Contrast
4) Color Quality

Grain. The surface of any film carries an *emulsion* that is sensitive to light. The emulsion has a grainy structure which, when examined under a strong magnifying glass or microscope, is apparent. The grain is generally much larger with fast films than with slow films with the grain structure generally apparent in large prints made from a high speed film.

Whether that is a problem depends upon circumstances and what is desired.

Sharpness is related to grain size. The detail that can be recorded on film, assuming both proper focus and proper exposure, is affected very much by the size of the grain. When a high degree of detail is necessary, a slower film speed is generally the choice because their grain structure tends to be much finer.

Contrast refers to the range of tones in a photograph. A high contrast negative will result in a print with pure whites and blacks, but a limited range of intermediate tones. A low contrast negative tends to not produce a print with a good range of tones. High speed films tend to feature less contrast than slow films.

Color quality tends to be richer with slower films, and although the photographer often considers that fact, the conditions under which photographs are to be taken also must be considered. One will not choose to use a slow speed film for its richer colors when it will be used under light conditions too low for that film to be useful, such as night time surveillance. Conversely, under normal day time conditions, when rich colors are desired, a high speed film would not be the choice. The surveillance photographer working with long telephoto lenses wants a fast shutter speed to eliminate blur from camera and lens movement and therefore will select a faster film even for day time use. The surveillance photographer is also concerned with getting a record on film to document the activity in question. Under both conditions the speed of a film is a greater concern than the color quality. When photographing a crime scene using a flash unit, proper color rendition and image sharpness for the recording of detail is important to accurately document the scene as-it-is. That concern takes precedence over the actual speed of the film.

Slow films, ISO 25 to ISO 50, tend to produce rich colors but a lot of light is necessary for proper exposure. *Medium speed films,* ISO 100 to ISO 200, are good general purpose films and produce good quality colors. *Fast films,* ISO 400 to ISO 3200 and more, generally do not produce as good a color result as the slower films. However, these films enable one to use a faster shutter speed when necessary to eliminate a blurred image from camera or lens shake, and they permit using a smaller aperture (lens opening) for increased depth-of-field when necessary. Further, fast films enable one to take pictures under low light conditions that would otherwise make nonflash photography impossible.

Because quality tends to be increasingly sacrificed the faster the speed of a film, a rule of thumb is to use a film speed no faster than what prevailing circumstances require in order to realize the best image quality possible.

The foregoing discussion should serve to illustrate why there is no one best film to use, and how needs and conditions will indicate the most appropriate choice. Although no single film type will serve all needs, most photographers attempt to use as narrow a range of film types as conditions within their realm will logically permit. By limiting the film types they use, they become very good at knowing which film to use under various conditions and what kind of result to expect. Again, talk with other photographers and experiment.

Latitude

The latitude of a film refers to the degree of over or underexposure it will tolerate and still offer a useful result. Color negative film has far greater latitude than slide film. The image resulting on color slide film is, in itself, the result. What you see is what you get and if the exposure was not correct one will have an unsatisfactory image that cannot be corrected. With negative film a great deal of correction for over or underexposure, and for color balance, can be made in the photo lab when making a print from the negative. For that reason, negative film is very forgiving for errors in exposure. Generally, one can deviate by as much as one f/stop underexposure and two f/stops overexposure. Beyond that range, a printable negative is unlikely; an acceptable print will not be realized.

Finally, some films within the same category will have more latitude than others. For example, even though color negative film has greater latitude than slide film, some color negative films have more latitude than others. And, fast films tend to have more latitude than slow films.

Photo Labs

When film has been exposed, it must be taken to a laboratory for development. But, not all photo labs are created equal. When one finds a lab that provides the desired quality and service, stay with it. The better labs may cost more, but their results tend to be more consistent. In general, you get what you pay for. If using specialized film or push-processing is frequently necessary, it will be necessary to investigate to determine what labs can best serve specialized needs.

Push-Processing Photographic Film

For nighttime surveillance photography, one may use infrared materials, or light intensification equipment. However, there are many times when the surveillance photographer must work without those benefits. *Ultra-high-speed-film* then is often necessary.

Fast lenses and fast films are essential for the surveillance photographer working with available light. By a fast lens is meant one with a large maximum aperture. Unfortunately, long telephoto lenses tend not to be as fast as the nighttime surveillance photographer would like. The maximum aperture for a 400 mm lens is commonly 5.6, for example, while the maximum aperture for many 800 mm lenses is no greater than f8.

Often the surveillance photographer will be faced with conditions where the light level is so low that obtaining a correct exposure with a fast film at its normal ISO rating is impossible. The solution then is to employ the technique referred to as *push-processing* or *force-processing*. Generally, when taking still photographs at night on a stake-out, one can work with a shutter speed as slow as 1/15th second with reasonable success if the camera is well stabilized and a cable release is used, but 1/30th second or more is certainly preferred. *Push-processing* is nothing more than overdeveloping the film to compensate for the underexposure that often cannot be avoided under nighttime surveillance conditions.

In practice, the photographer pretends that the film has a higher ISO rating than is actually the case. For example, while Tri-X film is normally rated at ISO 400, the photographer feeling that the film is too slow to allow a fast enough shutter speed for the particular task may choose to pretend the film is really ISO 1600 and expose accordingly. The negative naturally will be underexposed by two f/stops, so the photographer when developing the film will simply overdevelop to compensate for the resultant underexposure. The degree of overdevelopment must increase the more the film is underexposed. That is accomplished by either increasing the development time, the development temperature, or both. The best developer, times, and temperatures to use varies depending upon the film type used.

Unfortunately, push-processing film is a compromise situation since a great deal of quality is sacrificed in order to obtain a printable negative. Grain and contrast increase, often dramatically, when a film has been pushed. The photographer, with experience, will come to know when and how much to push, and what development provides him or her with the best results. While it is true that by pushing one can often obtain a photograph of much higher quality than would be possible with the film rated at its normal speed, one will begin to lose what could have been gained if pushing farther than necessary. Hence, one should never push film more than is necessary to obtain the necessary results.

Another point worth noting is the fact that when push-processing color and black-and-white film, there is generally an *actual* increase in film speed of only about one-third of an f/stop. When negative film is made, it is assigned an ISO rating, a rating calculated to provide the film the minimum amount of exposure necessary to obtain an acceptable negative of a scene with average contrast. There is, however, a safety margin of about one-third of an f/stop figured into the ISO rating of the film. Push-processing is possible because overdevelopment will serve to bring out an image that has been underexposed but is on the film nonetheless. Shadow areas that did not register on the film cannot be brought out by any amount of overdevelopment. The bright portions of a scene naturally can undergo a considerably greater degree of under exposure and still register on the film. That is why an *actual* film speed increase of only about one-third f/stop is possible. In a surveillance photograph where shadow details are generally of minimum importance and highlights such as a subject's face is of prime interest, a great deal of underexposure compensated by overdevelopment can be accepted.

When push-processing film, as stated, the more it is pushed the greater will be the increase in contrast and grain. Although a high contrast negative is generally printed on a soft paper (low contrast grade) to compensate, printing a push-processed surveillance negative on a high contrast grade paper, such as number four or five, tends to separate the features of the subject's face making them more distinct. The value of a surveillance photograph lies in its ability to identify a subject or subjects and to prove or disprove something. Therefore, the criteria by which general photographs are judged often do not apply when it comes to judging surveillance photographs. Keep that in mind when push-processing surveillance films; the objective is evidence, not art.

While push-processing does not significantly increase the film speed of negative films, push-processing color slide (reversal) film does cause an actual increase in the speed or ISO rating. Reversal films differ from negative films in that negative films get darker with exposure while reversal films get lighter with exposure. Unexposed portions of negative films are light while the unexposed portions of reversal films are very dense or black. A properly exposed reversal film does not use the full potential of the density of the film because if it did, it would end up being too dark to be viewed on a screen after a normal development process. As a result, reversal films have a lot of density potential which is not taken advantage of and not needed in normally exposed and processed films, even though the film is quite capable of recording details at much higher densities. In short, *a reversal film that has been underexposed and as a result is too dark for viewing often has recorded and contains both shadow and high light detail.*

By increasing the first development time, the exposed areas of the film can be lightened, with the film then light enough to be viewed normally when projected onto a screen. By increasing the first development time the proper amount and thus making the film lighter, a full compensation for underexposure has been achieved with an increase in the film speed resulting.

There are two development stages in the processing of color slide films, but when push-processing, only the first development time is increased. When pushing slide film there is a loss of image quality just as there is when pushing negative films. There is an increase in grain, the maximum density is reduced, and there is usually a slight change in color because of the fact that all the properties of the film's emulsion do not react the same way to the altered development procedure.

The reader who has need for high speed films is encouraged to research to determine what high-speed films are available at the time, for improvements in this area are a reality and those films discussed here can become obsolete by being superseded with something faster and/or better. Also, one should experiment to determine what works best relative to their own particular needs.

Kodak today offers black-and-white and color films that are much better and faster than when the first edition of this book appeared in 1976. For example, their T–MAX P3200 is a *multi-speed* black-and-white film with extraordinary latitude, making it useful at speeds of ISO 800 to as high as 25,000. In normal use, high quality negatives can be realized at ISO 1600 with little or no increase in grain and only a slight increase in contrast. Development formulas enable one to use this film successfully at ISO 3200 and ISO 6400 but with a resultant increase in both grain and contrast. Beyond those speeds, Kodak suggests conducting tests to determine the films suitability for one's particular needs. Kodak also offers T–MAX 400 which is an extremely fine grain black-and-white film. But, even the old standby Tri-X, ISO 400, responds very well to push processing. The authors have realized good results when pushing Tri-X film to ISO 4000.

Kodak Ektapress Gold 1600, a negative film, is rated at ISO 1600 but can be push-processed to ISO 6400 (2-stops). Kodak Ektachrome P1600 is a very high-speed slide film rated at ISO 1600 which can be push-processed two f/stops giving it a maximum rating of ISO 6400.

One other thing that the reader should be aware of when considering high speed films for night time surveillance work is the fact that with many films the ISO rating for sunlight is different, and greater, than its rating when used under artificial light. That holds true for both color and black-and-white films. For example, Kodak Vericolor 400 Professional film has an ISO rating of 400 when used under sunlight conditions. Under 3200°K Tungsten, it has an ISO rating of only 100, and under 3400°K Photolamps, it has an ISO rating of 125. Kodak Ektapress Gold 1600 Professional film has an ISO rating of 1600 when used under sunlight conditions, but ISO 400 when used under tungsten illumination. While that film can be push-processed by two f/stops, giving it an ISO rating of 6400 under sunlight conditions, it achieves an ISO rating of only 1600 when exposed under tungsten illumination and pushed two f/stops. That is something that the surveillance photographer needs to understand when selecting film for low light level work when anticipating push-processing.

16mm Films for Day and Night Work

There are several black-and-white and color films worth exploring for 16mm motion picture surveillance photography, for both daylight and low light level work. Many of the films can be push-processed for an increase of a couple of f/stops. One should consult a film supplier because, with time, faster and better films are developed. The best sharpness will tend to be obtained when working with a negative film and then printing that onto another film so that a positive projectable image is realized, especially when push-processing is anticipated. If push-processing is anticipated, discuss needs with the lab to determine how much they can or will push the film. Some labs will push by two f/stops; others will push as far as one requests.

FILTERS

Introduction

In photography, lenses are used to focus an image upon a piece of light-sensitive material. Properly executed, this creates a permanent record or likeness of the subject. The light being used to expose the image upon the film is, under normal conditions, comprised of red, yellow and blue colors. Although we see various colors as having varying tonal values and degrees of brightness, the film, if one is using black and white, may not reproduce them as we see them. Two colors whose striking difference made them very distinguishable may appear in a black and white photograph as possessing the same or very nearly the same tonal values and consequently not be readily distinguishable. A phenomenon such as this can and very likely will present problems under certain conditions. The resultant print of a scene photographed with black and white film may not have natural tonal values if photographed without employing the proper filter. When photographing with color, if proper filtration is not used under certain conditions with specific color films, the resulting photograph will in all likelihood be unacceptable because the colors will not be represented accurately as the scene existed at the time the photograph was taken. Proper use of filters enables control and modification of light under various conditions in order to achieve a true likeness of the subject matter.

There are basically three groups of filters or filter types that are necessary and useful: contrast filters control contrast, haze filters reduce the effects of haze and correction filters correct various conditions that would otherwise result in an unrealistic reproduction of a subject.

How Filters Work

Colors are really various wave lengths of electromagnetic radiation, and filters are simply designed to absorb certain wave lengths of this radiation; they work, therefore, not by adding colors but by subtracting or removing them. Also bear in mind that a filter absorbs its complimentary color, allowing the light of its own color to pass through, for all practical purposes, unaffected. A red filter, for example, allows red light to pass through but does not permit the red's complementary colors, blue and green, to pass. Instead, the blue and green are absorbed by the filter. If two filters are added together and the total consists of all three colors, *no* light will pass through, for it will all be absorbed. For example, if a magenta filter which absorbs green light is placed together with a green filter which absorbs red and blue light, no light will pass because the two filters together absorb all three of the colors.

The only filters in frequent use that do not remove certain colors of light are neutral density filters, which will be discussed later in this chapter.

Correction Filters

It was previously stated that although two colors may differ greatly in their actual shade, when photographed with black and white film they may well have the same or nearly the same tonal qualities. The result in such a case would be poor separation of the colors being photographed. By employing the proper filter, the tonal values and color contrasts can be effectively controlled, making them either darker or lighter.

In black and white photography, a yellow or yellow-green filter placed over the camera lens will make objects in the scene appear more natural insofar as tonal values are concerned than they would were no filter used. The photograph in Figure 2-1A was taken using no filter while the photograph in Figure 2-1B was taken using a yellow filter (K2) Number 8. The second photograph, which was taken using a filter, is a much more accurate portrayal of the original scene as its tonal values are much more natural. Without the yellow filter the clouds do not stand out as they do in the actual scene. The yellow filter functions by absorbing some of the blue and ultraviolet to which the film is so highly sensitive. With the excessive blue filtered out, the sky is reproduced in its natural tones (darker) rather than being washed out in appearance. When the sky is darkened in this manner, the clouds once again stand out from the sky, as one would expect them. Remember, there is a large amount of blue and ultraviolet from the sky, and photographic film is much more sensitive to it than a person's eyes. Photographic film has a tendency to see and record what the human eye does not see. This is true especially of haze.

Figure 2-1. (A) This scene was photographed with a panchromatic film without a filter. (B) Same scene photographed using the same film and a yellow filter Number 8 (K2). This photograph is a much more accurate portrayal of the scene as it appeared at the time it was photographed.

Correction filters are used not only in black and white photography, but in color photography as well. Probably the most notable are filters designed to correct color balance. Color film is designed to provide a correct rendition of colors under either daylight conditions (natural light) or tungsten (artificial light) such as from a common light bulb. When one film is being used under conditions intended for the other, the colors in the resultant photograph will not be natural or pleasing unless the correct filter is used. That is because the *color temperature* of each is different from the other. Film intended for daylight use, when used under tungsten lighting conditions, will result in too much red and yellow in the photograph. Conversely, photographing outdoors in normal daylight using a film intended for tungsten will result in too much blue in the photograph. Using outdoor film under fluorescent lighting will result in excessive green tones.

Conversion filters, also called *correction filters,* are used to prevent incorrect color rendition. When using daylight film indoors under tungsten illumination, use a blue number 80-series filter. When using tungsten rated film outdoors use an amber 85-series filter. When photographing under fluorescent lighting filtration is again necessary. When using daylight film an FLD filter (*fluorescent—daylight*) is the choice. When using tungsten film an FLB (*fluorescent—Type B film; 3200K*) is the choice.

One would be wise to consult a knowledgeable photo dealer to make the most compatible choice between film type and anticipated illumination. That is important because of the many film types available, lighting types in use, and filter choices to be considered. The correct combination is important!

There is an important exception to what has been said. Electronic strobe units, although emitting artificial light, emit light with a color characteristic (*temperature*) very similar to daylight. No correction filter is necessary. Hence, if all indoor photography is done using a strobe unit, one may use the same film whether photographing indoors or out. That simplifies matters for those photographing crime, fire, or accident scenes.

Haze Filters

Atmospheric haze is for the most part caused by light being reflected and scattered by very small particles of dust, water vapor and to a lesser degree, by the molecules in the air itself. Because the wave length of light gets shorter on the blue end of the light spectrum and even shorter in the ultraviolet region, these colors tend to scatter the most. The ultraviolet, however, is of much greater concern than is the blue light. It is this scattering of blue and ultraviolet light that causes distant scenes to appear to have a bluish cast. It should also be noted here, as has already been stated, that photographic films are much more sensitive to the blue haze and the ultraviolet than are the photographer's eyes. This is why a photograph will often show a greater bluish cast than the photographer observed at the time the photograph was taken.

Because this bluish haze does exist, and because photographic film is so highly sensitive to it, it is often desirable to use filters to minimize the effects of this haze when photographing.

When photographing with color film outdoors, it is advisable to use either a UV haze filter or a skylight filter. The UV haze filter absorbs only ultraviolet light and requires no exposure increase. If there is not a notable amount of ultraviolet light present, the filter does nothing. Many photographers make a practice of placing a haze or skylight filter on their camera lens and leaving it there as a means of protecting the front element of the lens against dirt, scratches or other harm.

Skylight filters are generally used to reduce some of the blue color and to add warmth to the photograph when taken outdoors using a reversal (slide) film. If too much bluishness is recorded with a color negative film, however, this can be corrected during the printing process. Skylight filters, in addition to absorbing ultraviolet light, will reduce the bluish cast when photographing on a very overcast day or in the shade.

Understand, however, that haze and skylight filters do not penetrate haze, they simply reduce its effects.

When working with black and white film, very effective use can be made of yellow and red filters to lessen the effects of haze. The deeper the yellow the greater will be its degree of effectiveness. The red filters will be found to be even more effective than the yellow filters. Similarly, the deeper the red, the greater its effectiveness will be.

One may question why a person would not always use a deep red filter as opposed to a light red or yellow filter if the deep red (most common being a Number 25A) is the most effective for reducing the effects of haze. It must be understood that the darker or denser the filter, the greater will be the necessary exposure increase. Also remember, a Number 8 yellow filter, when used in conjunction with black and white film, will generally render a photograph with tonal values that are quite normal. If a deeper yellow or a red filter is used, the effects become more extreme and radical.

The problem of haze and the need for filters to reduce its effects are very real factors to be considered in telephotography, aerial photography and the photography of distant landscapes. If a filter is not used, much of the detail in the scene will often be obscured by the haze.

Mist and fog, which are made up of water droplets and which have much the same effect upon a photograph as does haze, cannot be controlled through the use of filters.

Infrared for Haze Penetration

The use of infrared film with a red filter Number 25A is very effective as far as haze penetration is concerned. When using infrared for this application, it is necessary to greatly bracket the exposures (by several f/stops each way) because the level of visible illumination and its effect upon a light meter is not always indicative of the actual amount of infrared radiation present.

Contrast Filters

When using filters to control contrast in black and white photography, the main point to bear in mind is that to lighten a specific color, a filter of the same color must be used. Similarly, to make a specific color appear darker in the final print, it is necessary to use a filter of the complementary color. By using its complement, the light or a portion of the light reflected by that specific color is absorbed by the filter and is not permitted to reach and expose the film to the degree it normally would. Since that portion of the film is not exposed to such a great degree by that color, that portion of the scene on the negative will be very thin or clear and, as a result, will print very dark.

An area of police photography where the use of filters is highly desirable to control contrast is in the photography of fingerprints found at the scene of a crime. Consider, for example, that a fingerprint on a red surface has been developed by an investigator or lab technician and that the fingerprint has been dusted with a white or silver powder. If the fingerprint is photographed without the use of filters, the image may not be too bad insofar as contrast is concerned, but if that same fingerprint is photographed using a blue filter, the background upon which the finger-print is found will go much darker (almost black) and there will be very good contrast. Similarly, if the fingerprint is developed with a black powder and then photographed without the use of filters, there would be a very low contrast between the dusted latent fingerprint and the background. By employing a red filter to photograph the fingerprint, the background in the photograph will be very light and the print very dark. The resulting photograph would then be of high contrast. Filters of either the same color or of complementary colors can be effectively used in police photography to either lighten or darken various colors depending upon the specific needs of the photographer. The easiest way to determine what effect a filter will have on a given subject is to look at it through various filters.

Figures 11-12A and 11-12B in Chapter 11 illustrate the effectiveness of filters for contrast control.

When photographing latent fingerprints that have or may not have yet been dusted, the use of color film is usually both unnecessary and undesirable, for color in such photographs will in only the most excep-tional cases be of any value.

In cases involving blood, photographs should of course be taken using color film. This is true for any subject or scene where color itself is of importance. In many situations, however, it is desirable to photograph a scene or portions thereof with both color and black and white film. If blood is being photographed with black and white film, the use of contrast filters will prove to be desirable in many cases, depending upon the color of the background. Through the use of filters, the blood can generally be recorded as either lighter or darker than the background upon which it is found.

Polarizing Filters

Polarizing filters, often referred to as polarizing screens, will work only with polarized light. Polarized light is light that has reflected from a nonmetallic surface and is now vibrating in one direction rather than in all directions, as it originally did. The polarizing filter can eliminate that vibration. The surfaces from which light can be reflected and thus become polarized can be almost any nonmetallic surface such as wood, water, particles in the air and so forth. If the light is reflected from a metallic surface, however, it will not be polarized, since bare metal has a tendency to reflect all the vibrations. Finally, to get the maximum effect from a polarizing filter, it should be used at the same angle to the subject as is the original light source (see Figure 2-2).

Figures 2-3A and 2-3B illustrate subject matter photographed first without and then with a polarizing filter. From these illustrations it is easy to see how such a filter can be a valuable tool to the investigative photographer.

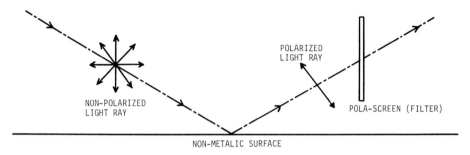

POLARIZED
LIGHT RAY

NON-POLARIZED
LIGHT RAY

POLA-SCREEN (FILTER)

NON-METALIC SURFACE

Figure 2-2. Polarizing filters are useful to the investigative photographer to remove glare from various objects. For maximum efficiency, the filter and camera assembly should be used at the same angle to the subject as is the original light source.

When using a polarizing filter, rotating the filter will make the scene appear to get lighter and darker. This effect, however, will make no appreciable difference as far as the basic exposure is concerned. The filter factor for polarizing filters is 2.5 or a $1\frac{1}{3}$ f/stop exposure increase and remains so regardless of how the filter is positioned and whether the scene appears light or dark. The only way the filter will require an additional increase in exposure over the filter factor of 2.5 is when deceiving reflections (glare) have been removed from an object. In such cases, an additional exposure increase of about $\frac{1}{2}$ f/stop over the filter factor is necessary. This is because light glare will often make an object appear brighter than it actually is.

Glass Filters

Glass filters, unlike gelatin filters, are not as susceptible to damage caused by dirt, scratches or fingerprints, but should nonetheless be treated with the same tender loving care as photographic lenses. Glass filters should be handled by the edges to avoid unnecessary soiling or

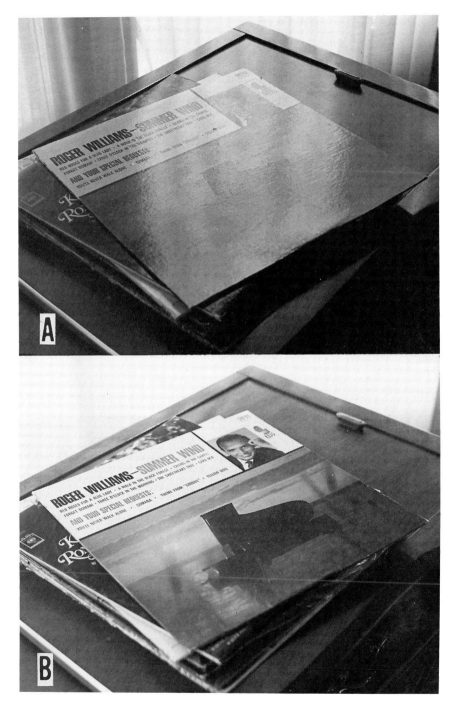

Figure 2-3. (A) The subject matter photographed without a polarizing filter. Note the pronounced glare. (B) Same subject was photographed at same distance and angle using a polarizing filter. Note the reduction of glare.

damage. When glass filters do become dirty, they should be cleaned in the same manner as lenses.

Glass filters are available in both square and discs. Discs are available which are mounted in a metal ring with male threads fitting the female threads on the camera's lens. This permits one to conveniently and quickly screw the filter directly to the lens. The other type of disc filters are mounted to the camera's lens by means of a special adapter. Some are equipped with threads to screw the adapter directly to the lens, whereas others simply slip over the lens. The best type to purchase will, for the most part, be governed by the type of camera with which the adapter will be used.

When purchasing a glass filter, one will generally find that they have been packaged in a small plastic container. It is advisable to keep these containers for storage of the filters because they offer excellent protection against dust and scratches. These containers also take up little more room than do the filters themselves.

Gelatin Filters

Photographers often purchase gelatin filters rather than glass filters for a number of reasons, but commonly it is because of the relatively low cost of gelatin filters. These filters can also be cut with scissors to any desired size or shape by placing them between two sheets of paper.

Gelatin filters are available in 2-inch, 3-inch and four-inch squares. Larger squares may be obtained from Kodak Company by special order.

A negative factor concerning gelatin filters is their susceptibility to damage from dirt, scratches and fingerprints. For this reason it is important that they be handled by the edges and stored in a cool, dry, dust-free place. Gelatin filters are very difficult to clean once they do become dirty or soiled, and photographers generally discard and replace them at that point.

Gelatin filters are generally placed over the camera's lens by use of a special holder designed for this purpose. The filter is placed into a filter frame, which in turn is placed into a filter frame holder. The holder is secured to the front of the camera's lens by use of an adapter ring which has threads matching those of the lens. Gelatin filters may also be taped over the lens or simply held in front of the lens when an exposure is made, although the latter method is not very convenient, especially on windy days.

Neutral Density Filters

Up to this point, the filters that have been discussed are those that absorb certain colors and thus modify the light passing through the lens to the film. With neutral density filters, however, this is not the case because they are intended only to reduce the amount of light passing through and no light modification is intended or desired.

Neutral density filters are available in a variety of densities. The three densities found to be the most useful are the ones that reduce the effective f/settings by 1 f/stop, 2 f/stops and 3 f/stops respectively. There are, however, a number of densities of both greater and lesser values as well as several in between the three mentioned. Neutral density filters may also be used in various combinations with one another to achieve specific desired densities.

Neutral density filters are often used on motion picture cameras when shooting movies under daylight conditions with a fast film. When shooting still photographs, neutral density filters are helpful if one desires to use a large f/setting under bright conditions to achieve selective focus. Under such conditions, one can use a large f/setting by reducing the light with a neutral density filter rather than the diaphragm. Neutral density filters are also helpful if one desires to use a slow shutter speed in order to pan action with a fast film. Tri-X® film with an ASA rating of 400 under bright daylight will have an exposure setting of about $1/500$ to $1/1000$ second at f11 or f16. In order to use a shutter speed of $1/60$ or $1/125$ second for effective panning, it will be necessary to further reduce the amount of light passing through the camera's lens. Since the lens is already set at the smallest f/setting, the use of a neutral density filter is essential.

The police photographer, however, will generally be concerned with neutral density filters under two conditions. These occur when using a motion picture camera with a fast film and when using a reflex-mirror lens which often has neutral density filters built into a turret mounted in the rear of the lens barrel. This being the case, the police photographer can expect to have a limited degree of contact and occasion to use such filters.

Filter Factors

Many photographers, when using filters with a camera equipped with an internal light meter, will make their exposure calculation simply by placing the filter over the camera lens and using the internal light meter. While establishing exposure in this manner will work, it is not always accurate, especially if a film with limited exposure latitude is being used, because the internal light meters in cameras are designed to operate under the influence of white light, which contains all three of the primary colors. If the meter reading is being taken when it is subjected to only a portion of the light spectrum, as is often the case when a filter is used, the accuracy of the meter reading cannot be relied upon. If exposure is determined in this manner, one should be sure to bracket making two additional exposures, one shorter and one longer than the indicated exposure.

A much more reliable method for determining the proper exposure when using filters is to use the factors that are generally provided with a filter. In many cases, the instruction sheet provided with the filter will give two different filter factors, one for use under daylight illumination and the other for tungsten. The reason for two different filter factors is that filters generally require a greater exposure increase when used under daylight illumination than when used under tungsten. Often only one filter factor, which is an average of the two, may be engraved onto the edge of the filter retaining ring. When the two specific factors are available, however, they should be used, because they are more accurate than the averaged factor. This, however, is not critical, and the averaged filter factor may be used with satisfactory results. It really depends, for the most part, upon how precise one desires to be.

Filter factors are not difficult to use. Assume, for example, that a red filter Number 25A is being used. When this filter is used under daylight illumination, it has a filter factor of ×8. In other words, the film, in order to be properly exposed when used in conjunction with this filter, will require an exposure duration eight times as long as it would without that filter. This means that the photographer must open the lens aperture three f/stops. Each f/stop the lens aperture is opened will double the amount of light that reaches the film. The same filter when used under tungsten illumination has a filter factor of ×6, which means the exposure time will have to be adjusted so as to pass six times the light that would normally be necessary were that particular filter not being used. To accomplish this, the lens diaphragm will have to be opened by $2\frac{2}{3}$ f/stops. If, when using filters, one should desire to utilize a specific f/setting, the exposure adjustment can be made by changing the shutter speed as an alternative to changing the f/setting. If a specific f/setting is not important, one may make the exposure adjustment by altering either or both the f/setting and the shutter speed.

Table 2-1 shows the proper amount of exposure adjustment necessary with various filter factors.

Table 2-1.

Filter factor	*Open lens by the indicated f-stop*
1.5	$\frac{2}{3}$
2	1
2.5	$1\frac{1}{3}$
4	2
5	$2\frac{1}{3}$
6	$2\frac{2}{3}$
8	3
12	$3\frac{2}{3}$
16	4

If, for some reason, the photographer does not wish to use the filter factor system as it was just discussed, there is another method by which filter factors may be used that does not require these calculations. Simply divide the film's ISO number by the filter factor, setting the meter's ISO according to the quotient, establishing the proper exposure before placing the filter over the lens, then placing the filter over the lens and taking the photograph.

For example, again assume that a red filter Number 25A is being used under daylight illumination. The filter factor is eight. Suppose also that the filter is being used with Tri-X film which has an ISO rating of 400. Begin by dividing the ISO number by the filter factor number, which will provide a quotient of 50. At this point, set the light meter at ISO 50 and establish the exposure (without the filter over the lens) as if one were using a film of 50 ISO. Having determined the exposure in this manner, place the filter over the camera lens and make the exposure. Both this method and the previously discussed method are accurate, so one must simply decide which will best suit his or her needs.

The following is a brief summary of commonly employed filters and their purpose. Specialized filters for infrared and ultraviolet photography are discussed in the chapters wherein their use for a particular technique is appropriate.

FILTER	FUNCTION
80 Series	*Color conversion* filters for use of daylight color film under artificial illumination.
80A	Increases color temperature from 3200°K to 5500°K. For use with 3200°K lamps.
80B	Increases color temperature from 3400°K to 5500°K. For use with photoflood lamps.
85 Series	*Color conversion* filters for use of tungsten type color films in daylight.
85	Decreases the color temperature from 5500°K to 3400°K. For use of Type A color films outdoors.
85B	Decreases the color temperature from 5500°K to 3200°K. For use of Type B color films outdoors.
FL Series	*Fluorescent illumination correction* for use of indoor or outdoor films under such fluorescent illumination.
FLD	When using daylight film an FLD filter (*fluorescent-daylight*) is the choice.
FLB	When using tungsten film an FLB (*fluorescent-Type B film; 3200K*) is the choice.
PL	*Polarizing* to eliminate undesired reflections from nonmetallic surfaces.
ND	*Neutral density* filters are used to control the amount of light entering a lens.
K2	*Yellow* to provide natural tone rendition with black-and-white film.
G	*Orange* increases contrast between reds and yellows with black-and-white film.
25A	*Red* is effective for increasing contrast with black-and-white film.
UV (0)	*Ultraviolet* filters are used to absorb ultraviolet rays to eliminate haziness of distant subjects.
1B	*Skylight* reduces excessive blueness when photographing outdoors.

Chapter 3

EXPOSURE DETERMINATION

There are four basic types of light meters with which the investigative photographer should be familiar. Each offers a feature not generally found on the other, although there are combination meters, a feature that will be discussed. The basic types of light meters are as follows:

1) Meters that measure *light reflected from* the subject.
2) Meters that measure *light falling upon* the subject.
3) Meters that measure *flash output.*
4) Spot meters that have a narrow angle of acceptance.

Incident and Reflective Light Meters

Of the above types, the investigative photographer will most frequently be found using a meter that measures light reflected from the subject. In Figure 3-1 is illustrated a Sekonic meter that measures reflected light. If there is a lot of snow or sand which has a tendency to reflect a large amount of light, this type of meter can provide erroneous readings when not properly used. Consider, for example, a situation in which one wishes to photograph an object surrounded by snow or sand. Under such circumstances, if the meter is pointed in the general direction of the object, it will for the most part measure the light being reflected from the snow or sand around the object rather than from the object itself. If this is not taken into consideration when determining the exposure, the resulting negative will be incorrectly exposed. If, however, the photographer was to walk up to the object being photographed and take the exposure reading directly from it, there would be no problem. If the subject to be photographed is such that it cannot be approached, the photographer can take a reading from the palm of his hand and then double the indicated exposure time. One's flesh tends to fool the meter, though to a lesser degree than does the snow and sand.

Figure 3-2 is an illustration of an incident light meter. They measure

Figure 3-1. This light meter measures reflected light. (Courtesy of Harry Gocho Enterprises, Inc.)

the amount of light falling on a given subject. Such meters are very effective and are used to a large degree by creative, commercial and portrait photographers. This is not to say, however, that these photographers do not make frequent use of reflected light meters also.

If it is not desirable or possible to approach the object to obtain the exposure reading, there are specialized light meters with a very narrow angle of acceptance that will enable the photographer to take a reading from small isolated areas of a scene without the necessity of walking up to the area to be metered. Figure 3-3 illustrates such a meter. The Minolta Spotmeter F is a sophisticated meter designed to take a *one degree spot measurement* of both flash or reflected ambient light. Of course, the photographer, when looking through the meter, sees a greater field of

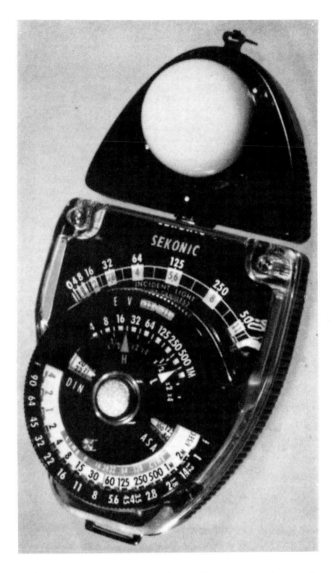

Figure 3-2. An incident light meter measures light falling on a subject. (Courtesy of Harry Gocho Enterprises, Inc.)

view. It takes little imagination to appreciate the usefulness of such meters under many surveillance conditions.

Related to the spot meters are zoom meters. Figure 3-4 illustrates a Sekonic Zoom Meter® which has an angle of acceptance ranging from 8.2° to 28°, which is the equivalent of a 300mm lens to an 85mm lens on a full frame 35mm format camera.

Figure 3-3. Minolta Spotmeter F features a one degree acceptance angle of ambient or flash light. The photographer of course views a larger area of coverage. (Courtesy of Minolta Corporation.)

When working under low light level situations using only the available illumination, and the illumination is so low that the meter fails to respond satisfactorily, try taking a reading from a white surface, such as a sheet of paper, and then increasing the indicated exposure by five f/stops. That method should yield satisfactory results or at least get one into the vicinity of proper exposure.

Multiple-Function Exposure Meters

It was mentioned earlier that there are combination exposure meters available that will perform several functions. Figure 3-5 illustrates the sophisticated Minolta Flash meter IV which is a multiple-function meter capable of measuring flash output, incident light and reflected light. Naturally, the usefulness of such a tool depends upon one's needs.

Figure 3-4. A Sekonic Zoom meter has an angle of acceptance ranging from 8.2°–28°. (Courtesy of Harry Gocho Enterprises, Inc.)

External and Internal Meters

The photographer using a 35mm SLR system generally enjoys the convenience of an internal light meter which has been built right into the camera. The photographer then does little more than line up a couple of needles, or perhaps center a needle between two indicator marks, and is thus ensured of proper exposure.

Internal Light Meters (Manual)

Internal light meters are very convenient to use because one can generally make the exposure calculation while looking in the viewfinder.

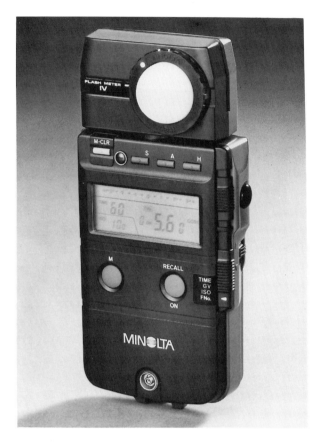

Figure 3-5. Sophisticated Minolta Flash Meter IV is a multiple-function meter capable of measuring flash output, incident light and reflected light.

Internal light meters are very handy if the person taking the photographs is not an accomplished or well-trained photographer, since all one really has to do is line up or center the needles in the viewfinder. Such a system makes it possible for a person without a proper understanding of the relationship between the shutter speed and the f/setting to obtain properly exposed photographs. There are, however, exceptions to this: A scene that is comprised primarily of snow or bright sand, would probably fool the meter, but as a general rule, if one lines up or centers the needles, a properly exposed negative will result.

The internal light meters built into 35mm cameras and 2¼ inch format cameras vary insofar as the portion of the scene from which they take the reading. Some such meters are designed to average the light reflected from the overall scene while others are center weighted, taking most of the reading from the center portion of the scene and only a small percentage from the outer edges. This information is generally furnished in the owner's manual provided with the camera and should present no problem.

External Light Meters

External light meters require the photographer to have a better understanding of the relationship that exists between the camera's shutter speed and the f/settings. The reason for this is that the photographer is no longer simply lining up the needles, but is faced with the task of interpreting the information provided by the light meter. This, however, is not at all difficult, and if one understands why it is necessary to set *both* the shutter speed and the f/setting, little difficulty should be encountered. The specifics involved in the operation of any light meter will be discussed in the owner's manual provided with that particular meter.

Cameras with Automatic Exposure Control

There are cameras available that feature automatic exposure control. Some are fully automatic, some feature what is called aperture-priority exposure control, and others feature what is called shutter-priority exposure control. The exposure control systems under discussion are most commonly available in the 35mm format.

With *shutter-priority* cameras, after the film speed indicator has been set to correspond to the speed of the film being used, one must simply select the desired shutter speed. The diaphragm or f/setting is automatically controlled and will vary in size depending upon the level of illumination. *Aperture-priority* cameras require one to select the desired f/setting with the shutter speed then being automatically controlled.

Some cameras feature both aperture or shutter priority modes allowing the photographer to choose one or the other depending upon circumstances. Yet other cameras featuring automatic exposure control are programmed so that the photographer need not choose either a shutter speed or f/setting, but rather, the camera will determine the optimum setting for both. When so doing, the camera will avoid, if possible, a shutter speed that is slow enough to cause blurring problems because of camera shake, or an f/setting large enough to unnecessarily limit depth-of-field. Fortunately, some such exposure systems, although fully automatic, feature a *manual override* so that the photographer may select either a desired shutter speed or a desired f/setting when challenging circumstances necessitate.

(Note ... cameras designed to accept DX-coded film do not require the photographer to set the camera according to the ISO rating of the film being used for such is set automatically when the film is inserted into the camera. Refer to Chapter 2, Film and Filters.)

Determining Basic Exposure without a Light Meter

When forced to calculate the basic exposure without the aid of a light meter, a simple rule of thumb may be utilized to obtain the correct exposure.

Consider that any film, when used under bright daylight (around noon), will require an exposure that has a shutter speed nearly equal to the ISO rating of that film when the lens aperture has been set at f16. For example, if one is photographing with Tri-X film which has an ISO rating of 400, the basic exposure under bright daylight conditions would be about 1/400 of a second at f16. If the day is overcast, increase the exposure by about one f/stop. If there exists a heavy overcast, increase exposure by another f/stop, or a total of two f/stops. One can, of course, make these exposure changes using the shutter speed, the f/settings or both. If the photographer is using Plus-X® film, which has an ISO rating of 125, the basic exposure for bright daylight would be about 1/125 of a second at f16.

When exposure is determined in the above manner, it is advisable to bracket the exposures by at least one f/stop on each side of the basic exposure to ensure a properly exposed negative. Bracketing can make the difference between a photograph of high or low quality. Nothing can replace experience and practice. The photographer should get into the habit of estimating the basic exposure before using a meter and then checking him or herself against the exposure meter. Although he or she will find the estimation is often a little inaccurate, it will also become evident that one can come fairly close without a meter.

Prior Exposure Readings and General Familiarization with Difficult Lighting Situations

Surveillance photography operations at night can present exposure determination challenges. In some instances the photographer will know in advance where photographing will occur and can determine proper exposure ahead of time. That can be done either by going to the anticipated subject's location and taking a meter reading, or by photographing it from the anticipated stakeout position and bracketing the exposures widely so as to determine, once the film has been developed, what exposure setting gave the best results. It is important to make exposure determination under the anticipated lighting conditions.

Another thing that can be tried when the security of an operation is critical is to make an exposure determination at a different location but one that has approximately the same illumination characteristics as the anticipated subject's location. Then, when photographing the subject, a greater likelihood of success will be realized. When guessing at exposure remember that it is better to overexpose a bit than to underexpose.

In many situations one will not have opportunity to determine exposure ahead of time and guessing will be necessary. For that reason, it is important that the photographer engage in experimentation and take test photographs under many varied lighting conditions, especially at night, to determine what exposure settings, with the film/s to be used, provide the best results. For example, take photographs of a coworker under a street light, in front of and inside a convenience market, standing on a street corner as the head lamps of a turning automobile illuminate him or her momentarily, when the dome light of their vehicle illuminates them momentarily when the door is opened, when lighting a cigarette, etc.

Directed experimentation and on-the-job experience will soon result in a frame-of-reference that will enable one to realize a surprisingly good percentage of success at estimating proper exposure under nighttime surveillance operations when using conventional photographic materials.

Subject Identification and Exposure Considerations During Surveillance Photography

During surveillance photography operations at night under existing light, it is the highlights of the subject's face that are important. A negative that is largely but unavoidably underexposed but contains the *highlights* of the subject's face so as to reflect subject identification is generally acceptable (see Figure 3-6).

A seriously back lighted subject presents a challenge. The backlighting will tend to fool the camera's internal light meter and suggest proper exposure when, in fact, the subject is little more than a silhouette and seriously underexposed. Serious overexposure of the background may be necessary in order to properly expose the subject. An example is provided in Figure 3-7.

Figure 3-6. Night photo of a subject illuminated by one nearby street light. 135mm f2.8 lens using push-processed T–Max film. Only the highlights recorded adequately.

Figure 3-7. Intensity of the background illumination makes an accurate meter reading difficult. Unless properly compensated for, the subject will be little more than a silhouette.

Chapter 4

FLASH PHOTOGRAPHY

Introduction

Many times it is possible to take a picture using no more than available light. However, there are many circumstances when supplemental lighting is necessary for proper documentation of a fire, crime or accident scene, such as would be the case indoors or outdoors at night. In yet other instances to properly document a crime or accident scene, to eliminate dark shadow areas, it is necessary to use what is commonly referred to as *fill-flash*. Properly executed such a photograph will depict the scene in a more *true-to-life* fashion. That is important for better documentation of evidence, and when testifying in court one will be asked whether the photograph is a fair and accurate depiction of the scene as actually viewed. Our eyes and mind tend to overlook shadows that can be pronounced in a photograph.

There was a time when the photographer using flash bulbs, or an early version electronic flash unit, had to manually calculate proper exposure. That involved determining the camera-to-subject distance and making a computation using what is referred to as a guide number assigned to the illumination source in question, and then setting the aperture (lens opening) accordingly. And one had to set the shutter at a designated speed so that synchronization between the flash and shutter would be realized; flash must occur while the shutter is open.

The method of determining a guide number, and its subsequent use, will be discussed although times have changed and so doing is not usually necessary with most of today's sophisticated *user friendly* equipment.

Because flash bulbs have largely become obsolete insofar as the investigative photographer is concerned, their use is not discussed in this second edition. And, because of the number of electronic strobe units currently on the market offering a host of features, and because of the rapidity with which advancements are being made, it is not feasible to offer more than a general discussion of basic features commonly encountered. Beyond that it will be necessary for the reader to assess his or her particular needs and determine product availability by obtaining manufacturers' data on the strobe units they offer at the time and make a selection accordingly.

Use of electronic strobe units is not difficult once one understands their general method of operation and has taken the time to read the owner's manual and experiment with one or more test rolls of film. In this discussion, we will consider that there are two primary ways in which strobe units are employed. We will examine their use as a *main lighting source* and as a source of *fill light.* In the final analysis, all flash techniques will be found to fall into one of the two noted categories.

Basic Strobe Function

Electronic strobe units produce a very brief but bright flash of light by storing electrical energy in a capacitor and then releasing that energy into a tube containing xenon gas. Typically the resultant flash duration is $1/500$ of a second or shorter. Hence, strobes tend to be effective in freezing the action of moving subjects. Naturally, some strobe units emit more light than others.

The recycling time of a strobe unit, the time it takes to recharge the capacitor and be ready for the next picture, will vary. With many units if one is using *alkaline cells,* which are disposable, the recycle time takes a bit longer than if one is using rechargeable *nickel-cadmium* batteries. However, alkalines, although offering a slower recycle time, produce almost twice as many flashes per set as will a set of nickel-cadmium per charge.

Because fast films need less light than slow films, it stands to reason that automatic strobe units must be set so that the type of film being used will be taken into consideration when the exposure is calculated. Proper exposure then is the result of the duration of the flash, the intensity (brightness) of the flash, the size of the lens opening (aperture), and the speed (*light sensitivity*) of the film being used. Fast films increase the maximum camera-to-subject distance possible with a given strobe unit.

With some strobes one must set a specific lens opening or proper exposure will not result, whereas more sophisticated strobe units allow one to choose from two or more lens openings depending upon such things as depth-of-field needs. Such strobes will adjust the duration of the light output accordingly. Some very sophisticated camera/strobe combinations will compute the exposure and set shutter speed and lens aperture automatically, leaving nothing for the photographer to calculate. Such a feature enables one to take quality photographs quickly and easily. For the creative photographer using the camera as a tool for the creation of art, such a feature will often not be desirable. But, for the investigator or police officer with a layman's knowledge of photography, such a feature can be very useful. The police officer investigating an accident during rush hour traffic has better things to do than begin making flash calculations. Quality point-and-shoot automatic cameras, many small enough to fit into the pocket, can be a very useful tool.

Automatic strobe units provide proper exposure by receiving information from a light sensor that tells it when the proper amount of light has been reflected from the subject and the flash output is stopped at that point. Some sensors are on the strobe unit itself, some can be positioned remote from the strobe, and some cameras have the sensor located in the camera body behind the camera's lens to measure light being reflected from the film. The latter is referred to as *Through-the-Lens (TTL) metering*. Such a method is helpful when lens accessories such as filters and/or close-up lenses are used, or when using a zoom lens.

When using a flash unit in conjunction with a zoom lens, proper exposure calculation can be a challenge. The effective aperture of a zoom lens changes as one zooms closer and further from a subject, a condition which can create practical problems when computing flash manually or when the strobe being used has a sensor on the strobe itself and assumes a constant aperture setting.

TTL (through-the-lens) usefulness results from the fact that it is not measuring the light reflected from the subject before some of its intensity is lost while passing through the lens and related accessories, or by being troubled by the varied effective aperture of a zoom lens, but rather, measures the light that has already made the journey and is reflected from the film in the camera. For some applications, such a system has limitations, but such is beyond the scope of this discussion.

On many early automatic models, or some of the least expensive models, when the proper amount of light had been realized for proper exposure, the flash output was interrupted with the excess electrical energy in the capacitor simply dumped into a quench tube and disposed of. Better units, in fact most of today's units, save the excess energy when the full charge has not been used, a useful feature that is accomplished through what is referred to as *thyristor circuitry.* The result is quicker recycle time and extended battery life when operating at ranges (camera-to-subject distances) that do not require the strobe unit's maximum output.

Establishing a Guide Number

Reference has been made to guide numbers, and it would be desirable to take a moment and discuss how a guide number is determined, and how a guide number is used. If working with manual equipment, this understanding is important. If working with modern automatic equipment, the photographer will likely not have to make such calculations.

To establish a guide number, simply take flash illuminated photographs of a subject at any known distance, 10 feet for example, using all the f/settings on the lens. After processing the film, examine each frame of the film and determine which f/setting (aperture) gave the best exposure and multiply that number by the camera-to-subject distance. For example, if the object photographed was 10 feet from the camera and the best exposure was achieved at f8, the guide number is 80 (10×8 = 80). Later, when taking a picture using that particular film speed (ISO rating) and flash unit, simply divide the guide number of 80 by the camera camera-to-subject distance and the quotient will be the proper f/setting (aperture) to use for correct exposure.

For the photographer who desires to be *very* accurate when determining a guide number, the proper method is to include an *18 percent gray card* in the scene and then use a densitometer to read the gray card on the negatives so as to determine which is most properly exposed. But, for the photographer with reasonable experience, good results can generally be realized by simply "guesstimating" which negative is most properly exposed.

Available to the photographer are many film types with varied speeds. When a variety of film speeds are to be used with a particular flash unit, a guide number will need to be determined for each film speed to be used.

When speaking of flash exposure calculation we commonly speak of *camera-to-subject* distance, because most commonly the flash unit is coupled with the camera and both are the same distance from the subject, at the same position. However, in reality, it is actually the *flash-to-subject* distance that is of importance in this calculation. For example, if the camera and flash are both positioned together at ten feet from the subject, then the guide number is divided by ten to determine correct aperture for proper exposure. But, if the camera-to-subject distance is ten feet, and the flash is positioned twelve feet away, the guide number must be divided by twelve to determine the aperture necessary to properly expose the film. Further, if the strobe is on the camera but a *bounce flash* technique is employed, the light will travel a greater distance which must be considered in the calculation. Additionally, the fact that the surface from which the light is being bounced (reflected) will not reflect 100 percent, that factor too must be taken into consideration. *When dealing with unknown factors or variables relative to exposure, be sure to bracket. By that is meant, take more than one picture giving some more, and some less, exposure than what is thought to be the correct exposure to compensate for possible error in exposure calculation because of variables.*

Red-eye Reduction

Many cameras feature built-in flash systems with the light source being very close to the lens. Hence, when photographing people they tend to result in a flat washed out appearance and also often result in a condition referred to as *red-eye*. Red-eye is the result of light reflecting off the veins at the rear of the subject's eyes. There are ways to avoid that effect. One way is, if using equipment that enables one to remove the strobe from the camera, locate it several inches above and/or to the side of the camera lens. That will minimize the red-eye effect. A second method, and this is especially helpful if the flash is built-in and cannot be removed from the camera, is to increase the level of the ambient light so that the subject's eyes constrict resulting in smaller pupils. So doing will noticeably reduce the red-eye effect. Doing both when possible is even better.

Pre-Flash is a simple feature offered on many automatic cameras to minimize the red-eye effect. It is designed so that when the shutter release button is depressed the strobe emits a rapid series of low level light pulses just prior to activation of the shutter and the main burst of light exposing the picture. The light bursts cause the subjects pupils to constrict so that the red-eye effect is minimized in the resultant picture.

Bounce Flash

Bounce flash is another technique that can be employed to minimize the red-eye effect when taking flash pictures of people.

Many strobe units have a flash head that can be articulated vertically and horizontally. With such a strobe one can employ a technique referred to as bounce flash if the ceiling and/or walls are white (*preferably*) and reasonably reflective. The result will be a photograph illuminated with somewhat indirect diffused light resulting in softer more even illumination.

Automatic strobes will calculate proper exposure when a bounce flash technique is employed with the flash duration being longer to compensate for the reduced level of illumination that results from the light being diffused, and the greater distance it must travel. If a manual strobe is being used, it is generally necessary to increase aperture size by two f-stops. But, the two f-stop compensation is a *rule-of-thumb* and bracketing is highly recommended.

If bouncing flash from a colored surface the light may become contaminated with that color to an undesirable extent and affect the color quality of the resultant photograph.

Fill-in Flash

When the police or fire photographer is called upon to photograph under normal daytime conditions, it is often possible to work without using artificial illumination by simply taking advantage of the available light. However, this changes in many daytime settings.

When photographing subject matter that is partially illuminated by direct sunlight and partially shadowed, it will often be necessary to use a flash to brighten the shadow area (see Figure 4-1). If exposure were set for the highlight areas only, the shadow detail would be lost. Conversely, if the shadow area were properly exposed the highlight area would be badly overexposed. The most practical solution is to use a flash unit to *fill-in* the shadow area resulting in even illumination. Such a technique is not intended to eliminate shadows entirely but only to lighten them and make details visible. If properly done, the resultant photograph will still appear to be a natural available light photo.

Many modern cameras have a feature that will automatically compute *fill-flash* for the photographer with no manual computations being

Figure 4-1. (A) Subject matter photographed without fill-in flash. Note that there is a disturbing loss of detail in the shadow areas. (B) Same subject matter photographed using fill-in flash. Note that the shadows are not as harsh and there is shadow detail that was lacking in the photo taken without fill-in flash.

necessary. If the system being used does not have such a feature, it will be necessary to make manual computations. The technique employed to properly fill-in with a flash unit is not difficult to learn and perfect. Although one can secure formulas and charts to precisely calculate the settings, there is a simpler and very practical method that will prove to be effective even though not as exacting under most circumstances. Such a technique is especially useful for the police or fire photographer in the field who may have to work quickly.

The following technique, with minimal practice, should prove to be effective. First, set the shutter speed for proper flash synchronization. When using a camera that allows properly synchronized exposures at several different shutter speeds, that will make the task easier and offer greater freedom with which to work. After setting the shutter speed, establish the f/setting (lens opening) that will provide proper daylight exposure with the chosen shutter speed. With that being done, the next step is to determine the correct camera-to-subject distance (*actually flash-to-subject distance*) for that particular f/setting. The photographer then takes a position just a little further from the subject so that the flash exposure will be slightly less than the daylight exposure.

With just a little experience one will become adept at consistently achieving the desired balance of illumination. When employing fill-flash some photographers like a ratio between the daylight and fill-flash of two f/stops, some prefer a ratio of just one f/stop. Each person is encouraged to experiment to determine what works best for him or her.

Multiple Flash

When taking a flash picture of a large area, if the exposure is figured for the foreground, the more distant portions of the scene will be underexposed and very dark in the resulting photograph. If exposure is figured for the central portion of the scene, the foreground will be burned out (overexposed) while the distant portion will be underexposed. The solution to such a problem is to use more than one flash unit to provide a more evenly illuminated scene. This can be accomplished by using slave units along with two or more flash units, by using extension cords or by using one flash unit and flashing it at various points throughout the scene while the camera shutter is maintained in the open position. The latter is known as painting with light.

When multiple flash is not possible, one may attempt to photograph from an angle that places as much of the subject matter as possible at basically the same distance from the camera. This will bring about a greater degree of sharpness because everything will be closer to the point of perfect focus with less demand being placed upon depth of field, and the subject illumination will be more even.

Painting with Light

Before becoming involved in a discussion concerning the techniques used to paint with light, let us take a close look at just what painting with light really is and what it involves.

When it is necessary to utilize a multiple flash technique because the area to be photographed is simply too large for one strobe or flash unit to handle effectively, one can use several strobe units coupled together with extension cords, several strobe units along with slave units or *one* strobe unit and walk about the scene flashing it at strategic points. The latter is called painting with light.

When a photographer uses a strobe or flash unit to paint with light, the end result of his efforts is the same as it would be were he to have used several strobe units and caused them to discharge (flash) all at once by way of extension cords or slave units. Figure 4-2 illustrates a scene photographed first using a normal one-flash technique and then a multiple flash technique.

The basic principles and techniques of painting with light are not difficult to understand or perfect. It will in all likelihood take a few experimental or trial sessions to familiarize one's self with these techniques to consistently obtain good results. It is also generally easier to obtain good results when painting with light indoors than out. The reason for this lies primarily in the fact that indoors one can take advantage of reflective surfaces such as light-colored ceilings and walls, making it easier to obtain even illumination since the light will tend to reflect about the scene and help fill in shadow areas.

When painting with light indoors, one will generally obtain the best results by standing around corners out of view of the camera and discharging the flash or strobe from that position. By so doing, the possibility of ghost images of one's self can be avoided. One should also consider taking advantage of bounce flash techniques when conditions favor it. If a bounce flash technique is utilized, however, there will be a necessary adjustment in exposure. This problem will be dealt with in

Figure 4-2. (A) This photograph was taken using a one flash technique. (B) This photograph taken using a multiple flash technique. (Courtesy of Lance Juusola.)

the section dealing with exposure calculation when using multiple flash techniques.

When painting with light outdoors using a flash or strobe unit, it is advantageous to use a stepladder so the flash may be discharged from a high point to avoid "hot" spots on the ground at each point the flash is discharged. It is also possible to fashion a 5- or 6-foot pole or stick upon which the flash can be positioned. The stick may be equipped with a length of cord and a switch that can be used to discharge the flash unit. With such a device, the strobe may be easily discharged from a high point. This is a little easier and more convenient than using a stepladder.

Exposure Calculation for Multiple Flash

Generally when one calculates exposure for using a flash or strobe unit, he makes the calculation based upon the camera-to-subject distance. The only real reason the calculation is based upon the camera-to-subject distance is that the flash unit is generally mounted on or near the camera; the flash-to-subject distance is the photographer's only real concern.

To better understand this, take a hypothetical situation and examine how the photographer may approach it with the idea of multiple flash. Consider that it is an indoor scene where an overall photograph showing all the rooms in relation to one another is desired. The photographer will first select the point from which the photo will be taken to most effectively portray the most essential subject matter. Whether the photographer decides to use slave units, or simply walk about the scene flashing one strobe several times will not concern the exposure calculation. The exposure calculation will be the same in both cases.

When painting with light, one will utilize what is known as an open flash technique. In other words, the photographer will open the camera shutter and let it so remain while he walks about the scene and discharges the flash unit. Consider now that the photographer has selected the point from which the photograph is to be taken. It is of extreme importance that the camera be mounted in such a manner that it is not permitted to move or shift at all while the exposures are being made, or a double image will result. A good tripod will generally take care of this problem. Next, it is important to adjust the lens aperture for proper exposure at a specific flash-to-subject distance. In this hypothetical situation, the most advantageous points from which to make the exposures are at roughly 10- to 15-foot points from the camera. Consider also that the proper f/setting for correct exposure at that distance is f11. That being the case, one would then set the lens at f11 and go about the scene making an exposure at every 10- to 15-foot interval from the camera position.

If the scene to be painted is large and without corners or obstructions, simply set the f/setting for a particular flash-to-subject distance and go about the scene flashing the unit. For example, if the lens is set at f11 and the correct distance for that aperture is 12 feet, fire the flash first from the camera position, then move ahead of the camera 12 feet and flash the unit again, being careful that you stand to the side and do not become a silhouette.

When painting with light indoors, if one decides to use a bounce flash technique to help eliminate harsh shadows, an exposure increase of about two f/stops will generally be necessary. If, however, the lens is opened up by two f/stops one will lose a significant amount of depth of field. If it is important to have as much depth of field as possible, a good alternative to opening up on the diaphragm is to flash the unit two or three times from each position rather than just once. It is also worth-while to consider not only flashing the unit three times or so from each determined distance, but from three different positions at each specific distance. Circumstances will dictate the desirability of such a technique.

Now, having discussed how to determine the proper exposure for multiple flash, it is time to examine a technique for going about the scene making the multiple exposures. As has already been stated, the camera must be mounted solidly to eliminate movement while the exposures are being made. The shutter is placed on time or bulb so that it will remain open. If the shutter has no time setting, it must be held open; most cable releases have this capability. The lighting should be made as low as possible so the photographer has as much control over the lighting situation as possible. This is also a good reason not to open the lens diaphragm to compensate for bounce flash but to leave the lens stopped down and make more flashes at each point as an alternative. The degree of unwanted exposure must be kept to a bare minimum. With the shutter open, walk about the scene to the various points and make the exposures. If the room can be completely darkened, the task is quite simple. If the room or area being photographed cannot be completely darkened, have someone, preferably departmental personnel, stand at the camera and place some object (a hat will work well) over the lens to prevent light from entering the lens between exposures. Take care not to touch and move the camera assembly. When ready to make an exposure, instruct the assistant to uncover; the assistant then uncovers the lens and indicates that he has done so. As soon as the flash is seen by the assistant, the lens can again be covered. Good coordination in this task will keep unwanted exposure to a minimum. After all exposures have been made, the shutter is closed.

Slave Units

When it becomes necessary to use more than one flash unit to adequately illuminate a scene, the use of a slave unit alleviates the necessity of bothersome extension cords or the need to paint the scene with light.

A slave unit is a device that is light sensitive and will react to a sudden increase in the level of illumination by discharging (flashing) the strobe unit to which it has been coupled (see Figure 4-3).

Slave units are very handy when taking a flash photo of a scene that is too large to be handled effectively with one strobe or flash unit. In addition to the main flash, one or more flash and slave units may be effectively used. There is no limit.

The maximum range at which a slave may be used depends for the most part upon the intensity of the main flash. The greater the light output of the main flash, the greater the distance at which the slave unit may be used. In most cases a maximum range of about 50 feet will be realistic. It is important that the slave be aimed directly at the primary or main flash unit. The flash unit which is mounted to the slave unit may be swiveled to point in other directions. When working with multiple flash units and slaves, be sure to exercise care so that the secondary flash does not flash towards the camera. When working with slave units, a simple ball joint will add to the flexibility of the unit (see Figure 4-4).

It should be understood at this point that when slave units are used to provide multiple flash illumination of a scene, the same thing is accomplished as by painting the scene with light. The only real difference is that by using the slave units the task is simplified.

When using slave units, there is a certain amount of unavoidable delay between the discharge time of the primary flash and the discharge time of the secondary flash. For this reason, a shutter speed of about $1/30$ of a second should be used. This will ensure that the shutter is open for *all* flash discharges. If shutter speed is too high, the primary flash will

Figure 4-3. An electronic strobe unit is mounted to a slave unit which will react to a sudden increase in the level of illumination by discharging the strobe unit.

probably be all right, but there is a good possibility of the shutter closing prior to the secondary flash units discharging. If this should occur, the purpose of using multiple flash will be defeated. This concerns only those cameras that have been designed to offer correct flash synchronization at several different shutter speeds. With many cameras, correct flash synchronization can be achieved at only one given shutter speed.

Available also are slave units that respond to radio frequency, eliminating the problem of other photographers' flashes discharging one's slave units.

Zoom Strobes for Zoom Lenses

Zoom lenses offer the photographer a great deal of convenient versatility by offering the use of various focal lengths without the inconvenience of carrying several lenses and losing precious time changing from one to

Figure 4-4. Using a ball joint will add to the flexibility of the flash and slave assembly.

another while in the field. Over the years the quality of zoom lenses has become increasingly better; hence, they have become very popular. But, because the *field of view* afforded by zoom lenses varies throughout the range of the lens, many going from wide angle to telephoto, and the effective aperture changing accordingly, their use with traditional flash units has been challenging. Challenging the photographer was both the uncertainty of proper exposure calculation and angle of coverage of the scene; the flash and lens may have two angles of coverage/acceptance. This is not to suggest, however, that the photographer had difficulty with proper flash coverage when changing from one fixed focal length lens to another, such as when switching from a normal to a wide angle lens. But, the difficulty tends to become more significant when using zoom lenses.

It has been said that need is the mother of invention. Today most automatic flash manufacturers offer one or more units that feature a flash head with an optical zooming capability. That is accomplished by varying the distance between the flash head diffuser relative to the flash tube. But this feature too has its quirks. When set for wide angle, the light output is spread over a wider area and thus will not carry as far. When set for telephoto the same amount of light output is concentrated into a beam and will illuminate subjects further away than when set for wide angle. Hence, the guide number changes throughout the zooming range of the flash head. Again, *carefully study the owner's manual for the equipment in question.*

When using a zoom lens with a zoom flash system, it is desirable to match their respective zoom ranges. Some flash systems feature three settings for wide angle, normal, and short telephoto lenses. Others feature a wider range of settings. The *Vivitar Auto Thyristor 5600 System,* for example, designed for the 35mm format camera, has settings to correspond to lens focal lengths of *28mm, 35mm, 50mm,* and *105mm.* Some manufacturers also offer flash lens kits for use when longer focal length lenses are employed, or when using wider angle lenses such as 21mm.

Battery Packs

When a great deal of flash work is anticipated, one may elect to obtain an electronic flash system that accepts power from an auxiliary battery pack. In that respect it is suggested that one obtain literature from various manufacturers to determine what is available and what features will be compatible with the anticipated use of the equipment.

Chapter 5

CRIME SCENE PHOTOGRAPHY

General Considerations

Before an attempt is made to make a detailed examination of a crime scene, it should first be photographed. By so doing, one is ensured of having a permanent record of the appearance of the scene and information and evidence when found. Often, if the investigating officer is a qualified photographer, he will do the photographing himself. If he is not, a qualified photographer should be called in to work under his direction.

Photographs of a crime scene, properly taken, are useful in a number of ways. Photographs often record small points of evidence and information that were overlooked when the actual crime scene investigation took place. Often a given item will have no apparent relevancy to the investigation at the time and is for that reason overlooked, but as the case develops, the item may take on a new meaning. If the scene had not been photographed, such evidence would very likely be lost. Photographs also serve to verify statements made by suspects and witnesses, and they show where the crime was committed and, often, how it was committed. By using photographs, investigators who were not at the scene of the crime themselves may assist in the investigation. Good photographs are also effective, just as are notes, to refresh the memory prior to testifying in court. Finally, photographs themselves often prove to be crucial as evidence in court.

Equipment

Until recent years, the 4 × 5 inch press camera was recognized almost universally as the most suitable camera for forensic and press photography. In recent years, however, the trend has been to use smaller format cameras such as the 2½ inch square formats and 35mm cameras. This is especially true of the press. Police departments have been slower to make the change, but the trend has shifted to the smaller format cameras and even to Polaroids in many cases.

Figure 5-1 shows a small press camera (2¼ × 3¼ inch format) next to a 35mm camera which would accomplish the same job in the field. By studying the illustration it is not difficult to understand at least part of the reason for the changing trend. Note how much less burden there would be on the photographer using the 35mm system. Consider also that modern 35mm cameras with a fine grain film will yield very good results. For every exposure a photographer makes with a press camera, a photographer using a 35mm camera could probably make five or more without any difficulty. By examining these points, it is not difficult to understand the reason for the shift from one system to the other. This is not to say that the 35mm camera systems are better than the press cameras in all respects, but that the 35mm camera systems do possess some very desirable features which tend to minimize their shortcomings.

Figure 5-1. A 35mm SLR is pictured next to a 2¼ × 3¼ inch press camera which is the smallest of the press camera family. The size difference between the two tends to indicate at least part of the reason for the shift from large to small format cameras in the police and fire fields.

In addition to a camera, the following items will prove to be helpful in photographing a crime scene. The camera should have, in addition to a normal lens, a wide-angle lens. If one does not use a press camera with double-extension bellows allowing close-up photographs up to a 1:1 reproduction ratio, close-up lenses and/or attachments will be needed. A good sturdy tripod, as well as a cable release, is essential. An exposure meter, and also a means of artificial illumination (photofloods or electronic strobe units) is desirable, as forensic photography is often done under lighting conditions that are less than ideal. An assortment of filters is essential for contrast control when using black and white film in photographing evidence such as fingerprints. A fingerprint camera facilitates documentation of fingerprints and tool marks.

Procedure

Photographs of a crime scene should show the sequence of events in a logical order even though they are rarely taken in that order. Often, the central area of the scene is photographed first and the exterior areas last. If, for example, the crime scene is that of a homicide which took place in an upstairs bedroom, it is very likely that the photographer would begin photographing in this location or at the point of entry, depending upon the specific circumstances, and then work his way throughout other parts of the house, photographing last the house, the grounds around the house and perhaps the grounds of neighboring homes.

The photographs of the above hypothetical homicide case, although taken first in the bedroom or at the point of entry and then working gradually away from the bedroom, would most likely be viewed in the following manner. The photograph showing, perhaps, a footprint outside the home would appropriately be marked *Exhibit A*. The photograph showing the jimmied window and the impressions left by the tool may well be marked *Exhibit B*. The soil deposit from the perpetrator's shoe on the carpet just inside the jimmied window would then be marked *Exhibit C* and so forth. Even though the scene is not generally photographed in the order in which the actual events took place, the resulting photographs should be placed in that order for viewing.

When photographing a crime scene, make overviews from eye level to provide four views from four directions. When photographing an indoor scene, take four photographs from each corner to show all four sides of the room. After this has been accomplished, gradually work in and take close-up photographs of small articles of evidence. When photographing small articles of evidence, be sure also to take photographs which show each particular piece of evidence in relation to fixed objects within the scene. Consider, for example, of what value is a close-up photograph of a fingerprint or jimmy mark if the mark or impression cannot be placed at the crime scene. If one can show that the impression was made by the suspect or his tool, but it cannot be shown that the impression was made at the scene of the crime, nothing of value will have been gained. When close-up photographs are taken of small evidence, a scale for size reference placed next to that piece of evidence is important.

Markings in the Field of View

When markings in the field of view are necessary to show important points and thus help the viewer to accurately interpret a photograph, chalk markings or small numbered signs may be used to mark such evidence as bullet holes, footprints and fingerprints. The only real consideration is that photographs should first be made showing the scene as it was before any markings were introduced. This holds true even if the marking is nothing more than a perspective grid placed in the field of view. Also worthy of consideration is the use of a transparent overlay upon which various markings can be made using India Ink. The overlay can be secured at one edge of the print with tape so that the print may be viewed both with and without the overlay in place.

When placing markings in or about a crime scene, be sure they do not in any way indicate prejudgments concerning the crime or its perpetrator. Words such as murder, rape or assault should be avoided.

As a final consideration, be sure that markings never obscure important details.

Point of View

Crime scene photographs should be from a position and angle that will produce both informative and realistic reproductions. Figures 5-2A and 5-2B illustrate how camera angle and position can have a great effect on the appearance of a scene. Correct camera positioning can make the difference between a natural and unnatural representation of the scene. When a photograph is intended to show what a witness was to have observed, however, the photograph must be taken from the position of the witness at the time of observation and at his eye level.

Aerial Photography

Aerial photographs can prove effective in showing the relative positioning of certain buildings and roads, and can illustrate to a jury the routes taken by a perpetrator going both to and from the scene of the crime.

Aerial photographs can in certain instances serve to prove or disprove that an individual could have committed a crime in a certain manner.

In arson cases where the burning of one building is alleged to have ignited a neighboring building, an aerial photograph can prove effective in illustrating the point that the distance between them is too great for this to have happened.

Photo Data

A record should be maintained regarding the time, date and location of each photograph as well as identification of subject. When photographing a crime scene or evidence at the scene, indicate the direction in which the photograph was taken and the distance between the evidence and the camera. Finally, a crime scene sketch should be made showing the position from which each photograph was taken. The seriousness of the offense will, of course, dictate how much time will be allocated for these things. Figures 5-3 and 5-4 illustrate two forms for recording photo data.

SPECIFIC TYPES OF OFFENSES

Uniformed Officers

Oftentimes uniformed street officers will be required to take photographs of various crime scenes which don't necessitate the response of a crime lab photographer. In those cases it will be up to the responding officer to take the necessary photographs of the crime scene. Listed are some of the crime scenes that officers most often will be required to photograph, and a few simple steps to adequately cover the scene.

Figure 5-2. (A) This living room has been photographed with a wide-angle lens. By positioning the camera midway between the walls on the right and the left, and somewhat centered between the ceiling and the floor, the lines within the scene remain parallel and very acceptable insofar as angular perspective is concerned. (B) The same scene is photographed with the same camera and lens. In this illustration the camera was moved to the right about three feet and elevated about two feet. That slight change in the camera position caused the scene to appear distorted. Note how the pole lamp appears to be leaning to the right while the gap in the curtains (left) appear to lean to the left.

Child Abuse

These photographs will usually be taken of a child or young person at a school, hospital, and sometimes at the child's residence. 35mm color photos of the injury should be taken. Polaroid photos of child abuse are not acceptable in most jurisdictions.

-Using color film take an overall photograph of the child showing the face and body.
-Be sure to take photographs which include the color chart as well as photos without the colorchart.
-Take close-up photos of the injury utilizing the color chart.
-If the injury depicts a particular shape, such as the outline of a coat hanger, belt, or extension cord, be sure to take close-ups with the color chart and also a forensic ruler to show the size of the mark.
-If the weapon which was used to cause the injury can be located, it should be placed alongside the injury in one of the photographs.
-In some cases it may be necessary to photograph the scene in which the abuse occurred. These types of photographs can substantiate or dispel statements made by the suspect/abuser. Photographs will also document if there are unkempt or dangerous living conditions that may be hazardous to children.

An important factor in photographing injuries close-up is to avoid washing out the picture. This can be done by using low power on the flash. Also when using a color chart hold it at a slight angle away from the camera lens so as to avoid a reflection.

Recovered Stolen Vehicles

-Overall photograph showing the vehicle and a reference point.
-Photograph all four sides of the vehicle, and include the license plates in one of the photos.
-Take close-ups of new damage or marks believed to have been made after the vehicle was stolen.
-Photograph the front and back interior from the entrance of each door.
-Photograph indications of method used to steal the vehicle. Such as damaged steering column, dummy ignition switch, screwdriver protruding from ignition, spliced wires.
-Photograph the odometer reading, and fuel gauge if possible.

PHOTO DATA

CASE NUMBER _____ FILM TYPE _____ ROLL NUMBER _____ CAMERA FORMAT _____

FRAME NUMBER	f SETTING	SHUTTER SPEED	LENS mm	CAMERA HEIGHT	CAMERA DISTANCE	FILTER	LIGHTING	LOCATION AND SUBJECT	TIME	DATE
1										
2										
3										
4										
5										
6										
7										
8										
9										
10										
11										
12										
13										
14										
15										
16										
17										
18										

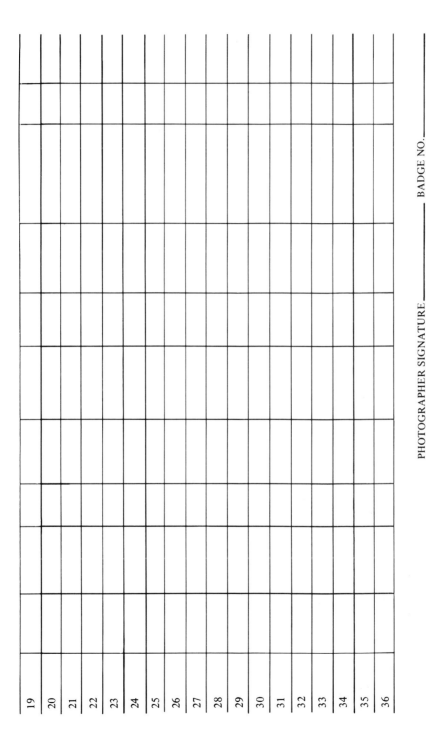

PHOTOGRAPHER SIGNATURE————— BADGE NO.—————

Figure 5-3.

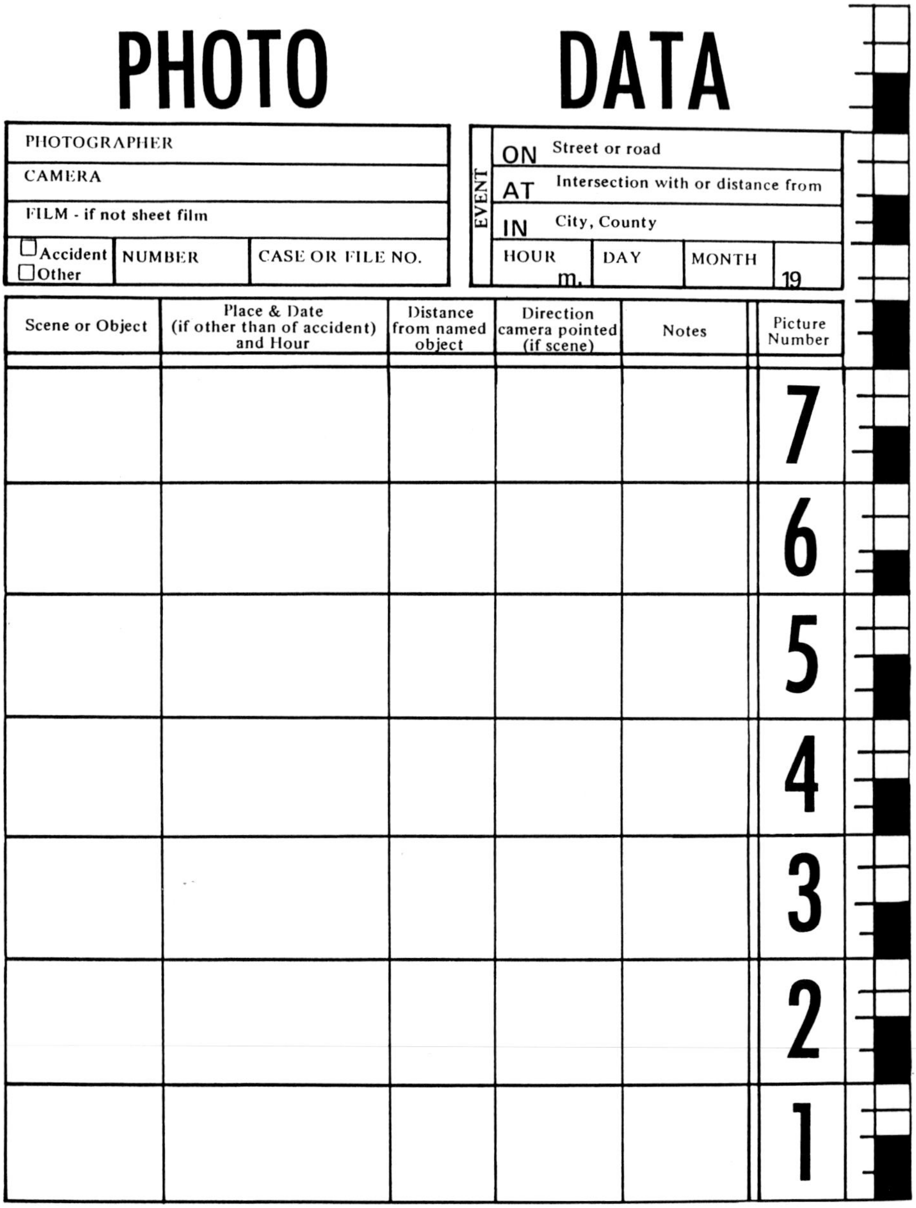

PHOTO DATA

PHOTOGRAPHER			
CAMERA			
FILM - if not sheet film			
☐ Accident ☐ Other	NUMBER	CASE OR FILE NO.	

EVENT
ON Street or road
AT Intersection with or distance from
IN City, County

HOUR m.	DAY	MONTH	19

Scene or Object	Place & Date (if other than of accident) and Hour	Distance from named object	Direction camera pointed (if scene)	Notes	Picture Number
					7
					6
					5
					4
					3
					2
					1

Figure 5-4. With this data sheet, a record of the photographs can be made by folding the bottom portion of the sheet under so that the last number showing corresponds to the number of the photograph being made. The markings along the right edge are one-inch markings. If placed beside small items of evidence, their relative size will be recorded. (Courtesy of Traffic Institute, Northwestern University)

-Photograph the driver's seat position. This could indicate the size of the person involved in the theft, or driving the stolen vehicle.

-Photograph the engine compartment, documenting stripped or missing parts.

Burglary

Proper photographic documentation of a burglary crime scene, whether residential or business can be imperative in pursuing an arrest and/or conviction of a burglary suspect. The following are examples of subject matter to be photographed in a typical burglary.

-Overall views of the surrounding area including the yard, parking lot, and immediate neighboring buildings.

-Overall views of the exterior of the building. One of these photographs should include the house number, or anything else that will identify the building or location in question.

-Point of entry. If marks of forced entry are visible, close-ups to show detail should then be taken.

-Point of exit.

-Photograph the condition of the rooms. A wide angle lens is acceptable if distance relationships are not an issue. The purpose of these photos is to show the extent of damage caused, and extent of ransacking.

-Photograph items left at the scene, such as burglary tools.

-Trace evidence, such as soda cans, or cigarette butts.

-Photograph tool mark impressions, as well as shoe or tire impressions (see chapter 12). It is also suggested that a photo be taken of the suspected tool alongside the mark (see Figure 12-7). The tool should not be placed in the impression, as this may alter the impression and render the photograph useless. This same practice should also be performed with shoes and shoe impressions.

-Photograph articles with visible fingerprints and shoeprints. If the item containing the print can be moved, oftentimes it is best to impound the item to the crime lab if one is available.

-Photograph the area from which the items were stolen. Such as a safe, dresser, or desk.

Chapter 6

ARSON AND QUESTIONABLE FIRES

General Considerations

Whether dealing with a large metropolitan area where the firemen are full-time employees of the city or with a small rural community where the staff of fire-fighting personnel are volunteer, there exists a need for men trained not only in the general characteristics of fires and how to extinguish them, but also in recognizing indications of whether a fire is caused by accident or arson. This is important, because an investigation into the fire's origin is usually initiated after fire-fighting personnel have voiced suspicions.

Illustrated in Figure 6-1 is the *arson triangle. Extinguishment* appears on the right side; this is the stage of the triangle discussed in the preceding paragraph. When arson is suspected, the second phase or *investigative stage* is entered. The investigation may be conducted by the police department, the sheriff's office, the state fire marshal's office, a special arson squad, or fire department personnel. In many cases the effort is joint, with much of the work being coordinated between any combination of the above-mentioned agencies. Following the investigation phase of the arson triangle comes the *prosecution stage.* It is at this point that the county or district attorney becomes involved.

The general procedure for the investigation of questionable fires is, for the most part, the same as that of investigating almost any crime scene. The first of three main steps in processing a crime scene is to secure the scene and protect it from damage by unauthorized persons; the damage caused by firemen while extinguishing the blaze is regrettable but unavoidable. The scene should be secured as soon as fire-fighting personnel have completed their task. The second step of a general crime scene investigation is to photograph the scene to create a permanent record of the appearance and general condition of the scene before anything has been handled or moved. This is important and can be applied also to the scene of questionable fires. The third step of a crime or fire scene

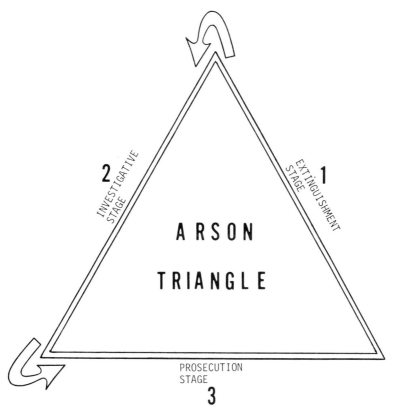

Figure 6-1. **The arson triangle.** On the right is the extinguishment stage. From there one goes into the investigative stage and finally into the prosecution stage which completes the arson triangle.

investigation is the search for information and evidence. This phase is conducted as soon as the scene has been photographed. When pieces of evidence and information are discovered, they should be photographed in detail as they are found, before they are disturbed, and again after having been uncovered and/or moved. It would be desirable to photograph each step as removal goes ahead during the search.

The photographer should understand the difference between evidence and information. There are many things that can be said to provide *information* which will serve to establish facts concerning the crime, but may have no evidential value should the case go to court. Information then has its primary value in aiding the investigator, while evidence not only provides information during the investigation but can prove or disprove a case in court.

Photo Equipment for Fire Photography

The photographic equipment suitable for the photography of fire scenes is the same as that used for general crime scene photography. The size of the camera is not an important consideration. A flash unit of some sort, as well as a moderate wide-angle lens, will prove to be essential for interior shots. If a wide-angle lens is not available, two overlapping photographs of an area is an effective alternative. Equipment for taking relatively close-range photographs is also desirable. Miscellaneous equipment will include such things as a tripod, cable release, a rule for size standard in close-ups, black and white and color film and a flashlight.

Buildings

The investigation of arson and questionable fires is not only a dirty task, but is perhaps one of the most challenging areas of investigative work since the physical evidence in many cases is either partially or completely consumed by the fire. In the investigation of fires, locating and photographing the point of origin is of primary importance, especially in cases in which multiple and seemingly unrelated fires point to an arsonist. If the point of origin is an unlikely location, such as in an area where there is no stove, electrical wiring or electrical utilities, the possibility of arson again becomes very real, and the course of the investigation should progress accordingly. In cases of arson, even though the point of origin has been located and photographed, it is desirable to photograph other points such as the fuse box and electrical utilities to document the fact that the fire did not start by accident at any of those points, but rather was started by an arsonist at a specific location. This can prove to be a worthy move should the case go to trial and the defense attorney attempt to cast doubt concerning the actual point of origin of the fire.

When the photographer first arrives at the fire scene, it is desirable to photograph the burning building from various angles and at various time intervals. Photographing a structure from a diagonal will enable the photographer to record two sides of the building with one exposure. Photographs should be taken at about 3- to 5-minute intervals. The reason for this is that photographs are helpful to the investigator in establishing the possible points of origin of the fire should the building be totally consumed. Some fire departments have placed Instamatic type cameras in the cabs of their trucks with the intention that the driver will, when he first arrives at the scene, snap one quick picture of the burning structure before going to work extinguishing the blaze (see Figure 6-2). The act results in virtually no time loss, and that one picture can prove to be valuable should an investigation be necessary.

Figure 6-2. Photographs of a fire in progress would aid the investigators tremendously if the building is totally consumed by the fire. Knowing where the fire was concentrated in the early stages helps to identify the origin of the fire. (Courtesy of Jack Jordan.)

The value of carefully sequenced photographs lies primarily in the fact that the rate of burning increases as a structure burns. Such photographs also provide a record of the position and condition of doors and windows; they may have been prearranged so as to control drafts. The color of the flames and smoke are good indicators as to the type of materials burning and the possible use of accelerants (see Plate I). The extent of the burning between each set of photographs will aid the investigator in establishing how rapidly the building was burning and whether that rate was in keeping with the type of structure and its purported contents. A time log should be maintained.

While the fire is in progress, it is very desirable to photograph the spectators every 10 or 15 minutes. This becomes doubly important if there has been a rash of fires in the area and arson is suspected. Often the identity of a pyromaniac will become apparent when his face begins to appear repeatedly in photographs taken at various fires at different locations throughout the area.

When photographing the spectators and a fire in progress at night, the illumination provided by the fire itself will often prove sufficient for available light photography. The 35mm camera systems are a good choice for such applications because they are not at all cumbersome to use and they generally have very fast lenses making low light level photography possible without the use of a flash unit. This is an advantage, especially when photographing spectators.

When the fire has been extinguished and the building or structure is still standing, the photographer should take a photograph of each exterior wall and then start on the interior of the building. The photographer should be accompanied and directed by the investigator and, if possible, the first officer on the fire scene. Each room should be photographed with a view of each wall. If there is any evidence found, such as remains of incendiary devices or unusual burn patterns, they should be photographed before anyone has disturbed them in any way, then photographed again after having been uncovered and/or moved. When the point of origin has been established, it is desirable to photograph it and the evidence. If the point of origin is in a location where there is no logical reason for a fire to have started, complete photographic coverage is important. The arsonist will sometimes use a petroleum product (liquid flammable) as an accelerant and will pour a trail of the chemical from one location to another to ensure that the fire will spread. Often such things as rags are soaked in a petroleum product and used as trailers to spread the fire. When this is the case, there is usually a deep charring pattern evidencing the use of such trailers. This charring will be found on such things as furniture, linoleum, carpets, wood and low spots or areas to which a liquid might cause a greater concentration. When this condition exists it should be photographed (see Figures 6-3 and 6-4). Any signs of forced entry should also be photographed (see Figure 6-5) as well as the position of interior doors, whether open or closed, locked or unlocked. If there is any evidence of protective devices having been tampered with, such as sprinkler systems, extinguishers or fire doors, they too should be photographed. Finally, if objects are removed from a fire scene without proper authorization, that act usually leaves telltale evidence. When such evidence is found, it should be photographed, since it may later prove to be important (see Figures 6-6A, B and 6-7).

Because fire scenes are generally very dark in color and reflect less light than is normally the case, the photographer should give the film one to two f/stops extra exposure to ensure against underexposure. If in doubt as to the correct exposure, it is advisable to bracket the exposures, that is, to take one shot at what is believed to be the correct exposure and then take two more shots, giving one shot more and the other shot less exposure.

Figure 6-3. This "V" burn pattern indicates the use of a liquid flammable. (Courtesy of Mel Hardy.)

Deaths

When there are deaths associated with a fire and the bodies are badly burned, identification can be a problem. Consider that with a badly burned body, friends or relatives will probably not be able to identify the victim, and fingerprints will be of no use. When dealing with such a situation, it is important to make notes and photograph anything that will have some identifying value, such as the location of the bodies in the building (see Figure 6-8). Concentrate especially on any jewelry that

Figure 6-4. **The underside of a balcony.** The dark areas are where the liquid flammable, which was poured about on the top side, has soaked through. (Courtesy of Mel Hardy.)

remains upon the victim's body. In addition to an overall view, a closeup of jewelry and related items is important. See Figures 6-9A and 6-9B.

The investigator and photographer at a fire scene involving farm buildings should examine each burned carcass carefully. One case that illustrates the importance of this point is a situation in which a barn containing a number of hogs burned to the ground. The farmer, while examining the badly burned remains of his hogs noticed what appeared to be a wrist watch on one carcass. Being unable to recall having furnished one of his hogs with such an item, he became suspicious and

Figure 6-5. When signs of forced entry are found, they should be photographed. Such damage could be the result of police or fire personnel gaining entry as rapidly as possible in an effort to save the occupants of the building, or it may mean that someone broke in to commit a crime.

Figure 6-6. (A) When something is removed from a fire scene, there is usually evidence of that fact. Illustrated here is the top of a stove before anything has been removed. (B) In this illustration the frying pans have been taken from the stove. Note the telltale spot where they had been.

Figure 6-7. Various items have been taken from this china cabinet. Note the white spots which are free of soot.

Figure 6-8. When the body of a fire victim is found, it should be photographed in its original position and location. However, when there is any possibility of life, the body is removed. In this case, there is often an impression where the body was found. When this condition exists, it should be photographed. (Courtesy of Wes Werner.)

contacted the local authorities. As a result of the farmer's noticing the watch on what appeared to be just another badly burned hog, it was established there had been a homicide, the victim had been placed in the barn and a fire set. The perpetrator was ultimately apprehended and prosecuted for this crime. Figure 6-10 should serve to illustrate how easy it would be to mistake a burned human for that of a burned animal.

Locating and Photographing the Point of Origin

It is not possible here to discuss every type of situation one will encounter over the years, but for the purpose of this discussion an examination will be made of some of the more common causes of fires, what to look for, what to photograph and why.

Fires are categorized as those that have been set, and those that are accidental. Obviously, a thorough investigation with proper photographic

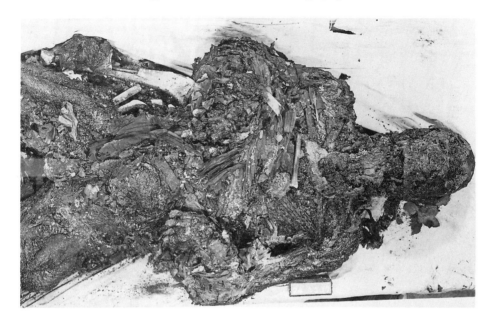

Figure 6-9A. From this illustration, the identification difficulties of badly burned bodies are readily apparent. In such cases, a photograph should be taken showing an overall view of the body. (Courtesy of Dr. Werner U. Spitz.)

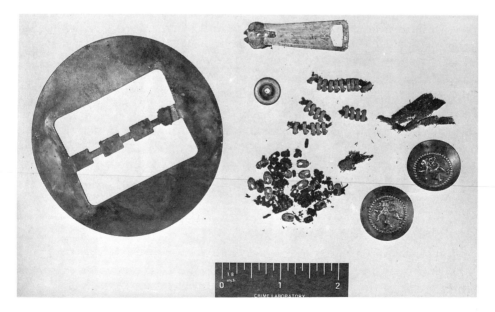

Figure 6-9B. In addition to an overall view of the burned remains of a fire victim, close-up photographs should be taken of jewelry and similar items because of their identification value. (Courtesy of Dr. Werner U. Spitz.)

Figure 6-10. This illustration should serve to emphasize how easy it would be to mistake, from an external examination, the burned remains of a human for those of an animal. This is why each carcass should be carefully examined when there has been a fire involving farm buildings. (Courtesy of Dr. Werner U. Spitz.)

coverage is important in a case of arson. With accidental fires, the photographs have their value in illustrating points of evidence which tend to show whether there was neglect involved. In order to establish the cause and origin of a fire, the investigator will endeavor to establish the point, or points, of the fire's origin. This the investigator does by studying what is referred to as *pointers.*

The reader will better understand what pointers are and their value by examining the following fires, their points of origin and the pointers which indicate that the fire started at a specific location. Figure 6-11 shows a hole in the floor of the living room of a home that was destroyed by fire. This hole is directly above the furnace. The arrow in this illustration draws one's attention to the phone box, which had been placed next to the furnace. In this particular fire, the body of the victim was found lying on the floor next to a telephone and it is questioned whether she was perhaps attempting to call for help but found the phone dead as a result of an explosion and subsequently a fire in the furnace. The hole in the floor above the furnace tends to indicate that the fire started in the furnace area. Figure 6-12 illustrates the living room ceiling directly above the burned hole in the floor. It is at that point where the deepest burning took place as is evidenced by the fact that the wood has burned completely through in that area. Further from the point, the depth and severity of the burns become progressively less. Figure 6-13 shows the doorway leading from the living room to the kitchen. Note that the wood molding around the door frame is burned from the living room side, not from the kitchen side. This indicates that the fire was traveling from the living room towards the kitchen rather than from the kitchen towards the living room. The fire in this particular case was determined to have started as a result of a faulty furnace. Figure 6-14 shows the furnace door as it was found after the fire had been extinguished. Figure 6-15 illustrates the door after having been placed back against the furnace. Note the pronounced bulge which indicates that the door had been blown off. Also note the mark on the wall (see arrow) which indicates that the door was leaning against the wall during the fire. Another indication that one should be aware of is the fact that a light bulb will often begin melting and bulge out in the direction from which the greatest source of heat is located (see Figure 6-16). In another case, the firemen were able to extinguish the blaze before it was able to do extensive damage. Upon examination of the scene it was found that the occupant had retired for the night, forgetting an aluminum pan over a lit burner on the stove (see Figures 6-17 and 6-18). In yet another fire it was found that the electrical wiring had been a "do-it-yourself" job and the fire started at the electrical box and traveled upward from that point (see Figures 6-19 and 6-20).

The fires that have been examined thus far were all determined to have resulted from accidental causes. In other words, they were not fires that were intentionally set by a pyromaniac, or for other reasons such as insurance fraud, hate, or revenge. There are times, however, when a building, after having burned either partially or completely, will bear evidence of having had more than one fire within it, or there will be signs of one or more incendiary devices having been used. As was pointed out, when there has been more than one fire without intercommunication, the possibility of arson should be considered. When a *set* (incendiary device) is found, that possibility becomes obvious. An unsuccessful set is illustrated in Figures 6-21, 6-22 and 6-23. Figure 6-21 illustrates the entire set as it was found. Figure 6-22 is a close-up view of the burning on the ground and the matches scattered about, probably a result of carelessness. Figure 6-23 illustrates the number of matches that were placed along the top edge of the window frame as a means of

Figure 6-11. The hole in the living room floor is directly above the furnace, indicating that the fire had started in the furnace area. The arrow in the upper left portion points to the phone box.

Figure 6-12. The living room ceiling directly above the hole in the floor was burned severely. As one moves away from that point, the depth and severity of the burns become progressively less.

ensuring that the fire would spread. When conditions such as this exist, it is obvious that the fire was set, and complete photographic documentation is essential.

Although it is not possible to cover the multitude of things one will come across over the years, the reader has been introduced to the type of conditions he will be seeking to identify and photograph. This section has examined the most common causes of fires.

Motor Vehicle Fires

When a motor vehicle has burned, the initial concern is locating the point of origin. An important consideration when examining and photographing a burned vehicle is the windows. Do they show signs of

Figure 6-13. The arrow indicates the burned molding on the door frame leading from the living room (right) to the kitchen (left). The fact that the right side of the molding is burned more severely than the left indicates that the fire was traveling from the living room towards the kitchen.

Figure 6-14. **The furnace door just as it was found after the fire had been extinguished.**

having been subjected to intense heat or melted to some degree, or have they been blown out by an explosion? As with all types of fires, if there is evidence of any equipment having been removed or substituted with cheaper equipment, that evidence should be photographed. If the vehicle fire had been set, the perpetrator would be likely to remove the battery, heater, radio, tape player, spare tire, hub caps and so forth. In sport models, the seats will sometimes have been removed. Remember also, as was stated earlier, that if things are moved after a fire, there is often evidence of that fact. It is also desirable to examine the lines leading from the fuel pump and the drain plug on the underside of the gas tank because the flammable used to ignite the vehicle is often acquired from these sources.

Figure 6-15. **The furnace door after having been placed back against the furnace.** Note the pronounced bulge which indicates that the door had been blown off. Also note the mark on the wall (see arrow) which indicates that the door was leaning against that spot during the fire.

Summary

What has been discussed are the general aspects of fire photography. When the investigating officer is not a photographer himself, he generally requests one. The photographer may not be an arson expert, but his work with the arson investigator will go much smoother and easier if he has some general understanding and appreciation for the reasons he will be asked to photograph various points.

Figure 6-16. Another good indicator is a light bulb; it will often begin melting and bulge in the direction of the greatest source of heat.

Figure 6-17. Note that the burner control (second from right) has been left on and the aluminum pan on the right rear burner has melted.

Figure 6-18. Overall view of the stove pictured in Figure 6-14. Note that the fire had started on the stove and traveled upward from there. These two photographs illustrate the point of origin of that particular fire.

Figure 6-19. An examination of the electrical box revealed a do-it-yourself wiring job. The fire had started in the box and traveled upward from that point. Note the arrow which indicates the melted cable which indicates a short in the system.

Figure 6-20. **A close-up view of the melted cable (note beaded wire ends) indicated by the arrow in Figure 6-19.**

Figure 6-21. **An overall view of an unsuccessful set.** Note the matches that were placed along the top of the window frame and the matches scattered on the ground. (Courtesy of Mel Hardy.)

Figure 6-22. **Close-up view of the burning on the ground and the matches scattered about, probably a result of carelessness.** (Courtesy of Mel Hardy.)

Figure 6-23. **Close-up view of the matches that were placed along the top of the window frame to ensure that the fire would spread.** (Courtesy of Mel Hardy.)

Chapter 7

TRAFFIC ACCIDENT PHOTOGRAPHY

General Considerations

Generally, when faced with a motor vehicle accident of very minor consequences, little more than the routine completion of an accident report is necessary. This fact changes when one is faced with an accident involving considerable property damage, personal injury or death.

Photographs of an accident scene, if properly taken, can be of value in a number of ways. Photographs can well serve the investigating officer as a memory refresher when asked to testify in court concerning his findings. In this respect, photographs can be as helpful as notes. Photographs can also be a very effective aid by which to illustrate or clarify a point in court, a sequence of events or a condition at the scene. They often record circumstances that were overlooked when the actual investigation was conducted at the scene. This is a very important point, for the investigator can often learn more about a particular scene if he has the opportunity to quietly sit back at a later time and date and make another detailed examination of the scene in the photographs. Consider also that many accidents occur at night when it is easy, because of the darkness, to overlook some important detail. Flash pictures will, however, generally provide a very good record of that overlooked piece of information. Photographs will also enable other investigators, who were not at the scene, to study and assist the investigating officer, and they will often provide a good record of weather conditions as they existed at the time of the accident. This is important, because weather is so often an important contributing factor in vehicular mishaps. Finally, photographs may serve to prove or disprove statements made by the parties involved and witnesses, and may also provide important evidence in civil suits that may result.

Photographing the Scene

Properly photographing an accident scene can often take as little as three or four minutes. The total number of exposures required to adequately cover the situation will, of course, depend upon the specific circumstances, but generally a minimum of six photographs will be necessary. The photographer is by no means limited to just one method or procedure by which to effectively photograph an accident, but one procedure which works well is simply to photograph the immediate scene and the approaches to it. The photographer should, before taking the photographs, look the scene over for a moment and formulate in his own mind what he intends to do and why. By so doing, the photographer can operate in a manner that is systematic rather than haphazard.

Figure 7-1 illustrates a typical intersection at which two vehicles have collided. A photographer should first photograph from about 100 feet from the intersection. This photograph should be taken looking straight down the roadway which one of the vehicles was traveling, looking towards the intersection in which the accident took place. The second photograph should be taken from the same basic position but this time looking in the direction from which the second vehicle was traveling to show whether or not there were any view obstructions which would have prevented either driver from seeing the other. After the second exposure has been made, approach the intersection and make a third exposure of that intersection from about 25 feet to provide a closer view of the vehicles and their final position, their license plate numbers, point of impact, resulting damage and so forth. This closer view will also record things in better perspective. This is an important point to bear in mind, since the photographs taken from a greater distance will tend to show a flat, compressed view of things. The problems that can result are apparent when examining Figures 7-2A and 7-2B. After the intersection has been photographed from about 25 feet, move in for any close-ups that may be necessary, depending upon the specific circumstances. The process is then repeated in reverse for the roadway upon which the second vehicle was traveling. In other words, go up the roadway about 25 feet and make an exposure of the intersection. After making that exposure, proceed to about 100 feet from the intersection and make two more exposures, one looking directly at the intersection and other looking in the direction from which the other vehicle was traveling. These photographs should be taken from the approximate eye level of the drivers involved. After these photographs have been taken, it is desirable to carefully photograph any skid and yaw marks that are of importance and which may not have shown up adequately in the general overall views. When photographing skid marks, be aware that there is generally a shadow area leading up to the skid mark itself. This shadow is often faint and can easily be overlooked if the investigator or photographer is not mindful to make a close examination of the mark. It is helpful, when seeking a shadow, to look from various heights and angles to the shadow in order to establish which position will bring it out the best. When this point has been established, take the photograph from that point. A photograph, or series of photographs, of the tires of the vehicles involved is often useful, especially if it is wet, icy or snowy and the tires happen to be bald or in generally unsafe condition. Such photographs are effective to show neglect or that a violation is in evidence (see Figure 7-3). Some states have a law stating that a tire worn beyond a certain tread depth is unsafe and therefore must not be used upon the streets and highways. When photographing the damage to the vehicles, do not overlook the possibility of the insides of the vehicles bearing important evidence and information. A photograph of the vehicle's interior is often desirable to show, among other things, the extent of the damage (see Figure 7-4). If there were any witnesses to the mishap, it is often advantageous to photograph the scene from their location when they made their observations.

When photographing an accident scene, it is desirable to employ some method by which to mark the point from which each photograph is taken so that a sketch can later be made reflecting this information. A yellow lumber crayon or can of spray paint works well for this purpose.

When an accident takes place at night or during dark rainy weather, as it very often does, it will be necessary to utilize a flash or strobe unit to illuminate the scene. If the scene should cover a rather large area, however, it may be necessary to use a multiple flash with slave units or paint the scene with light. For a detailed discussion of flash techniques, refer to Chapter 4, "Painting With Light." Also worth considering is the use of very large flash bulbs, approximately the size of 75- to 100-watt light bulbs to provide a tremendous amount of illumination. When photographing vehicles using a flash unit, the license plate of a vehicle will generally record so dark on the film because of the reflective characteristics of license plates that it will be necessary to "burn in" the plate when the negative is printed (see Figures 7-5A and 7-5B).

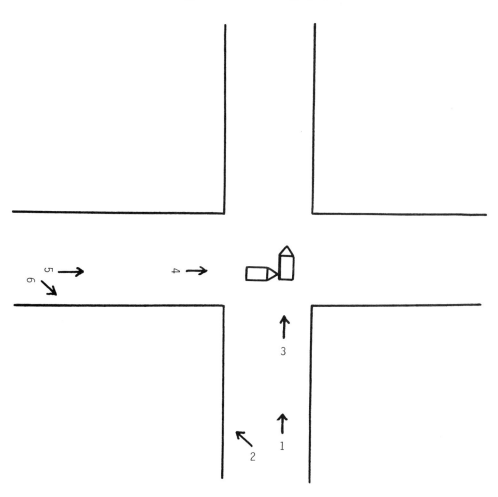

Figure 7-1. **A typical intersection in which two vehicles have collided.** This diagram outlines the positions and directions from which photographs should be taken.

When the photographer has completed photographing the scene, he should have a series of photographs that can be laid out in a sequence that will, in a sense, reconstruct the scene. Remember, however, that the photographs are intended only to supplement the written report, not replace it. The investigating officer should never neglect any portion of his investigation or investigation report, feeling that he can fall back on the photographs. This is not the purpose of the photographs.

When planning photographs that will serve to reconstruct a scene and illustrate the sequence of events, it is often desirable to begin at the final resting place of the vehicles involved and work backwards. This proce-

Figure 7-2. (A) **Skid marks photographed from a relatively long distance using a "mild" telephoto lens.** Note how short the marks appear to be. (B) **Same skid marks photographed from close range using a "moderate" wide-angle lens.** Note how long they appear to be. Use of a normal lens from a carefully selected position is desirable to offer true perspective. It is also advisable to include a side view if possible.

Figure 7-3. If the tires of any vehicle involved in an accident are badly worn or in generally unsafe condition, they should be photographed.

dure will often serve to give a clearer picture of what really happened. Again, as stated previously, the photographs of all scenes, whether fire, crime or accident, are generally intended to show the sequence of events by way of several photographs presented in a given order. However, the photographs are rarely taken in that order.

In summary, it is important to make a record of the location photographed, and the time and date it was done. Be sure, also, that the photographs will serve to identify the vehicles involved and their final positions. The license numbers of all vehicles involved should appear in at least one of the photographs (see Figures 7-6 and 7-7). If there is some small point of interest or article of importance and it is necessary to take a close-up photograph, be sure to include a scale for size reference and

Figure 7-4. Photographing the interior of damaged vehicles is often desirable to show the extent of the damage. In many instances, such photographs also show open alcoholic beverage containers.

also take an overall view photograph showing upon which vehicle and where upon that vehicle the particular point exists. This holds true of all accident and crime scene photographs. When photographing an accident scene, be as objective as when investigating a crime or fire scene. Strive to obtain facts and do not worry about, or attempt to show, fault in one particular driver. Sometimes the driver which first appears to be at fault later proves not to be.

One final statement concerning the photographing of traffic accident scenes: The basic procedure should remain the same whether one or several vehicles are involved. The photographs should show the approaches from about 100 feet, then from about 25 feet, and then any close-up views that may be necessary.

Color versus Black and White

The question of whether to use color or black and white photographic materials for the photographing of vehicle accidents must be decided

Figure 7-5. (A) When a vehicle is photographed at night using a flash unit of some type, the license plate will generally be so dark on the negative that it will print as white. This is because of the reflective characteristics of a license plate. (B) This print made from the same negative as the print in Figure 77A. The license plate was "burned" in for legibility.

Figure 7-6. This photograph identifies the vehicles involved in the mishap and illustrates the minor degree of damage to the truck, evidence that the train as not moving at a high rate of speed.

upon by the photographer and/or his department head. But, remember that black and white film does not provide as accurate or true-to-life resemblance of the scene as does color.

Photogrammetry

Not infrequently when a crime or accident scene is photographed, the scene is also sketched. The sketch is generally intended to supplement the photographs by illustrating the actual position of and relative distance between various objects. It is often desirable to make a second sketch to show the location from which each photograph was taken. When a sketch is made and measurements are included, it is important that an accepted method such as *triangulation* or *coordinates* be used.

As just stated, photography plays an important role in documenting the relationships between various objects. Although the actual mapping of the scene is most commonly done by taking measurements while at the scene, an accurate map of the scene can be made from the photographs themselves by using what is referred to as a *perspective grid,* also

Figure 7-7. Closeup view of the point of impact further indicates that the impact was not great.

called a *perspective template*. This process is referred to as *photogrammetry*. Figure 7-8 illustrates a perspective grid lying on a living room floor. This particular grid is a 2-foot square, and when properly used can provide most of the necessary measurements in a crime or accident scene. It is not essential, however, that the grid be a 2-foot square, for any square or rectangle of known dimensions will suffice. The reason for this will become clear when the workings of the grid are discussed.

The theory behind the perspective grid and why it works is neither complicated nor difficult to understand. Figure 7-9 illustrates how lines drawn from the edges of the grid will travel outward and eventually reach a vanishing point. Figure 7-10 is a photograph after having been subjected to this process. Each square in the photograph represents two square feet. This being the case, one can establish the distance between various objects by simply counting the squares. Finally, by taking a sheet of paper and drawing squares on its surface representing 2-foot squares (or whatever size the particular grid being used happens to be), draw a map with each square in the photograph having a respective square on the sheet of paper and the objects in the scene will be positioned accordingly.

When using a perspective grid, it is desirable to position it so that the bottom edge of the grid is along the lower edge of the field of view. Mapping the scene is much easier if the grid is so positioned (refer again to Figure 7-10). The grid will be accurate only if the surface of the scene upon which it is being used is reasonably flat. If there is a sharp incline or decline, the accuracy will be seriously impaired. When this is the case, the degree of accuracy will be improved if the camera position is elevated. On uneven ground, the higher the camera is positioned and the more directly it is looking down onto the scene from above, the greater will be the degree of accuracy offered by the grid. Finally, when a perspective grid is used for crime and accident scene photography, the focal length of the camera lens will have no effect upon accuracy. When using a perspective grid, use either a normal or wide-angle lens. It is very doubtful whether a perspective grid would ever be needed in conjunction with a telephoto lens. Technically, however, it would work fine.

The usefulness of a perspective grid will be appreciated when considering the problems encountered while investigating an automobile accident at a busy intersection or upon a busy freeway, especially if it is during peak traffic. Under such conditions, taking measurements is both time-consuming and hazardous. By utilizing a perspective grid, however, it is necessary only to place the grid within the field of view when the photographs are taken, and the necessary measurements can be established at a later date. In this way, the damaged vehicles can be quickly moved and normal flow of traffic promptly resumed. When using the grid in this manner, it is desirable to take one or two measurements to verify the accuracy of the measurements established by the use of the grid should the case go to court. The perspective grid is also helpful in

Figure 7-8. In the foreground is a perspective grid, which is simply a two-foot square.

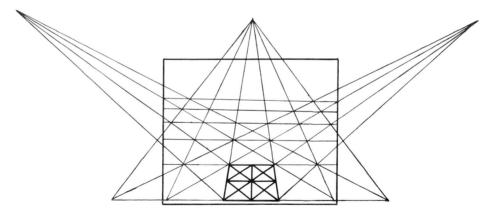

Figure 7-9. Drawing lines which coincide with the edges of a grid will converge and eventually meet. The result will represent two-foot squares, or whatever size the grid in use happens to be.

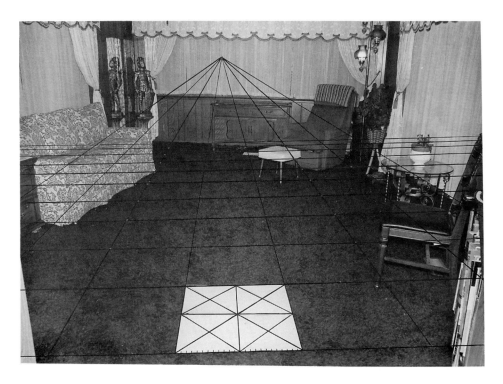

Figure 7-10. By using a two-foot square grid, it is possible to map out the living room to determine the distance between various objects by counting the two-foot squares.

cases where the seriousness of an offense is insignificant enough so that it is questionable whether complete measurements will ever be needed. It would be worthwhile in saving accumulated amounts of time to routinely place a grid in the field of view when the scene of minor vehicle mishaps are photographed, rather than taking time-consuming measurements. If, at a later date, it is learned that complete measurements are needed, they can be obtained from the photographs. In most cases complete measurements will not be needed, so it would not be practical to actually go through the entire process of mapping out minor accident scenes by use of the grid in every case. If, however, about 5 percent of the minor traffic accident cases were to end up in civil court and complete measurements were needed, the time necessary to map out those few scenes would probably be considerably less than that required to take complete measurements at every scene. The authors do not claim this to be the best and final solution to a problem, but it is worthy of consideration.

Should the reader desire a more detailed discussion of the perspective grid, he should contact the Traffic Institute, Northwestern University. Request P.N.81, which is a booklet titled *Perspective Grid for Photographic Mapping of Evidence.* *

---

*Traffic Institute, Northwestern University, 405 Church St., Evanston, Illinois 60204.

Chapter 8

DEATHS

General Considerations

While crime scenes are individual and unique in detail, they can generally be said to have certain common characteristics. For this reason, the general procedure for photographing most crime scenes is the same. Reference has been made to the point of entry, method of operation, sequence of events, as well as the various types of evidence often found such as tool marks, bits of clothing, footprints and fingerprints. These factors apply also to the investigation and photography of death situations. When photographing a death situation, the use of color film rather than black and white should be stressed.

At any particular scene, the investigative photographer should attempt to provide a complete and thorough photographic coverage, compiling photographs that can later be presented in an order that will portray the sequence of events and the manner in which they were committed. The photographs should include the point of entry, with close-ups of any evidence as well as signs of force having been employed. Often, for example, a small fragment of a suspect's clothing will be torn and left behind when he is crawling through a broken window or a cut screen. Close-up views of such evidence should be secured before the evidence being retrieved. Evidence which tends to indicate the movements of a suspect should also be photographically documented. Included in the photographic coverage should be overall views of the surrounding grounds where appropriate, as well as complete views of interior rooms. When taking photographs of the interior rooms, it is suggested that the photographer work in a clockwise direction. A wide-angle lens for interior views will prove useful. If none is available, take overlapping photographs of an area. Whenever a close-up is taken of a piece of evidence at a crime scene, a larger overall view should be included to show where the evidence was found. This is important, as a photograph of a piece of evidence is in itself of little value unless it can be connected to the incident under investigation. Close-up photographs of evidence should also include a scale for size reference, if appropriate. When photographing a crime scene, with the obvious exception of close-ups, one should take the photographs from a normal eye level so that the resulting photograph will depict the scene as an observer would normally view it (see Figure 8-1).

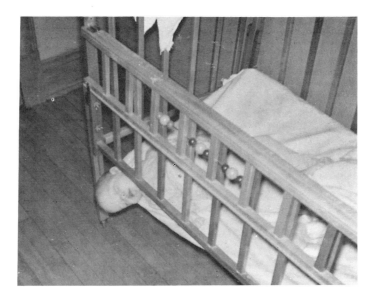

Figure 8-1. Overall views of a death scene should be taken from a normal eye level so that the resultant photograph will depict the scene as an observer would normally view it. Illustrated is the result of a defective crib. (Courtesy of Dr. John I. Coe.)

Special Points of Consideration

When photographing a homicide or death scene, special points to be documented are signs of a struggle, activity prior to the incident (position of furniture is often helpful in this respect), position of the body from at least two different directions as well as facial views for identification purposes. When photographing the facial features, it is desirable to include both a front and a profile view of the victim's face. Depending, of course, upon the specific circumstances, this is sometimes more easily done after the body has been taken to the morgue. If photographing the facial features of the deceased takes place a period of time since the death occurred and putrefaction has begun, the photographs may be of little value in helping family members identify the body by photographs. The facial views should, however, be taken in spite of that fact.

Suicide or Homicide

Careful photographic documentation of wounds in a death situation is very important because the location and nature of wounds are often a strong indication of a suicide or a homicide. Suicide committed with a knife will generally feature wounds in the throat, wrist or heart region. A stab wound or cut found in such a location could be indicative of either a suicide or a homicide. If, however, there exists a stab wound in the victim's back, suicide would be very doubtful. Similarly, wounds on the palms of the hands are indicative of an attempt at self-defense, and again, suicide is doubtful. When such wounds exist, it is important that they be photographed (see Figure 8-2). A person who commits suicide by stabbing himself in the heart will usually move the clothing to the side rather than plunging the knife through the clothing (see Figure 8-3). In a homicide situation this generally is not the case (see Figure 8-4). When a person has been cut more than once, and the cuts run parallel, there is a good indication of suicide rather than homicide. The presence of hesitation marks is also important evidence and tends to indicate suicide (see Figures 8-5 and 8-6). In the case of a homicide, however, the cuts run at any number of irregular angles and there is less evidence of hesitation marks (see Figure 8-7). In a suicide situation, unlike most homicides, there is also often evidence of a combination of methods having been employed or contemplated. A person may, for example, first cut his wrist and then his throat as insurance against failure in his attempt at self-destruction. Figures 8-5 and 8-6 are photographs of the same individual and illustrate this point well.

When the apparent cause of death is the result of a gunshot wound, the position of the body, the position of the gun and their relationship to each other is important and should be carefully photographed. Again, care should be exercised when photographing the wounds, because one committing suicide with a firearm will generally shoot himself through the temple, forehead, mouth or heart. A good indication as to the type of situation with which one is dealing is the fact that there are certain positions from which firing a gun is very difficult. This fact applies not only to gunshot wounds, but to wounds inflicted by any kind of a weapon. When a person has been shot, evidence which tends to indicate

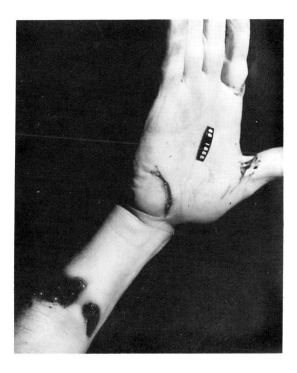

Figure 8-2. **Classical Defense Wounds.** Wounds on the palms of the hands are indicative of the victim having attempted to defend himself. In this illustration are also defense wounds on the upper forearm. (Courtesy of Dr. John I. Coe.)

the distance from which the shot was fired is important and should be photographed. If the shot was fired from relatively close range, there will generally be powder traces (tattooing) about the wound. When this is the case, one could be dealing with either a homicidal or a suicidal shooting. If the shot has been fired from a distance of several feet or more, the powder traces (tattooing) will generally not be present and suicide can generally be ruled out. When the barrel of the gun has been pressed against the flesh and fired, there often appears not a neat hole, but rather an irregular, star-shaped hole which is very often similar in appearance to, and can easily be mistaken for, that of an exit wound (see Figures 8-8 and 8-9). The entrance wound, unlike the exit wound, will often bear powder residue. Such wounds should be carefully studied and photographed, because it is important to know if one is dealing with two entrance wounds, a condition meaning that the victim was shot twice and that the bullets have possibly remained in the body, or that the victim was shot once and the bullet exited and is somewhere nearby.

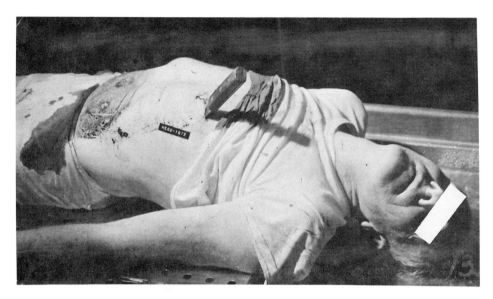

Figure 8-3. A person committing suicide by plunging a knife or some object into himself will generally move the clothing to the side prior to the act. (Courtesy of Dr. John I. Coe.)

Figure 8-4. Unlike the victim of a suicidal stabbing, the victim of a homicidal stabbing will have the knife plunged through the clothing. (Courtesy of Dr. John I. Coe.)

Also realize that with a contact wound one may be dealing with either suicide or homicide.

As previously stated, close-up photographs of wounds are important and should generally include a scale for size reference. When photographing a wound, it is important to include an overall view showing the person

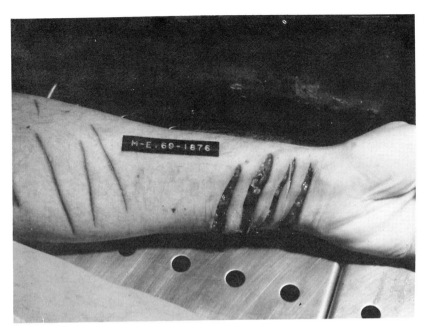

Figure 8-5. The cuts running parallel and the hesitation marks (upper forearm) indicate suicide rather than homicide. (Courtesy of Dr. John I. Coe.)

and the location of the wound (see Figures 8-10 and 8-11). Photographs of wounds can more easily be taken at the morgue in many cases. When the deceased is unknown, any identifying characteristics such as tattoos, scars and deformities should be photographed in color with a scale included where appropriate.

When photography at the scene has been completed and the body is moved, careful attention should be given to the area under the body. Any evidence found should be photographed prior to recovery.

Hangings

Hangings usually are an act of suicide; accidental hangings occur less frequently, and usually happen during the aberrant sexual practices of young men. Homicidal hangings are very rare.

In the case of a suicidal hanging, the motive is simply a desire to die. Contrary to what is generally portrayed in fiction, the suicide victim generally does not completely suspend himself from the floor by stepping off an object such as a chair. Kneeling, sitting and semiprone positions are most common. In cases of accidental hangings, it is most

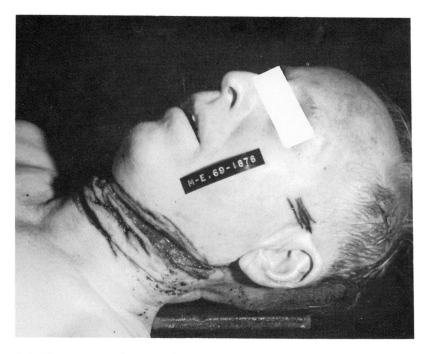

Figure 8-6. The presence of cuts on the throat and temporal artery running parallel to one another, and the hesitation marks, indicate suicide. (Courtesy of Dr. John I. Coe.)

generally a situation in which a man, usually young, has placed himself into various forms of bondage and simulated such situations as hanging as a means of achieving some form of sexual gratification. In such cases the victim did not intend or desire to die but simply made a mistake, went too far and was unable to free himself before being overcome by unconsciousness and finally asphyxia. Because the victim is usually bound, an inexperienced investigator could conceivably mistake an *auto-erotic* death for that of a homicide. Careful examination, however, will generally reveal that the individual had devised safeguards such as slip knots rather than square knots, for example. One will also find there are such items as mirrors, to indicate that the person was attempting to achieve sexual stimulation or gratification. All evidence, including the knots of the bonds, should be carefully photographed.

As previously stated, homicidal hangings are rare. One should not, however, rule them out until all aspects of the case have been carefully examined. One should also be mindful of the possibility of the victim's having been killed by another means and then set up so as to appear to

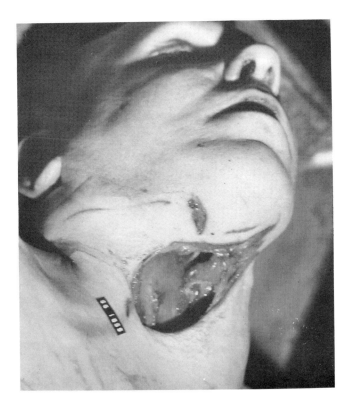

Figure 8-7. Unlike the suicide victim, the victim of a homicidal stabbing will be found to have wounds that run at any number of irregular angles. (Courtesy of Dr. John I. Coe.)

have committed suicide by hanging himself. However, this type of activity is rare.

Infrared Photography

An area of photography which can be helpful to one investigating a shooting death is infrared reflectance photography. This specific technique is explained in Chapter 13 "Document Examinations." The application of infrared reflectance photography makes it possible in many cases to establish and document photographically whether a bullet fired at a reasonably close range made a hole in a specific garment or piece of material. The tattooing can also give the ballistician an indication as to the range from which the shot was fired (see Figures 8-12A and 8-12B). Shown is a bandana handkerchief which has been shot twice at close

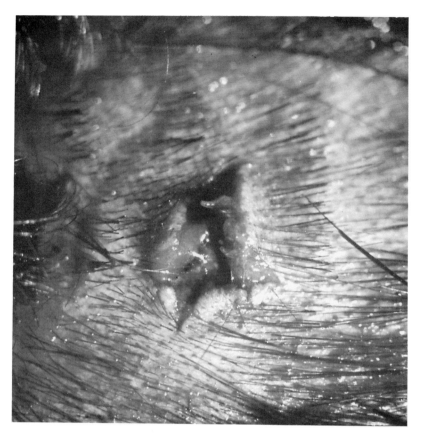

Figure 8-8. The exit wound caused by a bullet is generally characterized by a jagged "star shaped" hole while the entrance wound is more often a neat, round hole. (Courtesy of Dr. John I. Coe.)

range with a twenty-two caliber pistol. Note that in Figure 8-12A which was taken using a conventional photographic technique and pan film, it is impossible to see the location of the holes or their cause. In Figure 8-12B however, which was photographed using the infrared reflectance technique, the bullet holes and the tattooing around the holes are quite distinct, leaving little question as to the location of the holes and their cause. This results because many materials, when subjected to infrared photography, respond by recording as white while the powder traces record very dark, giving one the high degree of contrast between the two that was lacking when visually examining the garment or when photographing it using a conventional photographic technique.

Photographing invisible bruises on a body is also possible using this

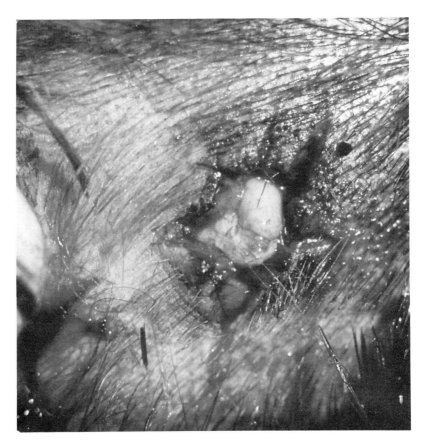

Figure 8-9. When a gun is held against the victim's body when it is discharged, the entrance wound, rather than being a neat, round hole, will be somewhat "star-shaped" and similar in appearance to that of an exit wound. Such wounds should be carefully examined and photographed. (Courtesy of Dr. John I. Coe.)

infrared technique, in cases such as the damage done to a body without leaving wounds that are readily apparent to the naked eye by an instrument such as a length of pipe wrapped in a towel.

Figure 8-10. When a wound on a body is to be photographed, it is essential that an overall view first be taken to show the identity of the person and location of the wound. (Courtesy of Dr. John I. Coe.)

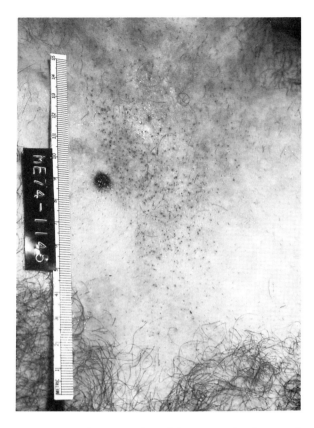

Figure 8-11. After an overall view has been taken of the victim, the photographer should move in for medium and/or close-up views of the wound. Note the tattooing which will indicate both the approximate distance from which the shot was fired and the fact that the shirt was closed when the shot was fired. (Courtesy of Dr. John I. Coe.)

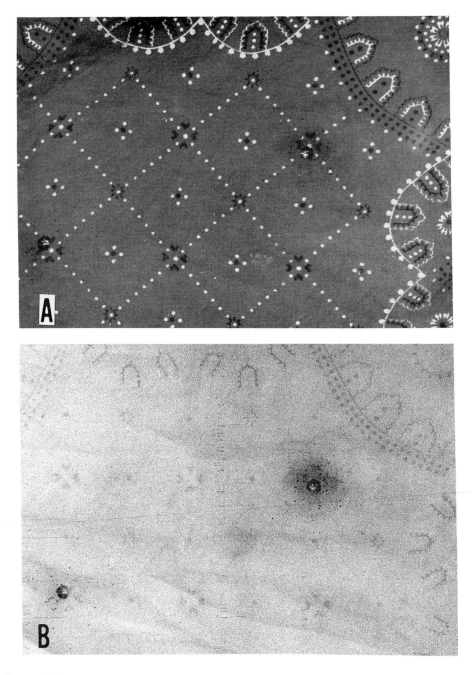

Figure 8-12. (A) This bandana handkerchief was shot twice at close range using a 22-caliber pistol and photographed using a conventional photographic technique. Note that in this photograph it is impossible to discern positively where the holes exist or what caused them. (B) This photograph of the same bandana was taken using an infrared reflection technique. Note that it is not only obvious where the holes are, but that there is no question as to their cause.

Chapter 9

IDENTIFICATION PHOTOGRAPHY

A Historical View of Civil and Criminal Identification

Throughout history, law enforcement authorities around the world have searched for a reliable means of identifying criminals, but it was not until the late 1800s and early 1900s that civil and criminal identification reached a reliable and scientific level.

Soon after the inception of photography, police employed it in that effort by taking an identification photograph of a person at the time they were charged. Commonly such photos are loosely referred to as *mug shots*. Photographs serve a useful purpose in the field of criminal identification even though they suffer acknowledged limitations. Photographs were, and remain, simply a supplement to other identification efforts.

Although police have been taking *mug shots* for years, photography was preceded by various other forms of identification efforts with methods varying considerably depending on time, place, culture, and the effectiveness varied. Significantly, some of the oldest methods are still used today in some form. For example, even before the origin of Christianity, the ancient Chinese used *finger prints* as a crude form of identification, and fingerprints are still used today. Some ancient cultures employed methods of *scarification* while others employed *tattooing*. And those methods are also still in use today in some places, and in some cultures. But, the results of scarification and tattooing can be altered just as a cattle brand can be altered with a running iron. *Personal descriptions* of a person have no doubt been used since the beginning of time, and that too is still used today even though, like other methods, the accuracy cannot be relied upon. In the late 1800s, Alphonse Bertillon (běr'tē'yôn'), a French criminologist, devised an elaborate system for describing people, a method that came to be known by the french term *Portrait Parlé* meaning *word picture*.

Anthropometry was introduced in France around 1879, also by Alphonse Bertillon, and introduced in the United States in 1887. Anthropometry came to be known as the *Bertillon System.* His was an intricate method of identification whereby various bony parts of the body were measured and recorded, and *it was his less than perfect system that was the first to put criminal identification on a scientific level.* But like all other methods, that too had its limitations. The error rate was excessive, it did not work with people not yet done growing, and it was time consuming to perform. The Bertillon system of measurements was later replaced by fingerprints, although there was a period of overlap and competition between the two as one phased in while the other phased out. That occurred during the early 1900s.

There was an early awareness of the fact that the friction ridges on the working surface of the hands and fingers tended to remain constant throughout a person's lifetime, an awareness going back perhaps as early as the 1600s. But there was no consideration for using them as a means of identification, and no method for their *classification* was proposed until 1823 when Professor *Johannes E. Purkinje* spoke of it in a thesis at the University in Breslau, Prussia. But, he did not go so far as to suggest their use for identification purposes.

Sir William Herschel, Indian Civil Service, Bengal, India, in the 1870s, began using hand and fingerprints to identify native pensioners to prevent surviving relatives or dishonest friends drawing their pensions subsequent to their death. And he devised a system for classifying finger prints. Although he used finger prints successfully the practice was not wide spread. In 1880, *Dr. Henry Faulds,* in Tokyo, Japan, began advocating the use of fingerprints to identify criminals. Soon thereafter, in the late 1890s, an Englishman, *Francis Galton,* began corresponding with Faulds and, as a result, a practical system for both the classification and filing of fingerprints was developed. From there the acceptance of fingerprints for purposes of civil and criminal identification grew rapidly with improvements being made by others as the science grew.

Eventually, *Sir Edward Richard Henry,* commissioner of the Metropolitan Police of London, modified and improved the system to where its use was even more practical. He published his system in book form in 1900. The next year, 1901, he was employed by Scotland Yard as Assistant Commissioner and fingerprints were officially adopted. Fingerprint science was officially adopted in the United States in 1902 when the authorities began fingerprinting civil service applicants in New York. The police department in St. Louis, Missouri, adopted fingerprinting in 1904, the first American police department to do so. The Army began fingerprinting in 1905, the Navy in 1907, and the Marines in 1908. Today, most law enforcement agencies in the English-speaking countries employ some variation of the Henry System of classification. To be sure, other countries that do not employ the Henry system do have a system nonetheless.

The previously mentioned Bertillon method grew widely and for a time was in general use but, with the growth of fingerprint science, began to die in the early 1900s. But its demise was gradual and there was a period of overlap. We see in Figure 9-1 that the identification portion of the file on the infamous Alphonse Capone, 1929, allowed for both fingerprints and Bertillon measurements although the latter portion received only marginal attention. The system had by that time largely fallen into disuse.

When photography was sufficiently developed as a science that police could begin using it as a tool for identification purposes, they did exactly that. And it did not take them long to determine that both a frontal and profile view was the preferred format. For the most part that has not changed over the years, although some departments do record only a frontal view. Note the *mug shot* of Alphonse Capone taken May of 1929 and compare its similarity with today's identification photographs.

Identification photographs serve a useful purpose and will no doubt continue to be used for a very long time. Indeed, there will probably never come a time when they are not used. But they do have their limitations. It has been said that everyone has a double, and that is very true. Another shortcoming is that the appearance of people changes over time, some very significantly. The photos in Figures 9-2 and 9-3 are of the same person with one photo taken approximately 22 years after the first.

Over the course of history, earlier methods of identification have given way to newer more promising methods. Less scientific and reliable methods gave way to Bertillon, which in turn gave way to fingerprints. Will fingerprints slowly give way to, or share a niche with, DNA? Only time will tell. Meanwhile, even if it does, the identification photograph, the so-called *mug shot*, will probably be around for a long time to come.

General Considerations

Identification photographs differ from portraits in that they are intended to be a true rather than a flattering resemblance of the person. In an

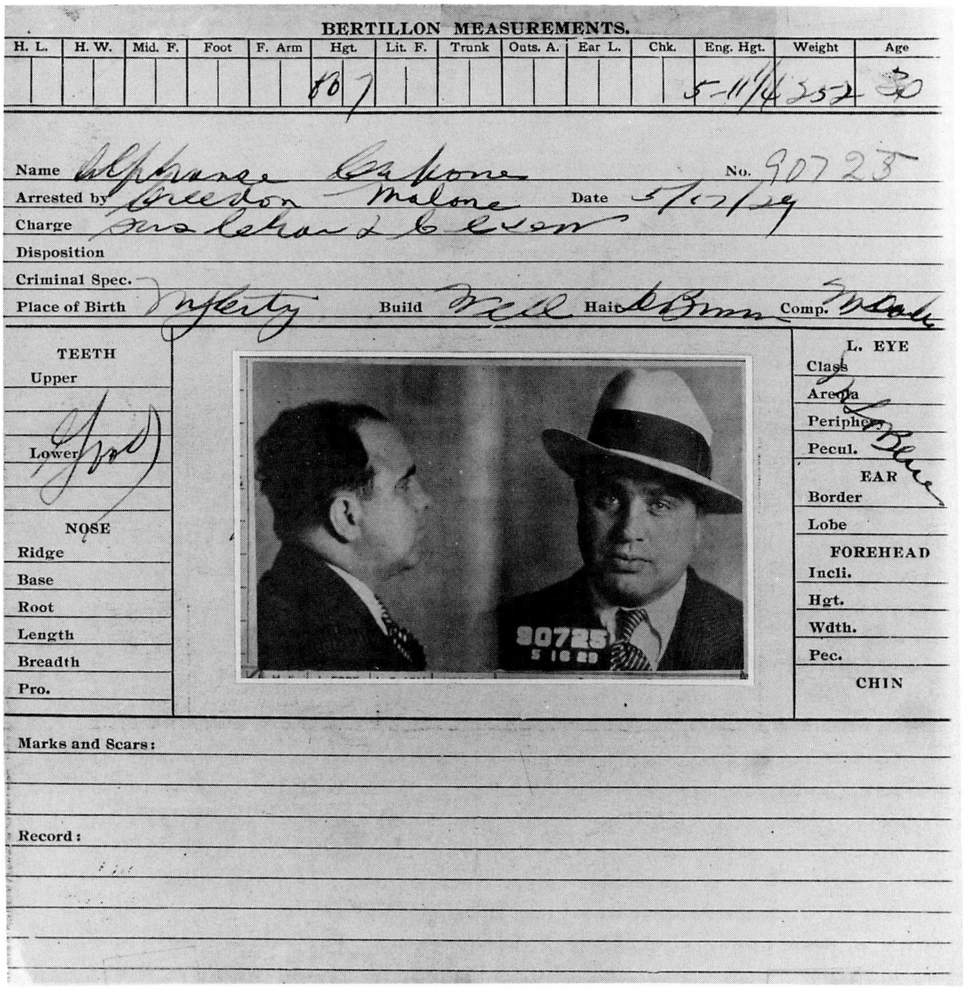

BERTILLON MEASUREMENTS.

H. L.	H. W.	Mid. F.	Foot	F. Arm	Hgt.	Lit. F.	Trunk	Outs. A.	Ear L.	Chk.	Eng. Hgt.	Weight	Age
											5-11½	255	30

Name *Alphonse Capone*   No. *90723*
Arrested by *Creedon Malone*   Date *5/5/29*
Charge *operating a casino*
Disposition
Criminal Spec.
Place of Birth *New York*   Build *Med.* Hair *Dk Brn* Comp. *Medium*

TEETH
Upper
Lower

NOSE
Ridge
Base
Root
Length
Breadth
Pro.

L. EYE
Class
Area
Periph.
Pecul.
EAR
Border
Lobe
FOREHEAD
Incli.
Hgt.
Wdth.
Pec.
CHIN

Marks and Scars:

Record:

identification photograph, it is desirable for every scar, mole and freckle to show up clearly. The most common type of identification photograph is a head and shoulder shot showing both a front and profile view as has been illustrated. With some identification cameras, a front and profile of the head and shoulders as well as a full length view may be taken. This feature is useful, especially when the person being photographed has an unusual stance or posture. Of less importance, but useful nonetheless, is a record of the individual's general mode of dress.

When preparing for identification photographs, one must decide whether to use a height scale or a neutral gray background.

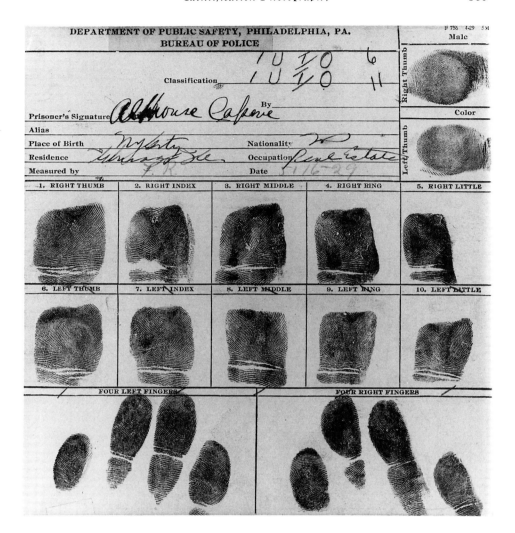

Figure 9-1 A & B. 1929 identification photograph and fingerprint card of the infamous Al Capone. Note that the Bertillon Measurements portion has been largely ignored in favor of the fingerprint section.

Photo Equipment and Film

There is no one type of camera that must be used in order to produce quality identification photographs. Almost any good camera will suffice. There are, however, various factors that should be taken into consideration when selecting a camera for identification applications. These include such things as the cost of operation, number of photographs

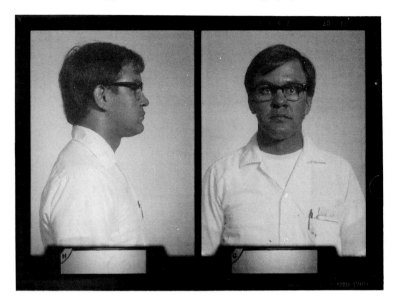

Figure 9-2. Typical identification photograph (mug shot) offering both a front and profile view. A neutral gray background rather than a height scale was used. (Courtesy of Minneapolis Police Department.)

generally being made over a given period of time and format of the equipment presently owned by the department. Some departments are utilizing 35mm cameras with an attachment that enables one frame, which is 24mm × 36mm, to record both the front and profile views of the person being photographed. There are also a number of cameras available which have been designed for the sole purpose of taking identification photographs.

Unless the decision is made to utilize a Polaroid film, it is desirable to stay with a film type and size that is widely used by the department. Anytime something can be standardized, the time factor can be kept to a minimum and the quality of the results consistent.

Lighting

In the past, photoflood lamps were the main source of illumination for identification photography. Since electronic flash units have become popular, however, they have come to be used for illumination when taking identification photographs. The short duration of electronic flash units completely eliminates the chance of blur due to subject movements.

Figure 9-3. Identification photograph of the same person appearing in Figure 9-2 taken 22 years later. Note the change in general appearance.

Strobe units are also small, compact, convenient and generally economical to use.

When using a strobe or flash unit, it is desirable to have the unit several inches from the camera lens so as to avoid the red eye effect, which results from the light's reflecting off the veins at the rear of the subject's eyes. In addition, if the location where the identification photographs will be taken is well-lit, the subject's pupils will contract, and the effect of red eye will be further reduced.

When utilizing photoflood lamps, two lamps positioned on each side of the subject and directed at the subject from a 45° angle will generally produce the best results. When utilizing a strobe unit, straight-on illumination will produce good detail even though it will generally not produce a flattering image.

The lighting arrangement and distance should be established and *all* identification photographs made with that specific arrangement. Operating in this manner will ensure uniformity.

Chapter 10

CLOSE–UP PHOTOGRAPHY
AND PHOTOMICROGRAPHY

Introduction

Close-up photography is referred to by various terms such as *close-up photography, macro-photography,* and *photomacrography.* Photography of this nature involves taking pictures of subject matter at near life size to well over life size, and it is done using special lenses or special attachments. Fingerprint and tool mark photography fall into this category. Close-up photography has its place both in the field and in the crime lab. *Photomicrography* refers to the taking of pictures through a microscope and is done done in the crime lab. While both are very technical applications of photography, the investigative photographer with a basic understanding of photographic techniques, and a bit of patience, can master both. In this chapter we will first examine close-up photography and then photomicrography.

CLOSE–UP PHOTOGRAPHY

Introduction

Frequently the photographer will be faced with a situation that necessitates close-up photographs of such evidence as fingerprints and tool impressions. Foot and tire impressions will generally not require a close-up technique because the minimum focus of a camera's normal lens is generally sufficient. Although close-up photography is a technical application, it is not difficult if one understands the technique that is being attempted and exercises care relative to lighting, proper exposure, camera stability, and focus. In fact, the very limited depth of field making critical focus essential is perhaps the most challenging part of close-up photography.

In close-up photography, there are basically five methods to consider. The five methods are:

1) use of a reversing ring to turn the camera's normal lens around so that the rear element faces forward;
2) use of auxiliary close-up lenses which mount to the front of the normal lens;
3) use of extension rings to increase the distance between the lens and the film plane;
4) use of a bellows to increase the distance between the lens and the film plane;
5) use of a macro lens with or without extension rings or bellows.

Reversing the Normal Lens

A very inexpensive means of doing close-up photography with a 35mm SLR camera is to purchase a reversing ring which permits the camera's normal lens to mount in a reversed position with the rear element facing forward (see Figure 10-1). A normal lens mounted in this fashion will offer a reproduction approximately 4/5 life size. The lens will not, however, work automatically, and it will be necessary to manually stop the diaphragm down to the desired f/setting.

There are two basic advantages to a technique such as this: (1) the low cost of being able to engage in close-up photography by use of this inexpensive accessory, and (2) the fact that a lens mounted in the reversed position will generally offer a greater flatness of field than it would if left in the normal position and simply extended from the film plane the necessary distance so as to offer the same reproduction ratio. This means that the lens, when reversed, will offer an image that is generally sharper and not quite so blurry or soft around the edges.

The greatest disadvantage of this technique is that the lens does not operate automatically, and the range of focus possible by rotating the focusing ring is so limited that there is really only one point of focus and one reproduction ratio. Since most lenses are not designed for optimum results at very close focusing distances, there will be some loss of image quality when using a camera's normal lens with a reversal ring or by extending the lens-to-film distance. The loss in quality is not extreme or highly objectionable, however, in moderate close-up work. If the normal lens is an f1.7 or f2, the results it offers will be better than if one were using one of the very fast normal lenses available such as f1.4 or f1.2.

Figure 10-1. A camera's normal lens may be turned around by use of a *reversing ring* so that the rear element faces forward. This allows the photographer to take close-up photographs of about 4:5 life size.

With very fast (large aperture) lenses, certain optical aberrations will be more pronounced than with slower (smaller aperture) lenses. Concerning exposure, if the camera being used is equipped with an internal light meter, there will be no problem in achieving or establishing the exposure in the normal manner. If, however, the camera being used is not equipped with an internal light meter, there is a necessary exposure increase of about $1^{1}/2$ f/stops when using a reversal ring. If unsure of the proper exposure, be sure to bracket.

When using a reversal ring, there is sometimes an advantage to placing a short extension ring onto the lens mount to serve as a lens shade, and also enables one to use the plunger that opens the aperture for focusing. Extension rings will be discussed shortly.

Use of a reversal ring can also be an advantage when using extension rings and bellows because of the greater flatness of field it affords.

Close-Up Lenses

Close-up lenses are very inexpensive. A close-up lens is nothing more than a simple miniscus lens mounted in a threaded ring which screws onto the front of the camera's normal lens in the same manner as a filter. A standard set of close-up lenses for a 35mm format camera is generally available in a set of three. The focal length of these lenses are commonly diopters +1, +2, and +3, although at this time Vivitar offers diopters +1 through +7. Diopters may be used individually or in any combination to achieve greater magnification.

Close-up lenses do not interfere at all with the normal operation of a camera's automatic lens, nor do they require a compensation in exposure. As a result, close-up lenses are very easy and convenient to use. They are especially well suited if the individual photographing the scene and taking close-up photographs of evidence is not a well-trained photographer. If an individual is capable of taking properly focused and exposed photographs with an adjustable camera, he or she should experience little or no difficulty when using auxiliary close-up lenses. Once the close-up lenses are mounted, the photographic procedure is the same as without the lenses. The only real difference is that it is possible to focus much closer than before; however, it is no longer possible to focus to infinity. Also, there is a rather short focusing range. The greater the reproduction ratio one wishes to achieve with these lenses, the shorter will be the focusing range and depth of field.

Concerning the statement that close-up photography is as easy as general photography when using close-up lenses, there is one consideration to bear in mind in order to obtain quality results when using close-up lenses, a depth of field of about 1/2 inch down to as little as 1/8 inch or less is a very real range. Considering then that one is now dealing with a distance of only a part of an inch rather than several feet, focus and camera stability are critical. If one achieves correct focus and then accidentally moves that camera closer or farther from the object being photographed when tripping the shutter, an unsharp photograph will result. Generally, however, when using close-up lenses, the reproduction ratio is small enough so that one can hand-hold the camera with little or no difficulty. If experiencing problems of this nature consider the use of a tripod or some other suitable means of support.

Close-up lenses, as is the case with the greatest majority of camera accessories, are manufactured by a number of lens manufacturers.

Extension Rings

Thus far we have discussed ways of taking close-up photographs by means other than extending the distance between the lens and the film plane. We have discussed reversing the lens as one method and the use of auxiliary close-up lenses as a second method. They both work well but they also have their limitations.

For extreme close-up photography, it is necessary to employ some means by which to greatly increase the distance between the lens and the film plane. This is generally accomplished by using either extension rings or a bellows. Figure 10-2 illustrates how an extension ring is placed between a camera lens and body to increase the lens-to-film distance. Extension rings are most commonly used with 35mm and 2¼ inch SLR cameras.

Depending upon the manufacturer, extension rings are often available

Figure 10-2. Extension rings are placed between the lens and the camera body to increase the lens-to-film distance.

in sets consisting of three rings, and, in some instances, up to as many as five rings to a set. More often than not, the rings are of varying widths, a factor which allows the photographer to achieve a variety of reproduction ratios.

With extension rings, the maximum degree of enlargement possible largely depends upon the focal length of the lens with which it is being used. The shorter the focal length of the lens, the greater the reproduction ratio possible. With a normal 50mm lens on a 35mm camera, a reproduction anywhere between life size to about 1¾ life size can generally be obtained. As stated earlier, there are a number of possible reproduction ratios between the smallest and the largest, but one does not have a continuous range. The reproduction ratios with extension rings go in fixed steps, depending upon which ring or combination of rings is used.

When using extension rings, focusing is achieved by adjusting the camera-to-subject distance, not by turning the focusing ring on the lens, because that will have no appreciable effect on either the reproduction ratio or focus. It is best that the lens be set at infinity and left there.

If the camera's normal lens is automatic meaning that the lens stays open for focusing no matter what aperture is selected, and then automatically stops down to the pre-selected aperture when the exposure is made, that feature will continue to work with many extension rings. With less expensive rings, the lens must be stopped down manually. The photographer will generally open the diaphragm all the way for a brighter image with which to focus and compose the subject, then stop down the lens to the desired f/setting and make the exposure. When operating in this fashion, the photographer should carefully observe the subject matter in the viewfinder when stopping down since there is often a slight shift in focus as a result of stopping down. That shift in focus can be a disadvantage when using the automatic feature. One must experiment and determine what works best for them. With the automatic feature one is sometimes able to pre-view for depth-of-field and focus. So doing is advisable.

With extension rings, the internal light meter will often solve the problem of exposure calculation. If, however, the camera is not equipped with an internal light meter, or if the degree of magnification is extreme and the resulting level of illumination is too low to get an accurate reading, the proper exposure will have to be calculated by another method. Details concerning this situation will be discussed later in this chapter. One may, however, simply run a series of exposure tests starting at several seconds and progressively working down to just a small part of a second, depending upon the subject matter, the level of illumination and the speed of the film being used. When making exposure tests, one may start at five seconds for the first exposure, perhaps three seconds for the second exposure, one second, then $1/2$ second, $1/4$ second, $1/8$ second, $1/64$ second, $1/30$ second, etc.

When using extension rings or bellows, the camera assembly and object being photographed must be absolutely motionless when the exposure is made. This consideration will also be discussed in detail later in this chapter.

Bellows

Figure 10-3 illustrates how a bellows is used to increase the distance between the camera lens and the film plane. A bellows system provides a continuous range of reproduction ratios. In this illustration a reversal ring has been used to reverse the camera's normal lens, not only for a greater degree of possible magnification, but for better flatness of field (refer also to Figures 10-4 to 10-5). Lenses are also made specifically for use with bellows.

Focusing with a bellows system is accomplished in the same manner as with the extension rings, i.e. by moving the camera and lens assembly as one single unit toward and away from the subject matter, not by turning the focusing ring on the lens barrel. When using extension rings or bellows, if the photographer desires to obtain a definite and known reproduction ratio, it is desirable to have the lens focusing ring set at the infinity mark.

It was just stated that the proper means of focusing is to move the entire camera and lens assembly as a single unit toward and away from the subject matter. The photographer could place the camera and lens assembly very close to the subject matter and then begin altering the lens-to-film distance, and at some given point the subject matter will be in sharp focus. The reason this is not done is because he or she will not end up with a definite, predetermined reproduction ratio. Adhering then to the idea that it is best to set the lens-to-film distance and focus by moving the camera *and* lens assembly, it would be advantageous to examine a few ways in which this can be done.

For example, the camera, bellows and lens assembly can easily be

Figure 10-3. Bellows are often used to increase the lens-to-film distance for close-up work. Bellows, unlike extension rings, offer a continuous range of reproduction ratios rather than just a few given ratios that go in fixed steps. In this illustration a reversal ring has been used to turn the lens around to achieve better flatness of field and a greater reproduction ratio.

mounted on a focusing rail, which is then mounted to a tripod. This permits the camera, bellows and lens assembly to be moved as a single unit. One may use a copy stand with a fine adjustment that permits one to raise or lower the camera and lens assembly after a rough placement has been accomplished. Depending upon the specific subject and situation under which it is being photographed, one may, as an alternative to moving the camera and lens assembly, consider moving the subject matter toward or away from the camera and lens assembly to obtain perfect focus. Doing this accomplishes the same thing as moving the camera and lens.

As is the case with extension rings, some bellows are automatic while others are not. With manual bellows, the lens must be manually stopped down to the desired f/setting after proper focus has been achieved. Because reflected light will often provide an image that is not very bright, it will, in extreme close-up work (photomacrography), be desirable for the photographer to use a dark cloth to exclude extraneous light.

Figure 10-4. Most press cameras feature what is referred to as a *double extension bellows system* which permits the photographer to engage in close-up photography (up to life size) without the use of accessory items.

This is preferable to opening the aperture to get a brighter image because depth of field is so very limited and focus often will shift somewhat when the lens is stopped down.

The use of a fast film is usually desirable, if not essential, because of the dim image. The best results generally will come from the lens being stopped way down (small opening) for maximum depth of field. The small lens opening, coupled with the low level of illumination, will mean either changing to a fast film or using a relatively long exposure time or both.

Macro Lenses

Macro lenses are designed to focus uncharacteristically close, thus enabling the photographer to take close-up photographs without having to use some of the accessory items that have been discussed. Although effective, a macro lens cannot produce as large a reproduction ratio as is

Figure 10-5. Enlarged photograph of a 38-caliber bullet taken using the camera illustrated in Figure 10-4 at a reproduction ratio of 1:1.

possible when using accessory items. Some such lenses will record a subject at life-size while half-life size or less is much more common.

Macro lenses are highly corrected for aberrations at very close camera-to-subject distances and therefore tend to work well when used with extension tubes or bellows. Naturally, that increases the range of their usefulness.

Macro lenses are available in a variety of fixed focal lengths, and there are also macro zoom lenses available. On a 35mm camera, a macro lens of normal focal length, or a zoom macro lens of say 28mm–85mm, would enable the photographer to take general crime, fire or accident scene pictures and then conveniently move in close to record small details without having to employ accessory items. The main disadvantage of a macro lens for such applications is the fact that they tend to be somewhat slow. Whether that is a problem depends upon circumstances.

Lens Extension and Reproduction Ratio

To determine the necessary degree of lens extension necessary for a specific reproduction ratio, the focal length of the lens must be multiplied by the desired reproduction ratio. The product will be the lens extension necessary to achieve the desired ratio. For example, a magnification or reproduction ratio of three is desired and the lens being used is 55mm. The reproduction ratio of three is multiplied by the focal length of the lens, which in this case is 55mm. The product of the two is 165. This means, then, that in order to obtain a reproduction ratio of ×3 when using the 55mm lens, it will be necessary to extend the lens 165mm from its normal position.

Establishing the reproduction ratio when the extension of the lens is known is done by dividing the extension by the focal length of the lens. For example, if a 55mm lens is being used and the lens has been extended 165mm from its normal position, simply divide 165 by 55. The dividend is three, which will be the reproduction ratio or the degree of enlargement.

Exposure

The f/setting of a lens is figured for that lens working at about one focal length. In other words, if a lens is set at f8, the opening of the diameter of the lens is ⅛ the focal length. If that lens is placed upon extension rings or bellows and thus extended some distance from the film plane, the *effective* f/value will change and an adjustment will be necessary in order to compensate for this change, or underexposure of the film will result. To get a better idea of how rapidly the effective f/value changes, and also to better understand how much to compensate for this change, study Table 10-1.

In Table 10-1, the magnification or reproduction ratio is multiplied by the indicated f/value, with the indicated f/value then added to the product. Example: One has increased the lens-to-film distance with a bellows (or extension ring) to achieve a magnification of ×5, and the indicated f/value is f8. Eight is multiplied by five, equalling forty, and the indicated f/value of eight is then added to the product, giving us an actual or effective f/value of f48. Actual f/value equals magnification multiplied by indicated f/value plus the indicated f/value. Stated another way:

Table 10-1.
This table illustrates the pronounced effect that
eproduction ratio has upon the actual f-value.

Magnification	Indicated Aperture	Actual Aperture
1X	f/4	f/8
2X	f/4	f/12
4X	f/4	f/20
8X	f/4	f/36
12X	f/4	f/52
15X	f/4	f/64

$$\text{True f/value} = \frac{\text{Indicated f/value} \times \text{lens-to-film distance}}{\text{Principal focal length of lens}}$$

It usually is beneficial to make the necessary exposure adjustment by increasing the exposure time rather than opening the diaphragm to its maximum diameter. If the lens is set at a very small aperture for maximum depth of field and the subject illumination is relatively low, thus resulting in a very long exposure time (fifteen seconds to one minute), the resulting negative may be underexposed even though the mathematics has indicated it should come out right. This is the result of what is known as reciprocity failure. To better understand, consider that one unit of light exposing film for sixty seconds will not have the same effect on the film as sixty units of light exposing the film for one second. The sixty units of light falling on the film for one second will cause the greater degree of exposure between the two. Remember that although the law of reciprocity tends to indicate that the two exposure times would have the same effect, they do not. Nothing has failed or gone wrong; this is a situation where the law of reciprocity simply does not apply.

When the correct exposure time is uncertain, the method that has been described may be used to roughly establish the exposure, and then several test or trial exposures made, giving some exposures more and some less light. Bracketing exposures in this way compensates for any deviations due to reciprocity or errors in figuring. Figuring the exposure compensation will give only the theoretical exposure, but not necessarily the best exposure. So again, it is wise to make a habit of bracketing about one f/stop on both sides of the basic exposure regardless of the type of photography, whether close-up or general. Making a few extra exposures when photographing under such conditions insures against losing the evidence permanently. Even in situations where retakes are possible, the added cost of working hours makes it impractical.

The police or fire photographer doing mild close-up photography in the field will generally not be faced with many of the highly technical challenges unique to extreme close-up photography as done in the crime lab.

Having considered some factors relative to proper exposure, factors such as the affect that reproduction ratio has on the effective f/value, and reciprocity failure, it is time to consider some practical approaches to lighting. In this endeavor, one may use a continuous light source, a common electronic flash unit, or a specialized ring flash unit.

A *continuous light source* enables one to manipulate the lighting angle until the subject, as seen through the camera's viewfinder, presents the desired detail. That is an advantage. And, often, if the camera is equipped with an internal light meter exposure may be set without having to make calculations. The disadvantage is that the exposure time is often long, thus increasing the chance of an unsharp image because of camera shake or vibration.

Electronic flash units are desirable because they are small and therefore portable, and their short flash duration minimizes the chance of an unsharp image because of camera shake or vibration. The disadvantage lies in not being able to manipulate the light source to find the best angle for detail rendition. However, one may use a continuous light source to determine the best lighting angle and then illuminate with the flash from that position. Although that approach is not a problem in the crime laboratory, it is not as conveniently done in the field.

If the camera features through-the-lens (TTL) automatic flash exposure determination, little problem generally exists because the flash sensing unit is inside the camera and measures the light being reflected from the film after having made the journey through the lens and any accessories being used. When the proper exposure has been achieved, the sensor simply interrupts the light output. If using a traditional automatic flash mounted on the camera, a flash that features the sensor on the flash unit itself, and the *lens-to-subject* distance is short, one can experience a problem with *flash-to-lens parallax.* The problem is that at very close range the angle of acceptance of the sensing unit on the flash is too narrow to take a reading from the subject itself and ends up taking a reading from what ever is above the subject. Improper exposure can result. A solution is to place an 18 percent gray card in front of the sensing unit at the same distance as the subject. The sensor then reads the light being reflected from the gray card and adjusts exposure accordingly. When a flash unit is removed from the camera and used on a cord so that exposure angle may be adjusted, and if the flash is sufficiently far from the subject as a result, flash-to-lens parallax will not tend to be a problem.

When doing extreme close-up work, a *remote sensor* can be useful, permitting off camera flash use with retention of automatic exposure control. Vivitar offers what they call a *Macro Flash Sensor.* That tool features a small lens that is attached to the front of the camera lens and the light reflected from the subject passes through that lens and to the strobes sensing unit via fiber optics. That tool permits automatic flash exposure from a range of 8 inches to 8 feet.

When using an electronic flash unit set for the correct ISO rating of the film, improper exposure will result if the lens and accessory set-up resulted in an effective aperture that is other than normal. One way to adjust for that is to fool the strobe unit. For example, if four stops more exposure is called for, set the strobe unit so that it thinks the film is four stops slower. It will provide the necessary greater exposure as a result.

Ring-strobes, also referred to as a *ring flash,* are specialized flash units designed specifically for close-up work. The advantage of such a tool is shadow free illumination of the subject. The strobe features a circular light tube that is mounted to the front of the lens and illuminates the subject evenly from all sides. Some such strobes also feature built-in continuous lights to aid focusing in subdued light, but those low intensity lights do not contribute to the film's exposure.

Some specialized macro lenses feature a built-in ring flash. One example is Nikon's *120mm f/4 IF Medical-Nikkor,* a useful lens that has been available for many years. That lens, to assure proper exposure, adjusts the aperture size as it is focused throughout its range. Without accessories the lens will record up to life size (1:1). By use of an auxiliary close-up attachment it will record up to 2:1.

Vibrations

When using bellows, vibrations of the camera and lens assembly will often present a much greater problem than when working with extension rings because of the greater degree of magnification possible. As previously stated, with extension rings a reproduction of about 1¾ life size is possible. With bellows, a magnification or reproduction of about 4 1/2 times life size is possible.

With an SLR camera, the mirror movement as an exposure is made often causes enough vibration to adversely affect the sharpness of the resulting photograph. A possible means of eliminating this problem is to make use of the self-timer which is built into many cameras. In using the self-timer, when the shutter release button is depressed, the mirror pops up and stays there for the period of time that has been selected, usually between 3 and 8 seconds. After the shutter has released and the film exposed, the mirror returns to its normal position. The several seconds between the time the mirror pops up and the shutter is activated allow the vibrations caused by the mirror to subside.

If the exposure time is going to be several seconds in duration or if a camera without a self-timer is being used, the room may be darkened and the shutter placed on *bulb* setting to keep it open. After the shutter is opened, a few moments should be allowed for any vibrations to subside, and then the exposure made by turning on the lights that will illuminate the subject matter. In all cases, a cable release should be used. Everything should be mounted solidly so it will not move about.

When using a bellows system, the camera's normal lens may be used in either the forward or reverse position. The results will be better, however, if the lens is used in the reverse position to lessen the curvature of field.

When reversing a lens, keep in mind that its effective focal length is not the same once reversed. For example, a 50mm Nikkor lens, once reversed, has an effective focal length of 33mm. For critical work, consider use of a macro lens with the bellows or a lens that is designed specifically for use on bellows.

PHOTOMICROGRAPHY

Introduction

For the most part, it can be said that the prerequisite for photomicrography is an extensive knowledge and experience in the use of microscopes. Taking quality photographs through a microscope is a skill that comes only after this proficiency has been achieved.

This chapter, although it will point out some of the more outstanding aspects of photomicrography, cannot and is not intended to make the reader proficient in this specific application of photography. It is the author's desire, however, to give the reader an understanding of the rudiments of photomicrography and its role in the fields of law enforcement and fire.

In the investigative field, basically two types of compound microscopes are used. They are the standard type of medical microscope shown in Figure 10-6, and the comparison microscope shown in Figure 10-7. The most notable difference between the two types is that the comparison microscope is, in a very real sense, two microscopes side by side and connected by a bridge containing prisms, an arrangement which provides a half field of view from each microscope. With such a microscope, one can take, for example, a bullet found at a crime scene or from the body of a shooting victim, and a second bullet which has been fired through a suspect weapon and examine the two to see if the minute markings on one match up with the other. When examining two bullets or shell cases through a comparison microscope, a portion of one specimen is seen in half of the eyepiece while a portion of the second specimen is seen in the other half of the eyepiece. There is a hairline dividing the two images (see Figure 10-8). If the two bullets or shell casings match, the findings can be photographed as a permanent record of the findings.

To fully understand the photomicrography process, it is necessary to first examine the basic principles of a compound microscope. With a compound microscope, the objective lens forms a real image in space (in the tube) and the eyepiece then magnifies that real image to an even greater degree (see Figure 10-9). If, for example, the objective lens magnifies the original specimen by ten times and the eyepiece then magnifies that image by another ten times, the specimen will be seen at a reproduction ratio of one hundred times its actual size.

Camera Types to Use

Almost any kind of camera may be used for photomicrography, although it will be found that cameras with both a removable lens and reflex viewing will be the most practical for such an application. While the instamatic type of cameras can be used, such cameras generally have no controls insofar as shutter speed and aperture settings are concerned; consequently they offer little in the way of versatility. Without reflex viewing, the photographer is not assured of what the camera really sees.

Figure 10-6. **Common compound microscope.**

The result can be poor framing, poor focus or both. If no other type of camera is available, however, such a setup does work.

Figure 10-10 shows how a press or view type of camera may be arranged over a microscope to record an image. The photographic recording of an image produced by a microscope involves nothing more than placing a film holder over the microscope eyepiece and then providing some means by which extraneous light is prevented from interfering with the exposure of the film. Since the microscope eyepiece projects the image onto the film, no camera lens is needed, nor is one desired. To exclude extraneous light a bellows system or even a simple black cloth bag may be used.

A 35mm SLR camera works very well for photomicrography. Most

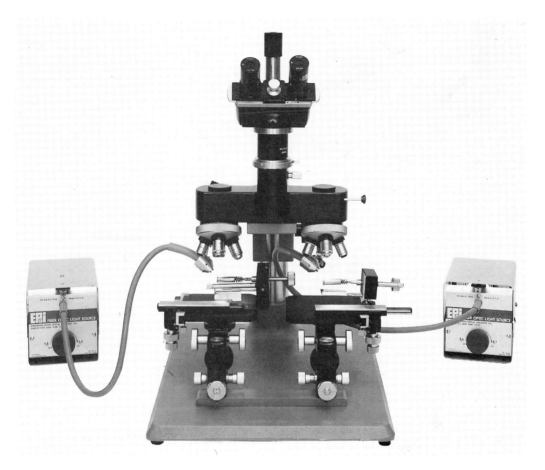

Figure 10-7. **A comparison microscope.** (Courtesy of Ehrenreich Photo-Optical Industries, Inc.)

manufacturers of these camera systems offer special microscope adapters which makes it very easy to utilize these cameras for purposes of photomicrography (see Figure 10-11).

Finally, commercially made cameras designed for the sole purpose of photomicrography are available. Such cameras may take either roll, sheet or Polaroid film (see Figure 10-12).

Focus

In photomicrography, focus is accomplished by varying the distance between the specimen and the objective lens. The objective lens, microscope tube and eyepiece (and camera if attached) should all move as one

Figure 10-8. Example of a photographed observation through a comparison microscope. Note the hairline. On one side of the line appears the test bullet while on the other side appears a portion of the fatal bullet. Note how the striations of each match with the other.

single unit. The focusing technique is much the same here as it was in photomacrography where the camera, bellows and lens all moved as one unit closer and farther from the object being photographed when a specific reproduction ratio was desired. The distance between the eyepiece of the microscope and the film plane will affect the brightness and intensity of the image as well as the size, but has no appreciable effect on the focusing of the image. Again, this is accomplished by focusing the microscope itself.

Another point to be considered when focusing for photomicrography is that the eyepiece projects basically two types of images. When looking through a microscope, the eye picks up what is referred to as a *virtual* image as shown in Figure 10-9 while the camera sees and records what is referred to as the *real* image, also shown in Figure 10-9. If one first focuses the microscope by looking into the eyepiece (he sees the virtual

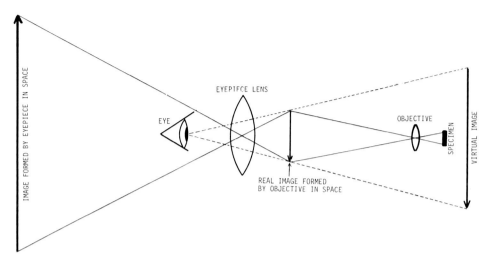

Figure 10-9. The objective lens of a microscope projects an image of the specimen in space. The eyepiece lens then magnifies that image. Note also that while the viewer sees what is referred to as a virtual image, the camera will pick up and record an image formed by the eyepiece in space. This is why it is not possible to look into the microscope, focus, mount the camera and hope to get a good sharp photograph.

image) and then mounts the camera which will record the real image, a sharp photograph will generally not be realized since the focus of the two images will generally vary to some degree.

Camera Movement and Vibrations

After considering the problems of focus, the photographer must consider how to make the actual exposure without causing camera movement and vibrations which will cause an unsharp image. In photomicrography, vibrations can easily make the difference between good and bad photographs, even if everything else is done right. Maintaining a vibration-free setup is very important, since magnifications are being recorded at a very high reproduction ratio, which tends to amplify the effects of any vibrations that may be present. Also, because the light intensity is frequently quite low, the exposures are often of a rather long duration.

To reduce the problems caused by vibrations, a good solid workbench is desirable. If a large view camera or press camera is used, a good support for that camera is essential. Also consider setting the camera on time and making the exposure by turning the microscope illumination

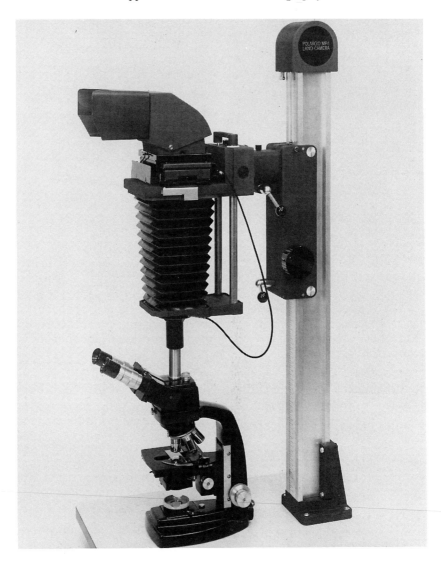

Figure 10-10. The Polaroid MP-4® being used to photograph through a microscope. This basic set-up is applicable for both press and view types of cameras when used for this purpose. In this illustration the camera is coupled to the microscope by means of a lensless baffle tube. (Courtesy of Polaroid Corp.)

on and off rather than by using the camera's shutter mechanism. This is especially worth consideration if the camera being used is equipped with a focal plane shutter, which causes more vibration than does a leaf shutter. If using a 35mm SLR camera, which generally has a focal plane shutter, use the self-timer. The mirror popping up in a 35mm SLR

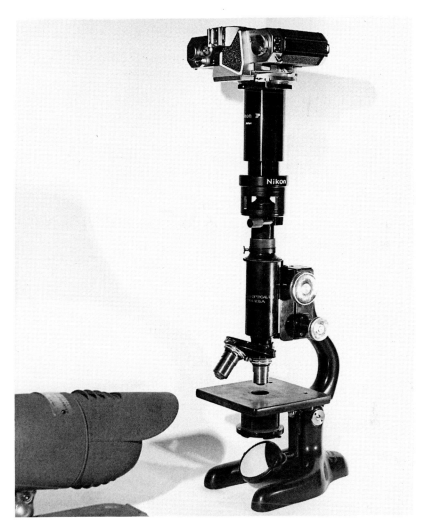

Figure 10-11. Most camera manufacturers offer microscope adapters which make for convenient coupling of the camera to the microscope.

causes considerable vibrations. If one selects a time lapse of a few seconds, the mirror pops up when the shutter release is depressed and stays in that position for the time interval selected, after which the shutter activates and the mirror returns to its original position. The time interval between the mirror popping up and the shutter activating allows for vibrations caused by the mirror to subside. If, however, a press camera with a focal plane shutter is being used, the method described by using the illumination switch should be considered. Also worthy of

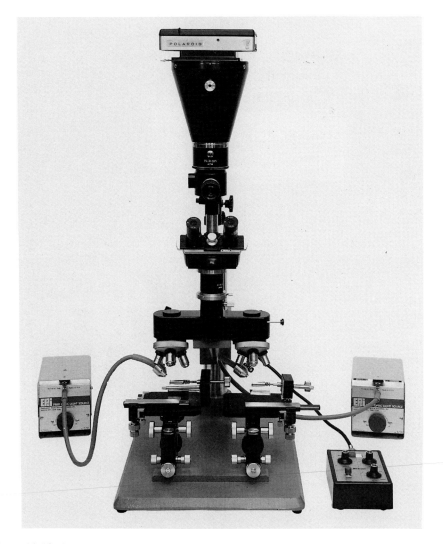

Figure 10-12. A comparison microscope with a Polaroid film holder designed specifically for that unit. One may also obtain film holders for roll or sheet film. (Courtesy of Ehrenreich Photo-Optical Industries, Inc.)

consideration is a special vibration absorbing pad that can be placed under the microscope assembly.

Film and Illumination

If one is taking black and white photographs, the color temperature of the lighting and film is of no consequence. If, however, one is photographing with color, the use of a light source with a color balance intended for the particular type of film being used is essential if proper color values are to be realized. Generally, a color film and light source balanced for 3200°K (Tungsten Filament) if the choice.

CP-6 Comparison Projector®

The CP-6 Comparison Projector illustrated in Figure 10-13 which has been made available by Ehrenreich Photo-Optical Industries, Inc., New York (EPOI), is a modification of the standard type of comparison microscope that was just discussed. The Comparison Projector has been designed to perform the same functions and fulfill the same needs as a standard comparison microscope. The difference lies primarily in the fact that it is not necessary to work over a microscope, which can be tiresome, but can look at the image projected onto the screen. The procedure involved in photographing the image on the screen is simple, with no necessary specialized or costly additional equipment or accessories. The photographer has only to focus, adjust for exposure and trip the shutter (see Figure 10-14). Figure 10-15 illustrates a match between two bullets that were photographed in this manner.

Polaroid MicroCam SLR

The Polaroid MicroCam SLR (single-lens-reflex), Figures 10-16 and 10-17, is a fully automatic camera designed specifically for photographing through a microscope with black-and-white or color film. The camera is conveniently coupled with a microscope by sliding into either the eye-piece tube or phototube. The camera features reflex viewing through a glass multi-element built-in 10× magnification lens. The camera features an LCD panel that reports all camera functions in any of six user-selected languages (English, French, German, Italian, Japanese, and Spanish). The camera features a sophisticated exposure control system with automatic compensation for reciprocity failure, a film's speed loss realized when long exposures. The internal photometer and microprocessor calculates proper exposure between 1/60 of a second and 16 minutes. The electronic shutter features a two second delay to permit vibrations to subside before activating. The camera also features an automatic internal color correction filtration system to compensate for both the color temperature of the illumination source and color shifts

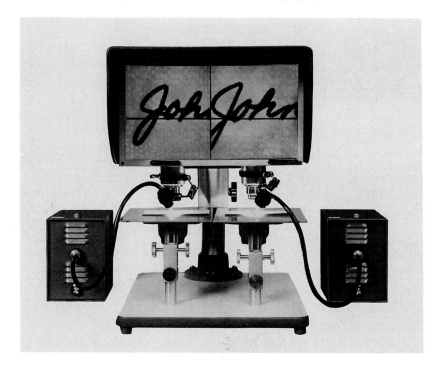

Figure 10-13. The CP-6 Comparison Projector®. (Courtesy of Ehrenreich Photo-Optical Industries, Inc.)

during long exposures. A manual override feature permits the operator to calculate exposure. At the end of an exposure the camera automatically ejects the 3×4-inch Polaroid print.

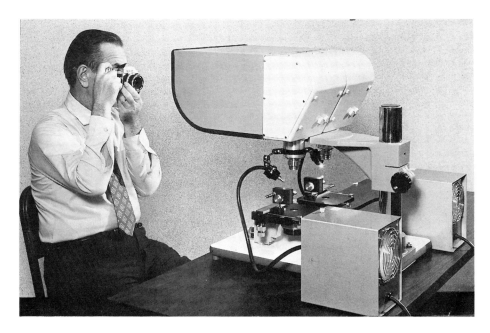

Figure 10-14. Photographing the image on the screen of the CP-6 Comparison Projector is easy; it requires only focusing, adjusting for exposure and tripping the shutter. (Courtesy of Ehrenreich Photo-Optical Industries, Inc.)

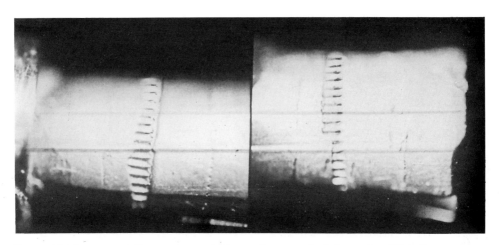

Figure 10-15. **A match between two bullets photographed from the CP-6 Comparison Projector.** While some technicians prefer to photograph directly through the microscope, feeling that they get sharper detail, many have found the convenience of the CP-6 to be a desirable feature. This is something the photographer must decide for himself. (Courtesy of Ehrenreich Photo-Optical Industries, Inc.)

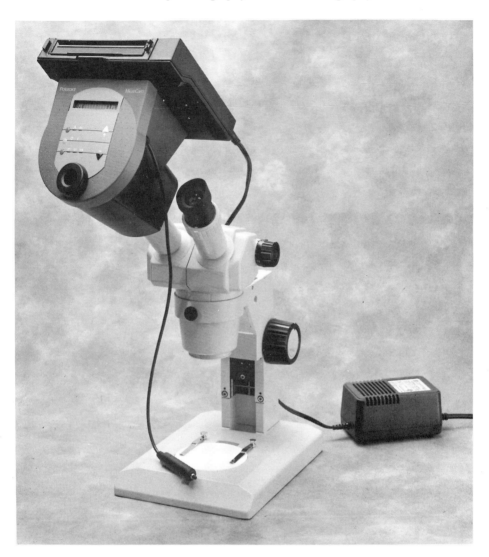

Figure 10-16. The Polaroid Microcam SLR produces instant photomicrographs.

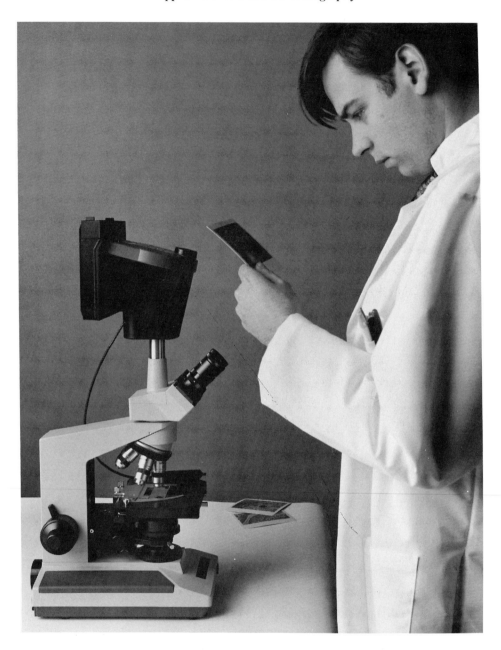

Figure 10-17. The Polaroid Microcam SLR produces instant photomicrographs.

Chapter 11

FINGERPRINT PHOTOGRAPHY

General Considerations

When it comes to the processing and photographing of fingerprints, the policy varies among law enforcement departments. Some departments rarely, if ever, photograph a latent print either before or after development, or before the print is lifted. Other departments will photograph prints only if the case is of a serious nature and the time and cost is justified. Ideally, however, a visible print should be photographed prior to any type of processing in order to decrease the possibility of losing the print should it be damaged or destroyed during the development process (see Figure 11-1). If a print is not photographed prior to being developed, it is desirable to photograph it prior to lifting, since damage can result during that process also. While it is true that many latent prints are not visible before being developed, many prints such as dust impressions and plastic impressions are.

Cameras and General Techniques

When photographing fingerprints, it is desirable to use a fingerprint camera that will photograph them at a 1:1 reproduction ratio, their actual size (see Figure 11-2). This camera is easy to use, for the operator must simply place the camera over the print to be photographed and make the exposure by depressing the shutter release button, which activates the self-cocking shutter. The illumination source is built into the camera and comes on automatically when an exposure is made. Fingerprint cameras are most commonly available in the $2^{1}/4 \times 3^{1}/4$ inch format size. There are also fingerprint cameras which accept Polaroid film. The resulting photographs measure $3^{1}/4 \times 4^{1}/4$ inches (see Figures 11-3, 14-3, and 14-4).

As stated, the fingerprint camera is designed and intended to be used to photographically document fingerprints, and it performs this task

Figure 11-1. **Visible print on a pistol photographed prior to development.**

well. Some fingerprint cameras, depending upon the sophistication and, consequently, the cost of the unit, feature a shutter mechanism which permits the operator to select the desired exposure time. With less expensive cameras one must estimate the exposure duration and hold the shutter open for that period of time. When using such a camera, a slow-speed film is desirable. The illumination source in even these less expensive cameras is automatic, and the intensity of the illumination remains constant except when the batteries begin to grow weak. Because of the internal illumination source, exposure determination is not difficult after a short series of exposure tests with prints on various surfaces have been performed. When doing this, remember that the exposure time will be longer for light prints on a dark surface than it will be for dark prints on a light surface. Once one is familiar with what to expect from different types of prints on various surfaces, no difficulty should be experienced when making exposures in the field.

In Figure 11-3, the camera was being used to photograph a fingerprint on a flat surface in a relatively open area, and it was necessary only to position the camera over the print. However, when photographing prints upon cylindrical surfaces such as drinking glasses and bottles, it is at times desirable to remove the front portion of the camera as shown in 11-4. When photographing evidence of this nature, the camera is placed

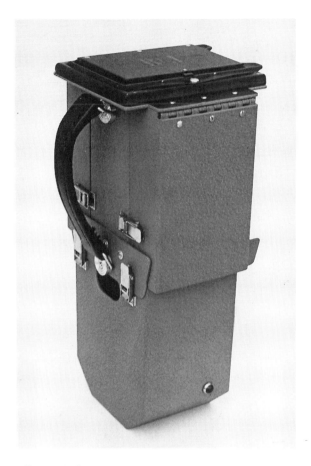

Figure 11-2. **Watson-Holmes fingerprint camera.**

on its side and the object bearing the print is built up so that the print will be recorded in the center of the negative (see Figures 11-4 and 11-5). When the print is upon a cylindrical surface, there will often be problems with light glare, and careful viewing of the object upon the ground glass (focusing screen) while manipulating the camera and/or object will be essential. Glare will be a greater problem with shiny surfaces such as glass. When two prints appear together on an object such as a drinking glass or bottle, they should be photographed separately, not together. Each print should be recorded in the center portion of the frame (see Figure 11-6). When photographing a print on a drinking glass or bottle, it is also highly desirable to place something dark behind the print and use a light powder. White or silver-colored powder is most generally used for such applications. With a drinking glass, black paper can easily

Figure 11-3. Polaroid fingerprint camera being used on a vehicle.

be inserted into the glass (see Figure 11-7). This, unfortunately, is not so easily done when working with a bottle, and a better alternative is to fill the bottle with a very dark solution. One such method which works well is to fill the bottle with water and add a small amount of potassium permanganate. This is a photographic product available from Kodak. The water will, as a result, become very dark and create good contrast between the bottle and the light colored print (see Figure 11-8). However, when using a technique such as this, extreme care should be taken to ensure that no liquid drips onto the print area and ruins the print.

Figure 11-4. When photographing prints on cylindrical surfaces, it is at times desirable to remove the front portion of the camera. Note how the object is positioned so that the print will be positioned in the center portion of the negative area.

When photographing a fingerprint on a small piece of glass, or on a rubber lift, it is desirable to place the object bearing the print on a flat surface and build the camera up with something that is the same thickness as the surface of the print (see Figure 11-9). This will ensure that the print to be photographed is the proper distance from the camera lens. This is very important because the camera contains a fixed focus lens, and features no means by which to focus other than placing the

Figure 11-5. The object bearing a print should be built up so that the print will be positioned in the center portion of the negative area.

subject matter the correct distance from the lens. When the subject matter has been properly positioned and is in correct focus, a 1:1 (life-size) image will be produced. When photographing a rubber lift, it is desirable to place it upon a dark surface. The lift in Figure 11-9 has been placed on a light surface only for the purpose of illustrating to the reader the use of an orifice made from a rubber lift to properly position the camera when photographing rubber lifts.

When photographing latent fingerprints, place some kind of identifying data beside the print so that there will be a means of recording where the print was found, and when and by whom it was photographed. This is best accomplished, in many instances, by numbering the print and making a separate legend. A grease pencil works well for this purpose, since the powder being used will adhere to the grease, and the number will show up very well in the resulting photograph (see Figure 11-10). When photographing a print upon a rubber lift, it sometimes helps to remove the acetate cover to reduce the problems that may result from glare. A number on a transparent material can then be placed in the corner, or next to the print when it is photographed. The number

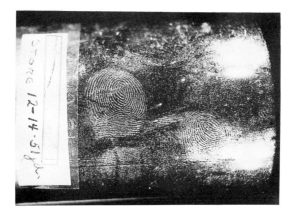

Figure 11-6. When there are two prints side by side upon a surface that will offer problems with reflections, do not attempt to get a legible record of both prints on one negative, but rather, concentrate on first one print and then the other. (Courtesy of John Douthit.)

Figure 11-7. When photographing a print upon an item such as a drinking glass, it is desirable to use a light-colored powder and place a piece of dark colored paper into the glass to provide a background of contrasting color. (Courtesy of John Douthit.)

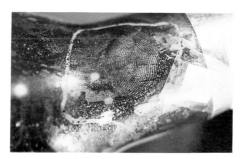

Figure 11-8. When photographing a print upon a bottle, placing a sheet of paper behind the print will not be possible and a better alternative is to fill the bottle with a dark colored solution. (Courtesy of John Douthit.)

Figure 11-9. When photographing prints upon such things as rubber lifts, it is desirable to use some means by which to build up the camera to the same level as the surface which the print is on. Here the center portion has been cut from a rubber lift for convenient positioning of the camera when photographing rubber lifts.

should be placed backwards so that it will be correct when the negative is printed. This is important because the print, when lifted with a rubber lift, is actually a mirror image of the original print. Similarly, the number must also be a mirror image so that when the negative is printed backwards in the darkroom, both the print and the number will be correct (see Figure 11-11). When printing a negative backwards, the negative should be placed into the enlarger emulsion side up rather than down, as is usually the case. After photographing the rubber lift, the acetate cover is replaced.

Film Choices

When photographing fingerprints, generally good results can be obtained through the use of almost any black and white film. However, if a greater degree of contrast is desired, try using contrast filters. If this does not

Figure 11-10. A grease pencil works well for numbering prints because the powder used will adhere to the number and provide a sharp image. (Courtesy of John Douthit.)

Figure 11-11. When photographing rubber lifts, it works well to place a number (reversed) on a transparent material next to the print. During the printing process, the print and number will be corrected. (Courtesy of John Douthit.)

produce the desired contrast, consider the use of a high contrast film such as Contrast Process Pan or Ortho film. A high-contrast film may also be used in conjunction with contrast filters. While a certain degree of contrast is essential, excessive contrast should be avoided or some fine detail can be lost. In this respect, experience will prove to be the best teacher.

Use of Filters

As just stated, the use of colored filters to control contrast is often desirable when photographing fingerprints. If a dark powder is used to develop a latent print, a filter may often be used to lighten the background. Similarly, if a light powder is used, a filter may often be used to darken the background, thus creating a sharper contrast between the print and the surface upon which it is found. This is possible because a colored filter will tend to lighten its own color and darken complementary colors when used with a black and white panchromatic film. For example, if no filter is used when photographing prints which are found on a red surface and developed with a dark powder, there will be poor contrast between those prints and the background, because the red will record as a shade of gray rather than the desired white (see Figure 11-12A). If the same prints are photographed using a red filter, the red background will be almost white rather than gray and thus give a much sharper contrast between the print and the background (see Figure 11-12B). If the print had been developed using a white or silver powder rather than a black powder, a blue filter could have been used to make the red go almost black rather than white, and the contrast between the print and the background would again be very good. The reader would do well at this point to refer to the section on Contrast Filters, discussed earlier in this book.

Ultraviolet Fluorescent Photography

When fingerprints appear on a multi-colored surface which contains both light and dark colors, contrast filters will not produce the desired results; problems will also be experienced whether using a dark or light powder. The best course of action under such circumstances is to use a powder that fluoresces under the influence of ultraviolet radiation and take an ultraviolet fluorescent photograph of the print. To take ultraviolet photographs of a fingerprint, dust the print by the usual method using a special fluorescent powder which is available through almost any fingerprint supply company. The camera is equipped with an ultraviolet

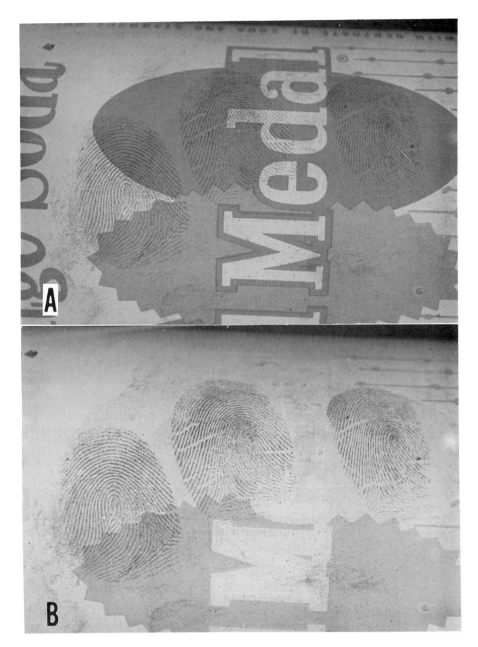

Figure 11-12. (A) Fingerprints upon a red surface (the oval shape), developed with black powder and photographed with a pan film without a filter. (B) Same print photographed with a pan film and a red filter Number 25A.

absorbing filter (Number 2A) to prevent ultraviolet radiation from passing through the camera's lens to the film when the exposure is made. This filter is referred to as a *barrier filter*. The electronic flash unit is covered with an 18A filter, which passes ultraviolet radiation but is opaque to visible light. This is called the *exciter filter*. Figure 11-13 illustrates this set-up. When an exposure is made, the ultraviolet radiation from the strobe unit causes the fingerprint powder to fluoresce brightly. The barrier filter over the camera's lens blocks out the reflected ultraviolet radiation, which is invisible, but passes the visible fluorescence. The resulting print will be a white image on a very dark background, because the print fluoresces brightly while the background does not, since it contains no fluorescent powder (see Figure 11-14).

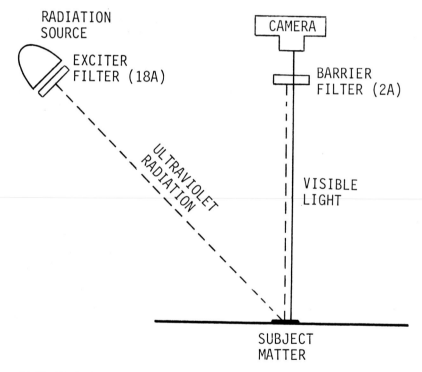

Figure 11-13. **Typical set-up for taking ultraviolet fluorescent photographs of finger-prints on multi-colored surfaces.**

When using ultraviolet fluorescent photography for fingerprints, it is desirable to position the flash unit as close to the dusted area as conditions will permit so as to achieve as bright a fluorescence as possible. It

Figure 11-14. **Ultraviolet fluorescent photograph of fingerprints on a multi-colored surface.**

will also be necessary to make a series of exposure tests. The prints in Figure 11-14 were recorded using Tri-X film with a camera-to-subject distance of about 3½ inches, with the flash positioned about 5 inches from the print. Proper exposure in this instance was achieved at f5.6. When using an electronic flash unit, exposure will have to be controlled by the f/setting (lens opening) and the flash-to-subject distance. Almost any black and white film will work well for this application. Although color film will work for this type of photography, it is neither necessary nor desirable in most instances.

Chemical Development and Photography

When dealing with prints on paper, the use of a powder is not recommended, so a chemical method such as iodine fumes, ninhydrin or silver nitrate must be used. When the print is developed, it can and should be photographed. If, however, the print is on a multi-colored paper, it may be developed with iodine fumes and then lifted with a silver plate. The image on the plate can then be photographed (see Figures 11-15A and 11-15B). When a fingerprint has been lifted with a silver plate, the image will be a mirror image of the original print, and the photographic negative, when being printed, should be reversed left to right, which means that the negative will be placed into the enlarger emulsion side up. This is also true with photographing prints that have been lifted using a rubber lifter. Refer also to laser and photography at the end of this chapter.

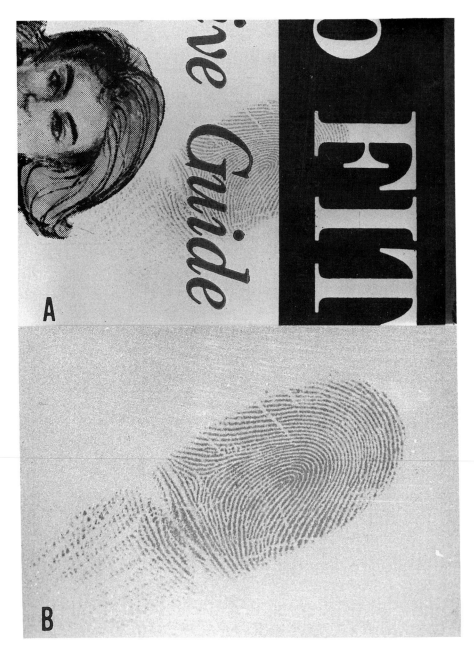

Figure 11-15. (A) Latent fingerprint on a multi-colored paper surface developed with iodine fumes. Note that much of the print detail is lost as a result of the dark portions of the background. (B) Photograph of the same print after being lifted with a silver plate.

Using Lifted Prints as a Photographic Negative

When fingerprints are lifted by means of a transparent lifter, they are most commonly placed upon a background of contrasting color. For example, if a black powder is used, the print is lifted and placed upon a white card. If a white or silver powder is used, the lifted print is placed upon a black card. Doing it in that manner is fine, but if the print was not photographed before it was lifted and a photograph is later needed, it will then be necessary to photograph it. If the lifted print had been placed upon a clear surface, however, rather than a background of contrasting color, the lifted print itself could very effectively be used as a photographic negative. A lifted print which has been placed upon a clear background should not be more difficult to study and examine than if it were originally placed upon a contrasting background, since the print on the clear surface can simply be placed over a surface of contrasting color for examination.

Using lifted fingerprints as photographic negatives can prove to be reasonably effective. Figure 11-16A illustrates a contact print which was made from a lifted fingerprint developed with black powder and placed upon a clear backing. Figure 11-16B illustrates an enlargement which was made using the same lifted fingerprint as a photographic negative and placing it in a photographic enlarger in the customary manner. Note, however, that the fingerprint ridges are white on a dark background. This results from the fact that the first print, which is made using the lifted fingerprint, is actually a negative image of the lifted print (the positive print). If a print with black ridges on a white background is desired, the first print made should be printed in reverse, that is, by turning the negative over and printing. In other words, if the fingerprint has a right slant, print it so that it has a left slant. With this procedure, when that print is used as a negative to make a contact print, the final print will be black ridges on a white background and correct with respect to the slant of the original fingerprint (see Figure 11-16C). The reason for printing the first fingerprint in reverse is because best results are achieved if the prints are placed emulsion to emulsion. If they are not, the thickness of the photographic paper between the two layers of emulsion will permit the light to diffuse somewhat, thus resulting in an image that is less than sharp. When making a photographic print from a photographic print, one should attempt nothing more than contact prints.

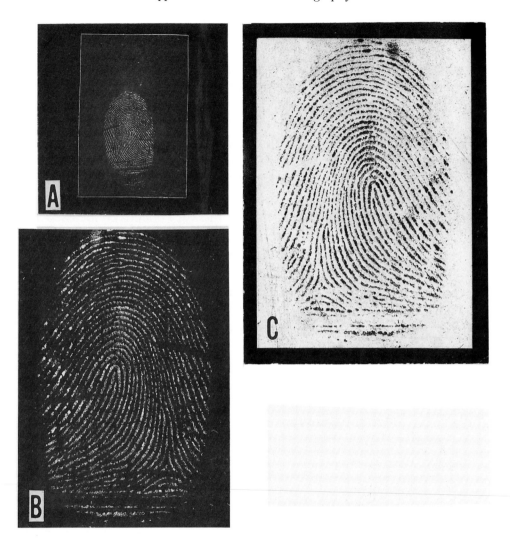

Figure 11-16. (A) Contact print made from a lifted latent print placed upon a clear backing rather than a backing of contrasting color. (B) Enlargement made from the same lifted latent print. Note that it has been printed so that the slant goes in the opposite direction from what it is supposed to go. (C) Contact print made from the print appearing in Figure 162B. Note that the slant goes in the proper direction and that the ridges are black on white. The contact print was made by placing the papers emulsion to emulsion.

If one does not wish to reverse the print by using a photographic print as a negative in the manner that has been discussed, the original print containing white ridges on a dark background may be photographed using a reversal film and the resulting transparency then used as a photographic negative. One may also consider placing the lifted print upon a clear slide which is then placed a few inches in front of a white card. The illumination source is then directed on the card which provides backlighting for the print. When the print is photographed, the ridges, regardless of the color of the powder used, will be shadowed and the final print will be black ridges upon a white background. This technique works well with white powder also.

Another technique the reader may wish to consider is producing a contact print of the original negative upon a piece of unexposed photographic film. When one employs this technique, it is essential that the negative and the unexposed film be positioned so that the illumination passes through the negative to the film. Quality results will be realized only if the surfaces of the negative and the unexposed film are held in firm contact by means of a print box, a printing frame, two sheets of glass or some similar means. When utilizing a technique such as this, it will also be necessary to experiment a bit with the exposure. Consider using the illumination source which is built into the print box, if such a device is being used. If a printing frame or a couple of sheets of glass are used, exposure may be provided by using an electronic strobe unit (either direct or bounce), turning the room lights on very briefly or placing the printing frame or glass sheets on the enlarger's base and using the projected illumination provided by the enlarger. If an enlarger is used for this purpose, the task of exposure control will be simplified by making use of the lens diaphragm.

Latent Prints on Glass and Mirrors

Fingerprints on glass and mirrored surfaces present special problems for the investigative photographer; for this reason one will devote more time to photographing these prints.

Because a thief will often gain entry by breaking a window, picking out the jagged pieces of glass, reaching in and releasing a lock or climbing through, fingerprints and/or glove prints will often be found on the glass. If the pieces of glass are lying about, often excellent results can be obtained by mounting the piece of glass in a small vice and manipulating the lighting until the print is visible. When a print on glass must be photographed at the crime scene, either a light or dark developing powder can be used, and a sheet of paper of contrasting color can be placed behind the glass. If, however, a black powder and a white sheet of paper are used, the need to reverse the print in the darkroom is eliminated.

If there are prints on both sides of the glass, one right behind the other, a white or silver powder may be used on one side of the glass and a black powder on the other. If powder of the same color is to be used on both sides of the glass, a short focal length lens on a bellows and a large lens opening should be considered. These techniques will tend to throw the second image out of focus enough to prevent interference in identifying the fingerprint.

When latent fingerprints are found on mirrors, such as the rear view mirror on a stolen automobile, a *light-colored* powder should be used because the background will go black when the print is photographed. A characteristic problem encountered in the photography of prints on mirrors is a very strong secondary image on the second surface of the mirror. The secondary image is apparent in Figure 11-17. One way to overcome such a problem is to use a lens of short focal length on a bellows and a large lens opening to throw the secondary image out of focus. If the mirror in question is cheap and easily replaced, consider the possibility of scraping the reflective backing from the glass and placing a sheet of paper of contrasting color behind the print. Fingerprint cameras perform very well in photographing of fingerprints on mirrors (see Figure 11-18).

If for some reason a good sharp photograph of the latent print on a glass surface is not possible, the most convenient route to take would simply be to develop and lift the print and then photograph it by the usual method.

PLASTIC IMPRESSIONS

Plastic impressions are those impressions which have been left in substances such as wax, putty or clay. Since such impressions are actually a reproduction of the ridge formations and contain depth, the most suitable method by which to photograph them is to use oblique (low-grazing) lighting so as to highlight the tops of the ridges while leaving the furrows shadowed. This is basically the same concept that is employed when photographing shoe and tire impressions. Figure 11-19 illustrates a plastic impression which has been photographed in this manner.

For a discussion on how fingerprints are prepared for evidence in court, the reader should refer to Chapter 17, "Photographic Court Exhibits."

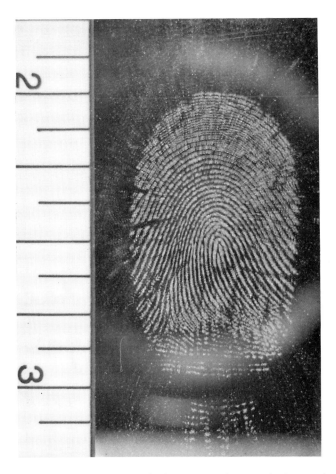

Figure 11-17. The strong secondary image of a fingerprint photographed on a mirror is shown in this illustration.

Laser and Photography

Laser, which is an acronym for *light amplification by stimulated emission of radiation,* can be utilized for the detection and photographing of fingerprints. Laser light enhances the eccrine residue's natural luminescence so that a print can be detected and photographed.

In the case of a latent fingerprint on a paper document that has been chemically treated with ninhydrin, the following process should be utilized to further develop the print thus making it more luminous for photographing with either laser or a conventional light source. Fingerprints developed with ninhydrin produce a dark purple color which is

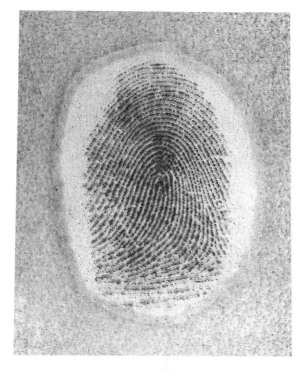

Figure 11-18. Fingerprint cameras are very effective for photographing fingerprints on mirrors. Note the very weak secondary image, and that a piece of black material with a hole was placed over the print to reduce glare.

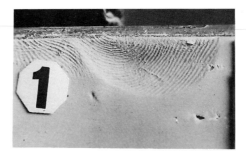

Figure 11-19. **Plastic impression found in soft putty.** Note how the oblique lighting has emphasized the ridge details. (Courtesy of John Douthit.)

referred to as Ruhemann's purple. A secondary treatment whereby the paper is immersed in a metal salt solution causes a chemical change thus making the print more luminous. The paper should then be placed in an insulated container and covered with a thin layer of liquid nitrogen. If cadmium salt was used in the secondary treatment, the complex formed can then be photographed by using a green (505 nm) exciter filter, and an orange (590 nm) barrier filter. Filters used for this type of photography are expensive, and if laser is utilized, only a limited number of wavelengths are available for a given type of laser. Additional shortcomings of laser as a means of achieving photoluminescence is its high cost and the responsibilities associated with safety precautions. Laser produces a very high concentration of energy, and thus safety must be a concern for those working with it.

Alternative Light Sources
(Xenon Arc Lamp)

Forensic light sources (FLS), such as the *Polilight,* are increasingly being used in forensic investigations. The *Polilight* which was designed by forensic scientists and manufactured in Rofin, Australia, offers many advantages over both laser and single light sources. Forensic light sources are able to provide a narrow band optical range output of 310–650 nm, and when utilizing a built-in fine tuner a peak wavelength between 320–650 nm may be selected. If infrared is desired, as it is with many forensic applications, an optional output of 650–1100 nm may be utilized. The biggest advantage of using a FLS versus using laser light is the flexibility it allows, and the low operating costs. The FLS is essentially many lasers in one, with the major difference being the ability to adjust and fine tune the light wavelength specifically to the forensic needs at hand. Whereas with a laser a person is dealing with one specific band of light, such is not the case with a FLS. As it can be imagined, employing many lasers with various wavelengths would be very costly.

Superglue Developed Latent

Oftentimes in the commission of a crime, the suspect will leave personal items at the scene which contain prints. In the case of a stolen vehicle that may have been used in a serious crime such as a drive-by shooting, the fingerprint left inside the vehicle are of great importance. The photo in Figure 11-20A shows a latent print developed with Superglue on a cassette tape found in a suspect vehicle as viewed under white light. Figure 11-20B is the same print stained with Rhodamine 6G and

Figure 11-20. (A) Shows a latent print developed with Superglue on a cassette tape found in a suspect vehicle as viewed under white light. (B) The same print stained with Rhodamine 6G and illuminated with 505 nm. (C) The same print has been color reversed thus making the ridges black, and easier to see. (Courtesy of Kevin De Nomie.)

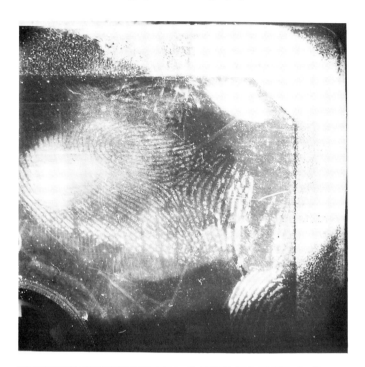

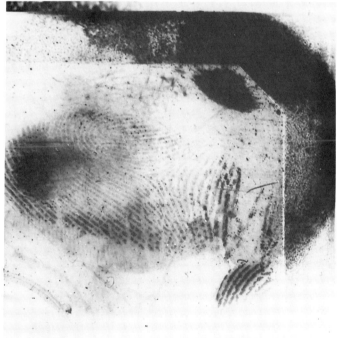

illuminated with 505 nm. In Figure 11-20C, the same print has been color reversed thus making the ridges black, and easier to see.

The applications and uses of FLS's in criminal investigations are numerous. The FLS system is an instrumental tool in forensic science being used across the United States, and in 30 countries around the world. A person desiring more information on the FLS system can contact a local dealer in fingerprint and identification photography equipment.

Chapter 12

IMPRESSION AND
TOOL MARK PHOTOGRAPHY

Impressions

When faced with impressions such as those left by footwear and vehicle tires, the investigator will often choose to have casts made. Before the casting is done, however, the impressions should be photographed to prevent any accusations, should the case go on trial, that the evidence was possibly altered by the casting process. Although casts are often made, identification work is generally done through the use of photographs.

If the object bearing the impression is mobile, it should be taken to the lab to be photographed under controlled conditions. Before the impression is moved, however, a photograph should be made showing it in relation to some fixed object, as a record of its original position and location. A fixed or permanent object may be a fire hydrant, telephone pole or a portion of a house. It is permissible to take chalk or some similar marker and circle the area to be moved. After an impression has been photographed at the scene, it is sometimes desirable to leave the tripod where it is, remove the camera, step back and photograph the tripod in relation to a permanent object because that will help to show and verify the original position and location of the impression.

When impressions are photographed, it is important to include a scale for size reference. The scale should be placed beside the impression and should also be at the same level as the impression. For example, if photographing a footprint in soft ground that is recessed one-half inch or so, the scale should not be simply laid on the ground beside the impression; it is best to very carefully dig out a bit of the ground beside the impression so that the scale is down to the same general level as the impression. When the scale has been properly placed, the camera should be focused on it. At this point, care should be taken to ensure that the camera's axis is perpendicular to the impression.

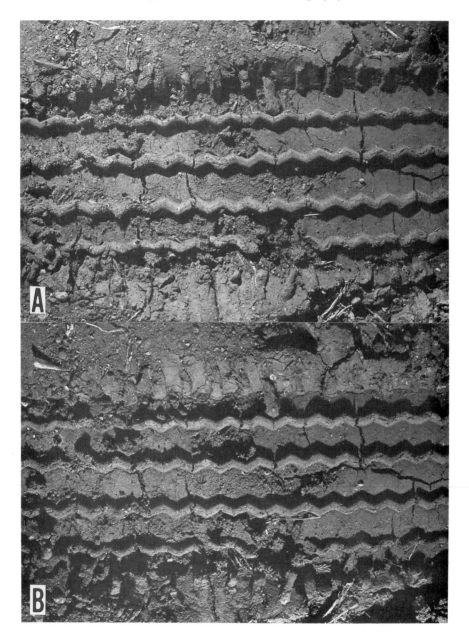

Figure 12-1. (A) While oblique lighting works well to bring out the surface texture of 3-D subject matter, it brings out detail on one side while creating a shadow on the other. In Figure 166A, the light was directed from the top, creating a shadow on the lower edges of the ridges that obscures detail. (B) The lighting was directed from below, creating shadow on the top portions of the ridges. (C) The illumination was directed from directly overhead, creating a washed-out appearance.

In the photography of impressions that are 3-D (three dimensional) a low-grazing illumination will tend to highlight the details and produce the best results (see Figures 12-1A, 12-1B and 12-1C). By examining these three illustrations, note that while the oblique lighting serves to bring out the pattern, it brings out detail on only one side of the impression. For this reason, the impression should be photographed with the light source first on one side and then on the other. This procedure is important, for it is generally not known at the time photographing takes place just what details will be important insofar as identification is concerned.

To illuminate 3-D impressions, a continuous light source such as a photoflood is more desirable than a flash unit, because the former can be manipulated to achieve the best results. In the field, however, it is usually necessary to work with a flash unit as opposed to a continuous source. Under such circumstances, several exposures should be made with the flash unit at various positions and angles to the impression. Be sure to record each exposure and how it was illuminated. Figure 12-2 shows a basic but effective method of photographing 3-D impressions in the field. When utilizing that technique, take care that the flash is not too high nor too low, because a high flash will tend to wash out detail, whereas a flash that is too low will not illuminate enough of the impression. In this case, experimentation and experience will provide the best results. Often, on a sunny day, the natural lighting will provide very good shadows and no flash is necessary; this should be taken advantage of. The sun, however, will be illuminating the impression from one side only. If it is necessary to illuminate it from the opposite side, a shade of some sort should be used to block out the direct sunlight and use a flash from the opposite side.

When photographing 3-D impressions, utilize as small a lens opening as conditions will permit in order to achieve maximum depth of field. Consider a time exposure if necessary.

Impressions in snow, ice and light-colored soil should be photographed as they are, even though the resulting photograph will have little contrast and many details will not show clearly, if at all. After the impression has been photographed as it is found, a powder of contrasting color may be lightly applied by use of a blower and the impression photographed again (see Figures 12-3A and 12-3B). Strong oblique lighting will also prove useful in many cases (see Figure 12-4).

If after impression photographs have been made, a suspect is located and test impressions are made from the shoes, tires, etc., it is important

Figure 12-2. When photographing foot or tire impressions, the camera's axis should be perfectly perpendicular to the impression and the illumination should be directed from the side.

that the test impressions be illuminated from the same direction and angle as were the crime scene impressions when photographed to show the same details in the same manner. The resulting photographs will be the most useful if done in this manner. Also, when questioned footwear, etc. is examined, photographs of the items will generally show more detail than will the actual test impressions.

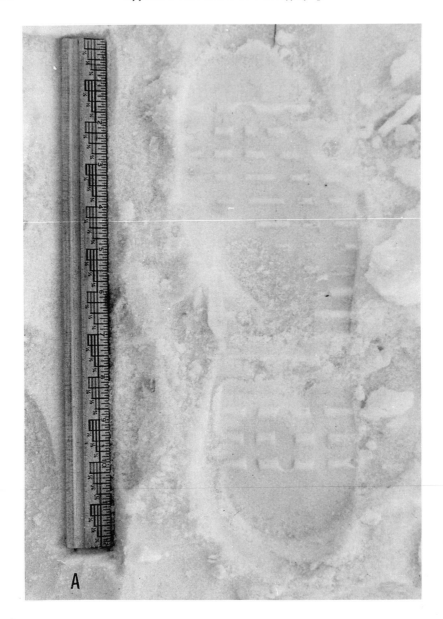

Figure 12-3. (A) **Footprint in snow on overcast day.** Note the obvious lack of detail.

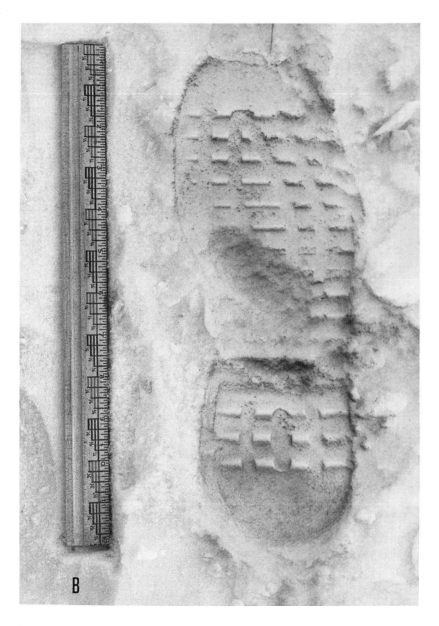

Figure 12-3. (B) **Same print as in Figure 12-3A after having black fingerprint powder lightly applied with a blower.**

Figure 12-4. **Footprint in snow photographed with strong oblique lighting.**

When photographing a 2-D impression on a multi-colored surface such as a freshly waxed floor, careful and meticulous positioning of the lighting is essential in bringing out the detail in the impression. Under such circumstances, a continuous light source is absolutely essential (see Figure 12-5). If conditions are such that a flash must be used, use a flashlight to establish the best point from which to discharge the flash unit.

In impression photography, like many other applications of police photography, if the evidence is of a perishable nature, speed is essential. Whenever faced with impressions in substances that can melt, dry or shrink from drying, the photograph should be made as soon as possible (see Figure 12-6). In the meantime, a sunshade of some sort should be used to protect the impression from the direct rays of the sun. If the impression is in snow, a box should not be placed over it, because the dead air within the box could melt the impression enough so that valuable detail will be lost.

When preparing photographs of impressions for court presentation, it is desirable to enlarge them to life-size (1:1) so the jury can view the impressions at their actual size. When it is necessary to show the impression left by the full circumference of an automobile tire, there will naturally be several photographs involved, and each should be numbered to show the proper sequence.

Tool Marks

Photographing tool marks is very similar to photographing foot and tire impressions. Oblique lighting will most often produce the best results, and an overall photograph should be taken to show the impression in relation to some permanent object.

Unlike the photographing of foot and tire impressions, however, tool impressions will very often necessitate the use of bellows extensions or close-up lenses, as the details in the markings are generally very minute. If using a press camera, take advantage of the double-extension bellows system. The reader may at this point wish to refer back to the chapter on close-up photography. As was the case with foot and tire impressions, a scale should be used for size comparison as shown in Figure 12-7.

As with foot and tire impressions, tool impressions should be photographed before any attempt at moulding. If a suspect tool, such as a jimmy, is found, and it is desirable to take a photograph showing the tool by the impression, the tool should be photographed beside the impres-

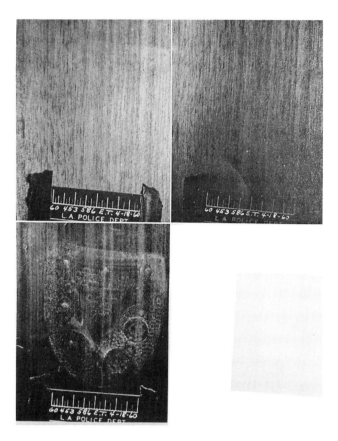

Figure 12-5. The three photographs in this illustration are of the same foot impression on a freshly waxed floor. While the upper two show no detail, the lower photo illustrates the results of properly using oblique lighting. (From Abbott, John R., *Footwear Evidence*, 1964. Courtesy of Charles C Thomas, Publisher, Ltd., Springfield, Illinois.)

sion rather than touching it. This will prevent any accusations in court that the impression had been altered.

Electrostatic Dust Print Lifter (EDPL)

Oftentimes footprints or tire mark impressions at a crime scene cannot be photographed effectively using the previously explained methods. In areas where a suspect has walked, the footprints can be recorded often with dramatic results using a Electrostatic Dust Print Lifter, referred to as a EDPL in the forensic field (see Figure 12-8). During a crime, a suspect leaves prints in the dust, thus making a "dustprint." This print, which is usually not visible to the unaided eye, can sometimes be observed if a light is shined at an angle to the print. The EDPL is also

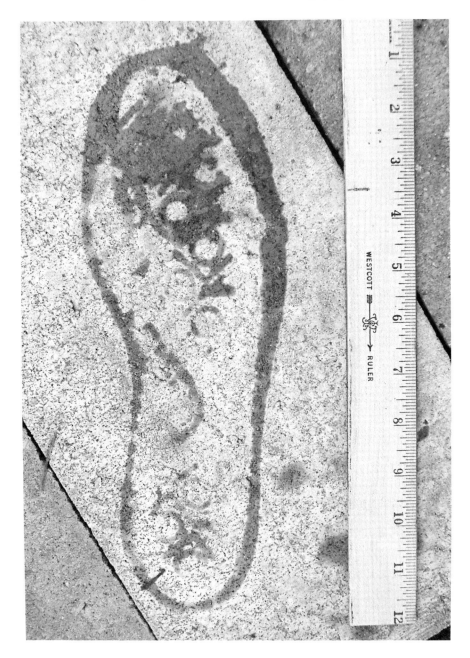

Figure 12-6. **Foot impression left by wet shoe on patio bricks.** Such evidence is short-lived and should be photographed immediately. This is true of any perishable evidence.

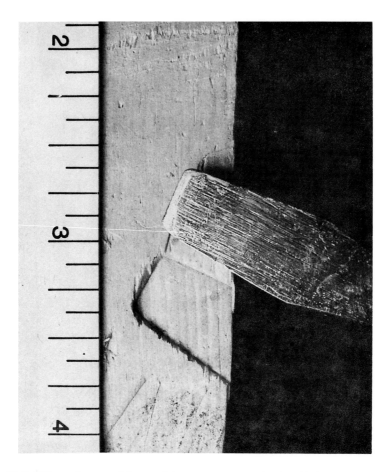

Figure 12-7. When photographing tool impressions, a scale should be included. When it is desirable to show the suspect tool beside the impression, do not permit the two to make contact as that could result in an alteration of the impression.

very effective in recording tire "dustprints" from a vehicle that has driven across a surface where tire impressions were otherwise not obtainable.

The EDPL that is available from the Kinderprint Company comes complete for field use except for an optional cabinet which is used to preserve lifts. When it is decided to utilize a EDPL at a crime scene, it is extremely important that the crime scene be preserved as soon as possible as this type of evidence can easily be disturbed and rendered useless. Once the crime scene is secure and dust prints are suspected to be present, the EDPL can be utilized. The operator should wear shoe covers so as to not contaminate the scene. The process of obtaining the

Figure 12-8. Footprint on a bank's counter top, not visible to the unaided eye, lifted using the Electrostatic Dust Print Lifter, and then photographed with a Polaroid CU-5. (Courtesy of Kevin De Nomie.)

dust prints is quite simple. The evidence area is covered with a metalized sheet of plastic film. Electric current is then applied to the film causing a static charge which attracts dust particles on to the surface. It is important to ensure that no bubbles appear while applying the electricity as the dust particles will not transfer to the areas where there are air pockets. After applying about 15 seconds of current, the power is shut off. The metalized film can then be turned over and inspected by applying oblique light. The portion of the lifting film that contains evidence should then be photographed. The EDPL can be used to obtain dust prints from most anything including fabric, cardboard, paper products, carpet, and deceased bodies.

Photographing Electrostatic Dust Prints

Photographing the electrostatic dust prints is very important, as the dust particles are not permanently attached to the lifting film. Sprays or tape coverings will destroy the dust print. The contrast of the print will vanish in the adhesive layer of the tape, and the spray will distort the print altogether. The most effective way to record a dust print is to photograph it. Dust prints after photographed can be stored by taping them to a board, and then placed in a slotted storage cabinet offered by the Kinderprint Company. Photographing the image immediately is important, for over time dust particles may accumulate on the surface of the metalized film, thus reducing the detail of the image.

To photograph the dust print image it is best to use laser light or a FLS. Good results can be obtained, however, by using a photoflood, and allowing the light to escape through a narrow slit. Photography should be performed in low light conditions by applying oblique lighting, as an undirected light source results in scattered light, resulting in a poor photo. Electronic flashes can be used; however, they are not recommended as this type of light produces scattered light. The Polaroid CU-5 (Figure 14-3) camera is designed for close up photography, and is excellent for this type of photography. It takes 4×5 inch format photos and offers an optional film holder which will accept traditional film such as Tri-x. It is important to include a ruler in all photographs taken. Also important to remember is that dust print lifts are a reversed image, in order to obtain a photograph that can be compared with a shoe, the negative must be reversed during processing so that the photograph is not reversed.

Chapter 13

DOCUMENT EXAMINATIONS EMPLOYING PHOTOGRAPHY AND COPYING TECHNIQUES

PHOTOGRAPHY

General Considerations

This chapter is not designed to make the reader a competent document examiner. Document examination is a very specialized field in itself, and to treat it properly would require an entire book, perhaps many. An effort will be made, however, to give the reader some of the highlights of the role and application of photography in the examination of questioned documents, as well as a general discussion of a few basic photographic techniques which have proven to be effective.

Often information on a document has been changed, added or deleted. When such a document is received, the first step is to photograph it for a permanent record of its original condition. The document examiner will then employ various methods and techniques in an effort to determine whether any changes have been made. A document undergoes numerous tests: chemical, visual examinations using various types of lighting and filtering, microscopic examinations and finally, photographic examinations. In some instances photography is used to discover alterations on a document, while in others the alterations are discovered by nonphotographic means, and photography is then employed simply to make a record of the discovered alteration.

Equipment

Document photography can be done with almost any camera which is capable of taking close-ups. The format of the camera is generally not a critical concern except in the photography of infrared and ultraviolet luminescence, which is often of weak intensity. This type of photography requires the use of a 35mm camera system and fast lenses. Otherwise, for general photography of documents, a view or press type of camera works very well; the type of lighting units needed will depend entirely upon what is being attempted. Usually, a standard type of copy stand for mounting the camera, as well as a cable release, will prove to be essential.

Infrared Reflective Photography

The investigator is at times faced with a document whose writing has been obliterated by charring, deterioration from age, chemical bleaching, accumulation of dirt or censoring by ink to blank out certain passages, dates or names.

Many of the above conditions, depending upon specific factors such as the original type of ink used, can be dealt with effectively through the use of infrared reflectance photography.

Taking an infrared reflective photograph is, generally speaking, no more difficult than taking a normal flash picture (see Figure 13-1). There is only the consideration of one filter which must be used and a small adjustment in focus. In Figure 13-1 note that there is a Kodak Wratten Filter Number 87 placed over the camera lens. The camera is loaded with Kodak High Speed Infrared film, which is available in 135 cassettes and which must be placed into the camera in total darkness, since the cassette is capable of keeping out visible light but not infrared radiation. The most convenient radiation source to use for this type of photography is a common electronic strobe unit. As for the focusing adjustment that was mentioned, it is necessary to increase the lens-to-film distance by about 1/4 of 1 percent of the focal length of the lens being used. This adjustment is necessary because the lens elements refract the infrared radiation to a different degree from that of the visible light, due to a difference in the wave length between the two. Most lenses for 35mm SLR cameras have an infrared auxiliary focusing mark engraved near the infinity mark on the lens barrel (see Figure 13-2). To use the auxiliary focusing mark, simply focus using visible light, then rotate the lens barrel just enough so that the point that previously lined up with the distance indicator now lines up with the infrared auxiliary focusing mark. This extends the point of focus by 1/4 of 1 percent of the focal length of the lens. After proper focusing has been accomplished, the infrared filter should be placed over the lens to block out visible light. Exposure is best determined by conducting a series of exposure tests. Vary the exposure by changing either the f/settings, the flash-to-subject distance or both. Be sure to keep a record of all significant exposure tests for future reference.

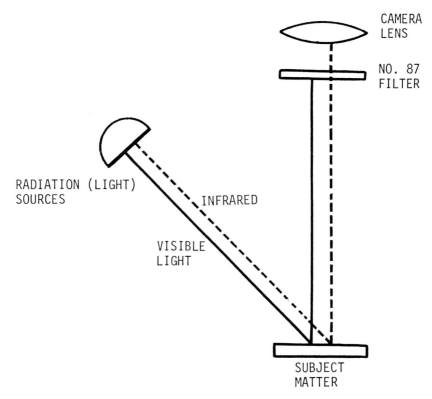

Figure 13-1. The technique involved in infrared reflectance photography is simply that of taking a flash photograph. One simply uses infrared film and places an infrared filter over the camera's lens to exclude visible light.

The basic concept of infrared photography and the reason it will serve to bring out details which have been obscured is not difficult to understand. For example, observe the two photographs in Figures 13-3A and 13-3B. Figure 13-3A shows a typed message which has been obliterated with a magic marker, and then photographed with black and white pan film using a normal photographic technique. It is impossible to know what the typed message was. Figure 13-3B shows the same obliterated writing photographed using the infrared reflectance technique just discussed. Very little can be seen of the magic marker deposit which served to conceal the typed message, while the typed message itself is quite clear and easily read. The reason for this is that the typewriter ink, which is a pigment type of ink, reflects the infrared radiation to a high degree while

Figure 13-2. When taking infrared photographs, an adjustment in focus is necessary. This is accomplished by extending the lens-to-film distance by ¼ of 1 percent of the focal length. The arrow indicates the infrared auxiliary focusing mark.

the magic marker, which is only a water color, reflects very little infrared radiation, allowing most of it to pass through.

If writing has been chemically bleached, there may be enough pigment left in the paper to make it possible to restore the original message enough to see what it was. If this is not possible, infrared photography will often serve to at least show that an alteration was made, though it may be illegible.

Infrared Luminescent Photography

In relatively recent times it has been found that, when infrared reflective photography will not produce the desired results, utilizing an infrared luminescent technique will (see Figures 13-4A and 13-4B).

The technique for taking such photographs is not difficult. A box or housing can be constructed of plywood ¼ to ½ inch in thickness. It must be well built to prevent all extraneous light from entering while an exposure is being made. Windows can be equipped with two squares of

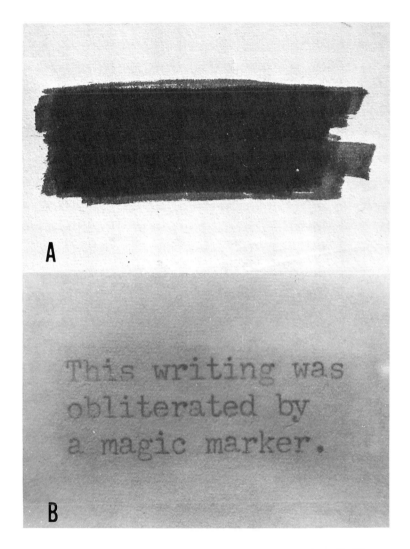

Figure 13-3. (A) A typed message was obliterated using a magic marker. (B) The same message was photographed using infrared reflectance photography. Note the clarity with which the message can be read.

Corning Glass Number 9780® (available from the Corning Glass Works in New York) and common fluorescent light tubes or 500-watt photoflood lights used to provide the radiation. If a photoflood light is being used, a piece of heat-absorbing glass should be placed between the light and the filter. A Kodak Wratten Filter Number 87 must be placed over the camera lens to exclude all visible light.

Figure 13-5 shows what is actually happening when an infrared lumi-

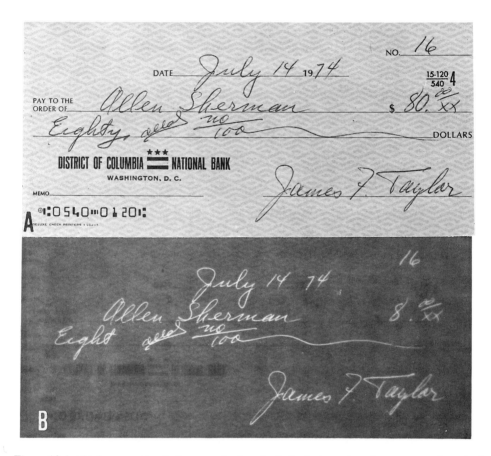

Figure 13-4. (A) A conventional photograph of a raised check shows how it appears to the naked eye. The check appears to have been written in the amount of $80.00. (Courtesy of the Federal Bureau of Investigation.) (B) **An infrared luminescent photograph of the same check.** Note that this photographic technique reveals the check to have actually been written in the amount of $8.00. (Courtesy of the Federal Bureau of Investigation.)

nescent photograph is taken. Note that the Corning Glass filter stops all infrared rays and allows only the visible light to pass, whereas the infrared filter over the camera lens passes only infrared light and stops all visible light. The principle then is that the visible light excites the specimen and causes it to emit an infrared luminescence which is recorded on the film. Remember that there is also visible light being reflected from the specimen, and the visible light will be stronger in intensity than will the infrared luminescence, which is very weak. If the infrared filter was not placed over the camera lens to stop the reflected visible light, it would register on the film much stronger than the weak infrared luminescence and the exposure would be undesirable. Similarly, if the Corning Glass filter were not used to stop the infrared rays emitted by the radiation source, they would reflect from the document, and the results would be nothing more than an infrared reflected photograph. The reflected infrared radiation would be much stronger in intensity than the infrared luminescence.

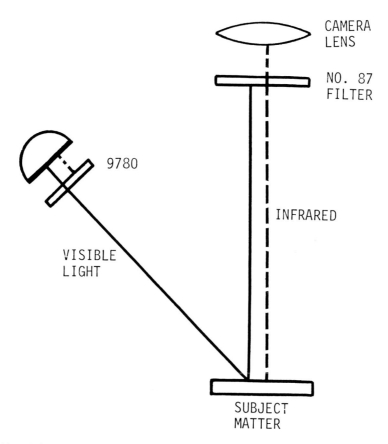

Figure 13-5. Infrared luminescent photography calls for the use of both an exciter filter and a barrier filter. The visible light causes the specimen to emit an infrared luminescence which is recorded on the film.

The exposure time for infrared luminescent photography must be established by conducting a series of exposure tests. The exposure time will in most cases be quite long, anywhere from several seconds to several minutes. A small lens opening is desirable to achieve maximum depth of field to ensure good image sharpness. Again, as always, keep a record of all significant exposure tests.

Ultraviolet Reflective Photography

In examining questioned documents, ultraviolet reflective photography will often provide useful information. This is especially true in cases of documents bearing invisible writing or erasures. There are many chemicals which will work as well as invisible ink: photographic film and paper developer, urine, lemon juice and diluted India ink, to name only a few. Invisible inks may be developed by exposing the document to iodine fumes, by applying heat and often through the use of ultraviolet reflective photography. In the case of erasures, the erasing process very often disturbs the fibers of the paper and, although this is often not apparent to the naked eye, it becomes quite evident when the document is photographed with ultraviolet radiation.

The application of ultraviolet reflective photography is not difficult. All one needs is a common black (ultraviolet) light tube and a Number 18A filter placed over the camera lens which allows ultraviolet radiation to pass through while stopping any visible light (see Figure 13-6). It is necessary to place the 18A filter over the camera lens because the ultraviolet light tubes emit both ultraviolet radiation and visible light. The 18A filter serves to stop the visible light.

Figures 13-7A and 13-7B illustrate a document that was first photographed using a normal photographic technique and pan film, and then again using an ultraviolet reflective technique. Note the difference in the information provided between the two photographs of the same document.

Filters for Data Separation

Chapter 11, "Fingerprint Photography," states that if the photographer, while photographing with black and white panchromatic film, wishes to cause a specific color to reproduce lighter than it normally would, all he needs to do is photograph that color through a filter of a like color. If, however, he desires a specific color to appear darker, that color should be photographed through a filter of its complementary color. This technique is often helpful if a document or check is suspected of being altered and the two inks on the document differ in color. If the upper ink and the original marking underneath differ in color, the document should be photographed through a filter of the same color as the upper markings. This will often cause the upper writing to become almost transparent. The easiest way to determine which filter should be used is

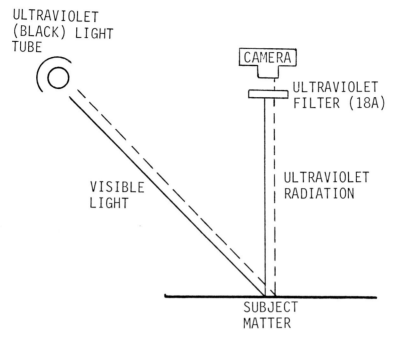

Figure 13-6. **Ultraviolet reflective photography.** Illumination is provided by a common black light tube. A U.V. filter Number 18A is placed over the camera's lens to absorb any visible light.

to view the subject matter through various colored filters. The reader would do well at this point to refer to Chapter 11 where contrast filters are discussed.

Photomacrography

Often, when letters and numbers have been changed, such as one would expect to find on a raised check, for example, an examination of the document under a low-power microscope will show the changes. Such changes can effectively be documented by extreme close-up photography. This method is also effective to show that specific writing may have taken place after a given piece of paper had been folded (see Figure 13-8) or that one stroke with a writing instrument was made either before or after another. In cases of erasures, photomacrography is useful. Figures 13-9A and 13-9B illustrate the importance of a very low grazing illumination for such applications.

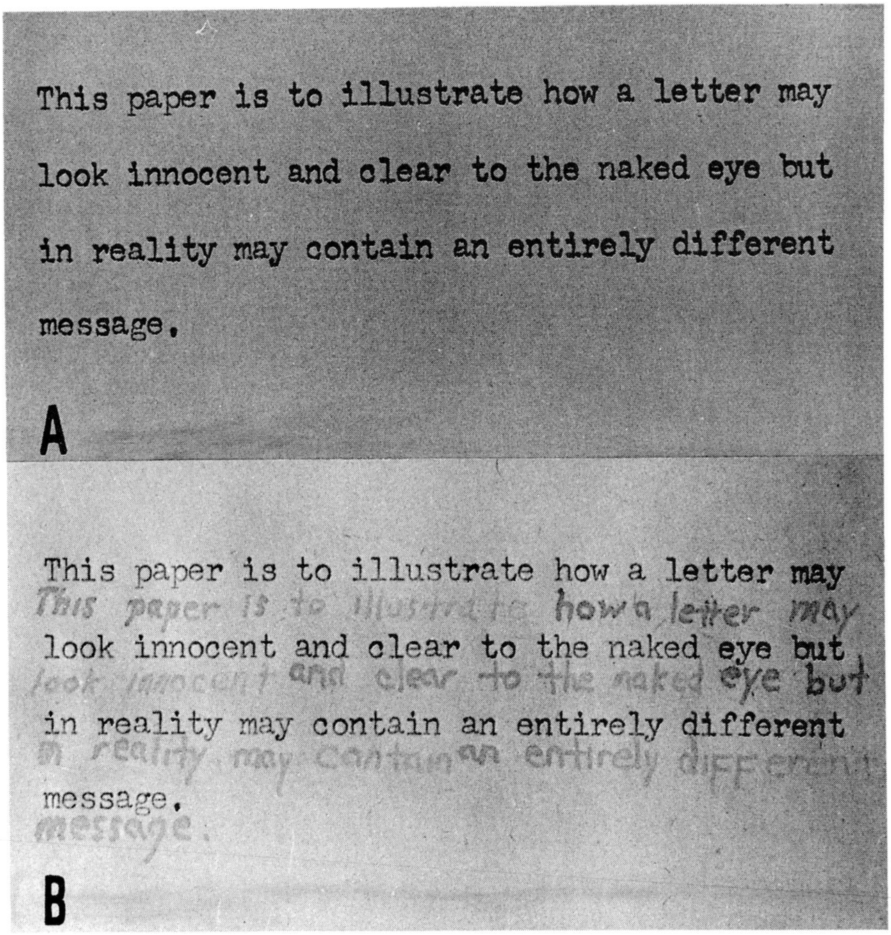

Figure 13-7. (A) **A typed message photographed using a conventional technique.** This photo is the message as it appears to the naked eye. (B) Ultraviolet reflectance photograph of the same paper. Note the clarity of the secondary message written using an invisible ink.

Infrared Transmitted Illumination

In cases where the contents of a sealed envelope are of interest, such information can, under certain conditions, be recorded by making a contact print of the envelope and its contents on a piece of infrared sheet film. Figure 13-10 illustrates the results of such a technique. While this technique can be useful, should the envelope contain several sheets of folded paper, or if the paper has been written or typed on both sides, the

Figure 13-8. Photomacrography can be used to document the fact that something was written before or after the paper had been folded. The ink line on the left was made after the document had been folded, while the ink line on the right was made prior to being folded.

effectiveness of this technique will suffer. Control of exposure is best accomplished by varying the flash-to-subject distance. A sheet of paper should be placed between the flash and the subject matter to cut down the level of illumination if there is a problem with overexposure.

Photographing Carbon Paper

When a message is typed or written and there is carbon paper involved, the carbon will usually contain the original message. This, however, ceases to be true in cases where the carbon paper has been used to a great degree because there will be little more than a complete obliteration left. When the carbon has not been used excessively, however, there are basically three methods that may be employed to create a photographic record of the information on the carbon.

One technique is to lay the carbon paper flat with the carbon side up. By using oblique lighting it is often possible to get a good reproduction through a normal photographic technique. It will be necessary to manipulate the light source a bit to obtain the best results. Another technique is

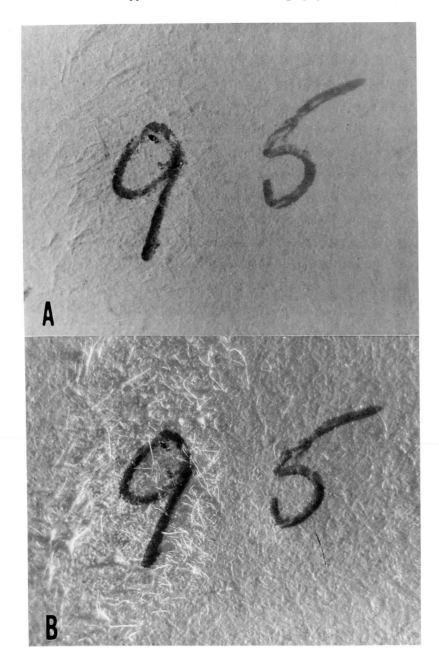

Figure 13-9. (A) When photographing erasures, direct illumination will provide a flat appearance which will often fail to reveal what it is intended to illustrate. (B) A low-grazing (oblique) illumination will reveal the disturbed fibers much better than direct illumination.

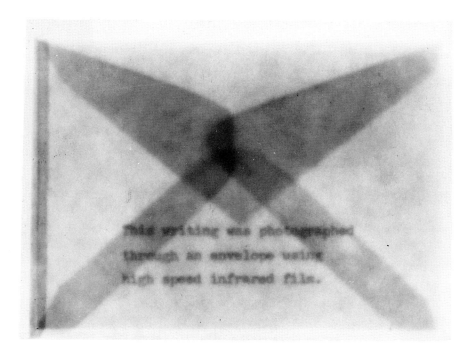

Figure 13-10. The typed message that appears was on a sheet of folded paper and sealed in a small manila envelope. This is the result of a contact print of the envelope made on a sheet of infrared film.

to use transmitted illumination (light at the rear of the paper) and a Number 25A red filter over the camera lens. Use Kodak Contrast Process Panchromatic Film® when photographing a carbon paper in this manner. Finally, it is often possible to obtain a good reproduction of the original message by making a simple contact print using the carbon paper as a photographic negative; with this technique, a photographic paper grade of high contrast should be used. Expect the exposure time to be relatively long.

Indentations

When a message is written on the top page of a pad of paper, there is often a trace of that message left on the next lower page. This is caused by the pressure of the writing instrument. When handling such evidence, take care that nothing is done that will have a tendency to flatten out the paper and decrease the depth of the depressions.

If there has been sufficient pressure involved, it is sometimes possible to photograph the second sheet of paper and make a record of what was originally written. When photographing such evidence, it will become necessary to use a very low grazing light angle to cause a shadow in the depression caused by the pressure of the writing instrument. When attempting this, it is desirable to work in a darkened room so that lighting can be controlled. A useful lighting unit is a slide or motion picture projector since it throws a strong, concentrated beam of light. There is a variation or addition to this technique that can often produce very good results. First of all, a low grazing illumination and a contrast process film should be used in order to produce a high contrast negative. With this technique, two exposures are made, varying only the direction of the illumination; the first is directed from the side of the document and the other from the top or bottom. The two negatives are then sandwiched. This is done because the impressions running across the beam of light will be shadowed, but those running in the same direction will not. By combining the two negatives, a print with shadow highlighting going in both directions is produced.

COPYING TECHNIQUES

General Considerations

The application of photocopy techniques is an important aspect of police photography. When a questioned document is received in the laboratory, it is photographed in its original state before any attempt is made to analyze the document. The copy camera is also used to make infrared and ultraviolet photo examinations of various articles of evidence ranging from documents to bullet holes in clothing. Often it is deemed necessary to copy various photographs.

While copy work is a reasonably technical area of photography in itself, the general techniques are not difficult to master, nor is there a rigid requirement concerning the type of camera used for copy work. Actually, when one takes a close look at copy work, it does not differ radically from general photography.

Equipment

To do copy work, basically only a suitable camera, a means of mounting the camera securely, a means of providing evenly distributed illumination and a means of obtaining close-ups with the camera are needed. Most commonly used for copy work is a view type of camera with a bellows system capable of extending a distance of two to three times that of the focal length of the lens to make it possible to obtain close-ups. Ideally, the camera should be equipped with a ground glass focusing screen for critical focus. If a view or press type of camera is not available, 35mm camera systems can very effectively be used for such applications. It will, however, be necessary to use various accessories in order to make close-up photographs of a copy subject. The reader should refer to Chapter 10 "Photomacrography," where various close-up accessories and techniques are discussed. There are also a few models of Polaroid cameras available which can be used effectively for copy work. Shown in Figure 13-11 is the Polaroid Land MP-4 Multi-purpose camera®. Finally, if there is no suitable camera available, one may effectively use a photographic enlarger for the task without undue difficulty. There are several models of enlargers also available that are designed to be used for copy work. Among such enlargers are some models of the Durst.®

Copying with an Enlarger

Photocopies may be made using a standard type of an enlarger, with photofloods to illuminate the copy subject and a black cloth or some other suitable means of preventing light from fogging the negative in the enlarger head.

The easiest method of using an enlarger as a copy camera is to take a thin negative and scratch the emulsion surface with a needle making an "X" in the center. The negative is then placed in the negative carrier, inserted into the enlarger, and the image is focused on the plane at which the copy subject will be placed. The next step is to substitute the scratched piece of film with an unexposed piece of film. Wrap the black cloth around the enlarging head to prevent extraneous light from exposing or fogging the film while the exposure is made. When the film has been placed into the enlarger and the cloth wrapped around the enlarging head, the exposure is made by turning on the photoflood lights briefly. Expect that it will be necessary to make a few trial exposures in

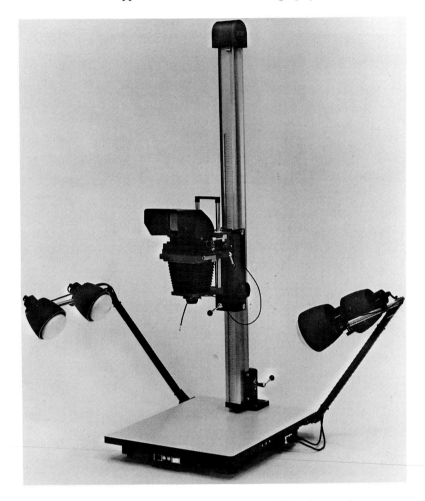

Figure 13-11. **Polaroid MP-4 Multi-purpose camera.** Note the lighting arrangement.

order to obtain optimum results. If the findings are recorded, good, well-exposed copy negatives of almost any subject matter will be reproduced at nearly any reproduction ratio simply by referring to the record to see what exposure time worked best for a similar situation in the past.

Alignment of Subject and Equipment

To produce quality results when engaged in copy work, it is very important that the back of the camera (film plane) be perfectly parallel with the subject matter. When using a professional copy assembly and camera as shown in Figure 13-11, or a copy stand either commercially made or homemade, as shown in Figure 13-12, proper alignment will be little trouble. This is also true when using an enlarger for copy work. If, however, one is using a standard type of tripod, great care in alignment must be exercised or the results will be less than acceptable.

When a tripod rather than a copy stand is being used for copy work, it is desirable to use a bubble level to ensure that the camera is perfectly level. After this has been done, it is a good idea to take a measuring tape and measure the distance from each side of the camera to the subject to ensure that the camera is also aligned in that respect. The camera lens should also be the same height as the center of the copy subject when the subject is mounted to the wall.

Stopping Down the Lens

It is not correct to believe that the farther a lens is stopped down the sharper the resulting image will be. It is true, however, and perhaps this is where the common misconception is introduced, that the more a lens is stopped down the greater will be the depth of field. Depth of field has little to offer the person engaged in copy work, however, since copy work generally involves a flat subject.

Most lenses have what is referred to as a *critical aperture,* a specific f/setting at which the optimum resolution that specific lens is capable of producing is achieved. This point is generally in the vicinity of half stopped down. A lens that has an aperture range of f2.8 to f16, for example, will generally offer the finest resolution when set at somewhere between f5.6 and f8. To learn what that setting is for a specific lens, the manufacturer of that lens should be consulted.

Lighting

The most common lighting arrangement for copy work is to have two to four photoflood lamps (depending upon the size and area of the copy subject) on either side of and shining on the copy subject from a 45° angle (see Figure 13-13). When illuminating the subject, it is important to exercise care that the illumination is even, or a negative of inconsistent density will result. Such negatives are difficult to print.

Ordinary tungsten (3200°K) lamps are adequate for black and white copy work of both continuous tone and line copies. If one chooses to use

Figure 13-12. Copy stands need not be expensive or fancy to be useful. The stand illustrated has been homemade. Proper use of a copy stand will help to ensure that the camera's axis is perpendicular to the subject matter.

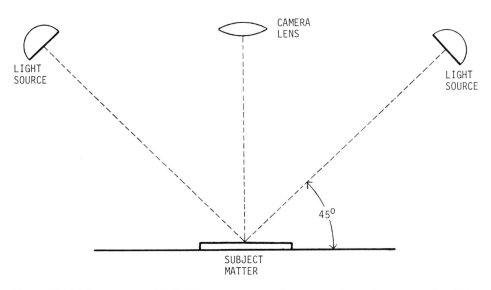

Figure 13-13. The most suitable lighting arrangement for copy work is to have two to four lights shining onto the subject matter from a 45° angle.

photoflood lamps (3400°K), do so realizing they have a life of only four to six hours and are, for this reason, not economical to use. To copy color subjects, use a color film balanced for tungsten illumination. If by chance electronic strobe units are being used, it will be necessary to use a daylight color film.

Reflections

Often, when copying materials that have a glossy surface, reflections of the lighting units and/or the camera will present problems. One easy method of dealing with such a problem is to take a flat, black piece of cloth or paper with a hole large enough for the camera lens to poke through and place it as a shield in front of the camera (see Figure 13-14).

Darkfield Illumination

Darkfield illumination is used with transparent objects and specimens which are for the most part colorless. With subject matter of this nature, reflected and transmitted illumination would generally be of little avail.

The light source is placed behind the subject matter and directed through it at a 45° angle (see Figure 13-15). This produces a bright

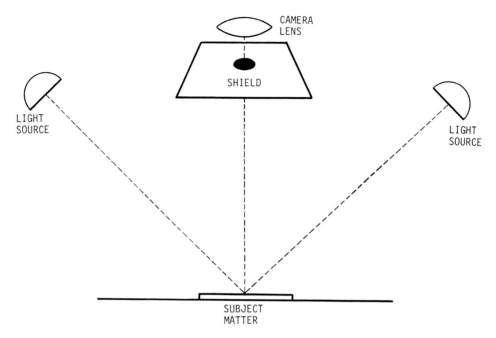

Figure 13-14. When reflections from shiny or glossy subject matter cause problems, take a black cloth or paper with a hole large enough for the lens to stick through and place it in front of the camera.

image against a dark background. Darkfield illumination is very useful in the area of photomacrography and, as is evident in Figure 13-16, it is also effective for photographing bullet holes in glass.

Vertical Illumination

In the section on photographing impressions and tool marks, oblique lighting was discussed. While oblique lighting works best under many circumstances, there are cases where a type of lighting called *vertical illumination* will produce the best results. As shown in Figure 13-17, vertical illumination consists of a light source whose beam is directed parallel to the surface of the specimen. A small piece of glass is placed between the specimen and the camera lens at a 45° angle. The glass acts as a reflector which directs a portion of the light straight down at the specimen, and the lens, of course, sees the specimen through the glass. Figure 13-18 was illuminated and photographed in the above manner.

When vertical illumination is used, it often works well to set up the equipment as has been described, then, while viewing the subject on the

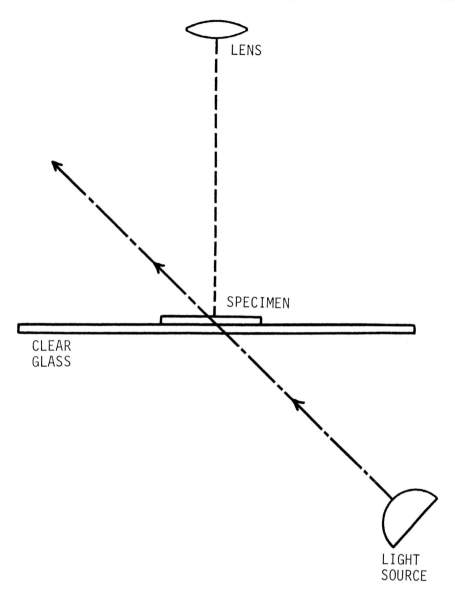

Figure 13-15. Darkfield illumination is accomplished by placing the light source behind the subject matter and directing it through at a 45° angle.

ground glass or through the viewfinder, move the light source around a bit. This procedure will have a tendency to bring out some details while at the same time suppressing others.

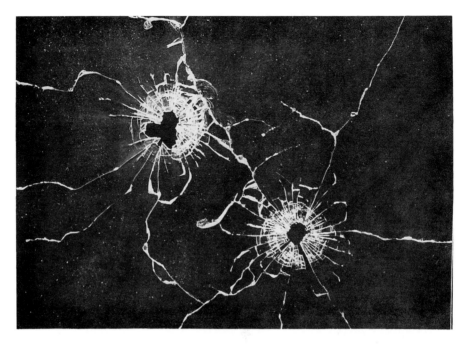

Figure 13-16. **Bullet holes in glass photographed using darkfield illumination.** Such photographs also document, by way of the cracks, the order in which the shots were fired.

Forensic Light Sources
and Document Examination

Forensic light sources, discussed in greater detail in chapter 11, can also be used extensively in the area of document examinations. The U.S. has seen an alarming increase in check forgery crimes, and it is estimated to cost billions of dollars a year to the American people. FLS can be used very effectively for assisting in document crime investigations. If a document has been altered, or censored such as by certain parts of it having been obliterated, a specific band of light can often be used to illuminate and reveal the altered or obliterated writing, then an appropriate filter utilized to photograph it.

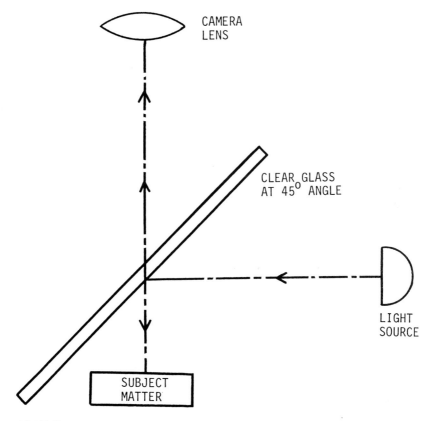

Figure 13-17. Vertical illumination consists of a light source whose beam is directed parallel to the surface of the specimen. A small piece of glass is placed between the specimen and the camera lens at a 45° angle.

Negative Materials

There are many films suitable for copy work, and the reader would do well to obtain copies of Kodak publications* which provide technical data on their various films. As a starter, however, the reader may wish to try Kodak Professional Copy Film®, which gives reproductions of continuous tone prints that are almost indistinguishable from the originals. Other black and white films which may prove satisfactory for various copy applications are Kodak Contrast Process Pan®, Kodak Contrast Process Ortho®, Royal-X Pan, Royal Pan®, Panatomic-X®, Plus-X

*Kodak Professional Data Book Number F-5 (Kodak Professional Black and White Films) and Kodak Professional Data Book Number M-1 (Copying).

Figure 13-18. **Serial numbers on a pistol photographed using vertical illumination.** Oblique lighting would also work for such subject matter.

Pan, Professional Line Copy, Tri-X Pan®, and Ortho. The reader is by no means limited to the several films which have been mentioned here. Exactly which of the above films will serve the photographer's needs best depends entirely upon the type of photography being done.

Chapter 14

POLAROID

This chapter is intended to make the reader aware that the Polaroid system has carved out a well-deserved niche in the field of forensic photography. Polaroid offers some very fine quality cameras with a full range of aperture settings and shutter speeds as well as fine lenses. These cameras are suitable for many professional and technical applications. Polaroid also offers a number of films that provide not only instant photographs in either black and white or color, but they also offer black and white films that provide both an instant photograph and a negative.

Over the years, Polaroid, like other camera manufacturers, has made an effort to offer cameras that are increasingly user friendly. Perhaps the most notable advantage of Polaroid products in the police and fire field, aside from the obvious advantage of having instant photographs of evidence, is the fact that the police officer or investigator who is not a polished photographer can go into the field and come away knowing exactly what was obtained in photographic coverage of a given scene. This factor eliminates the possibility of leaving the scene with film that is either over- or underexposed, or which for various other reasons may be of little or no value. This point should prove to be of greater interest to the smaller departments which do not have a staff or division that specializes in photography, but must rely on their line personnel. It should also be recognized that the small departments are in the majority.

Another point worthy of consideration is the added security and confidentiality of Polaroid evidential photographs. The small department that has been making use of commercial laboratory services, often by sending films out, will no longer find that necessary. In some cases, however, the scene may be photographed using a conventional color film, with Polaroid photographs used as a back-up.

The reader should, however, be aware of two main areas of police and fire photography where the usefulness of a Polaroid camera is to be questioned. The two areas are surveillance photography and photography of a fire in progress, and its spectators, especially at night. The reason is the fact that the two types of situations tend to be very fast-moving and the photographer must use a camera that will accommodate such a situation. In a stake-out, for example, the photographer may find it necessary to make a series of several pictures in rapid succession, and the use of telephoto lenses is generally necessary. Polaroid cameras do not address either need well. When photographing a structural fire in progress, the photographer will very often photograph the building from all sides at intervals of three to five minutes, as well as the spectators every ten to fifteen minutes. That can take place for one to several hours, and it often occurs after dark. Under such circumstances, one should consider using a 35mm SLR (single-lens-reflex) system. Such cameras are small and light. They have a variety of fast lenses available for them, and rapid sequential photographs are possible.

In the area of fire photography, a Polaroid camera is adequate for photographing the scene after the fire has been extinguished and the photographer is no longer faced with the fast-moving situation described earlier, and the use of flash is feasible.

Cameras

It would not be practical here to make an attempt at illustrating and discussing every Polaroid camera presently on the market. The reader will, however, be introduced to a few cameras that have a strong potential in the area of police and fire photography.

Polaroid Procam

The Polaroid *Procam*, Figure 14-1A and 14-1B, is a user friendly folding camera featuring auto focus, automatic exposure control, built-in automatic flash for main illumination and fill computation, and an optional date or time code that will imprint the data on the 4 × 4-inch picture. Additionally, although the camera features a minimum focus of 18 inches, use of the auxiliary close-up lens enables one to focus down to 12 inches, a 33 percent decrease in camera-to-subject distance with a corresponding increase in image size. The built-in flash is effective up to 18 feet.

Spectra System

The Polaroid Spectra Law Enforcement Kit, Figure 14-2, was designed specifically for crime scene photography. The camera features auto

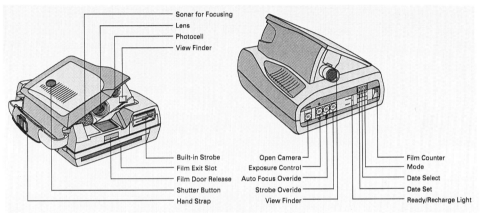

Figure 14-1A & B. The Polaroid ProCam features auto-focus, auto-exposure, built-in flash and close-up capability. (Courtesy of Polaroid Corporation.)

focus, automatic exposure control, built-in flash, a snap-on close-up lens, and 1:1 copy stand.

Polaroid CU-5 Close-Up Land Camera

The CU-5 camera, shown in Figure 14-3, is designed for close-up photographs of evidence such as foot and tire impressions, tool marks and fingerprints. The standard CU-5 camera records evidence on a $3\frac{1}{4} \times 4\frac{1}{4}$-inch image format at reproduction ratios from $\frac{1}{4}$:1, which covers an area of $11\frac{1}{2} \times 15$ inches, to 3:1 (three-times life-size), which covers an area of $1\frac{1}{16} \times 1\frac{9}{16}$ inches.

With the CU-5 camera, various reproduction ratios and framing are easily and effectively accomplished by choice of lenses, ratio multipliers and framing attachments which mount to the front of the camera (see Figure 14-4).

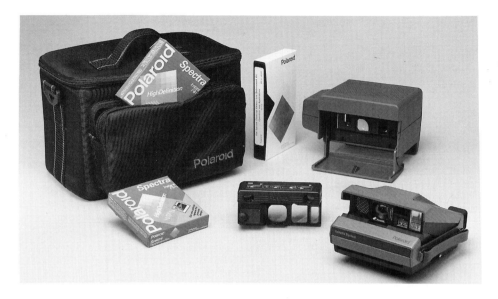

Figure 14-2. The Polaroid Spectra Law Enforcement Kit was designed for crime scene photography. The camera features auto-focus, automatic exposure control, built-in flash, a snap-on close-up lens and 1:1 copy stand. (Courtesy of Polaroid Corporation.)

Illumination is provided by a ring strobe which encircles the lens. Such a set-up will generally offer photographs with little or no shadow. For exposure control, the photographer will find it is necessary only to set a selector switch for either color or black and white, depending upon the type of film being used. This type of operation is suitable for most situations. When dealing with a unique and difficult situation, however, exposure control can be set manually. Also, oblique lighting may be used for showing a subject's surface texture. In reference to manually controlled exposure, the shutter has speeds ranging from 1 second to $1/125$ second, as well as a provision for making timed exposures. There are two interchangeable lenses available for the CU-5 cameras. The 3-inch (75mm) lens has f/settings from f4.5 to f45. The 5-inch (127mm) lens has f/settings from f4.7 to f45.

For field applications, a $3\frac{1}{4}$ pound battery pack is necessary to provide energy for the flash unit. The battery pack contains a 510 volt, nonrechargeable battery which will provide about one-thousand flashes before becoming exhausted (see Figure 14-3).

The CU-5 camera is simple to operate and is intended to be used easily and effectively by anyone, whether knowledgeable in photography or not.

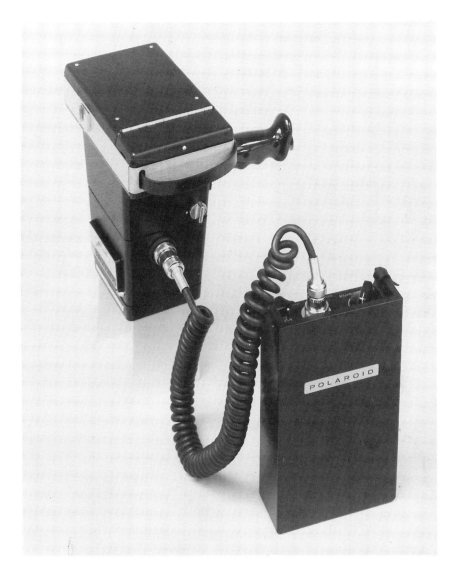

Figure 14-3. The CU-5 Close-Up Land camera is designed for close-up photographs of evidence such as foot and tire impressions, tool marks and fingerprints. This camera must be used with the battery pack shown. (Courtesy of Polaroid Corporation.)

Figure 14-5 illustrates a fingerprint that was photographed using the CU-5 camera.

MP-4 Multipurpose Land Camera

Figure 14-6 illustrates the MP-4 Multipurpose camera, so called because of its versatility. Basically, the MP-4 is a copy camera which is

Figure 14-4. Various reproduction ratios and effective framing are easily accomplished by use of the various ratio multipliers and framing attachments. (Courtesy of Polaroid Corporation.)

especially effective for the copying of line and half-tone specimens as well as photographing small objects such as hand guns and small tools. The MP-4 is designed to be used for photomacrography (see Figure 14-7) and photomicrography. See Figure 10-10 in Chapter 10, section discussing photomicrography.

The MP-4 system features reflex viewing, as well as a sliding head which eliminates the need to remove the film holder while framing and focusing. The sliding head permits the photographer to slide the ground glass into place for framing and focusing and then slide it to the side, bringing the film holder into place. This system virtually eliminates the possibility of accidentally moving the camera when the film holder is replaced.

The camera is designed to rotate 360° around the film plane and can be locked in any desired position. There is also a calibrated scale for reference as to the exact position and elevation of the camera. In addition to the camera's ability to rotate, the column of the XLR model will rotate completely around for easy positioning over the floor. This is a useful feature when photographing large objects or using the enlarger head available specifically for this camera.

The four lighting units, which are a standard part of this assembly, are

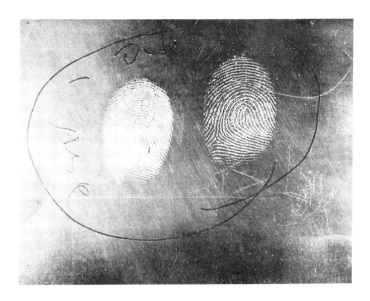

Figure 14-5. **Life-size photograph of fingerprints made with the CU-5 Land camera.** (Courtesy of Polaroid Corporation.)

completely flexible, making it possible to illuminate subject matter with either direct or oblique lighting.

Figure 14-8 shows the MP-4 camera with a condenser enlarger head mounted to it. This is a quality unit and will accept negative formats from 35mm to 4 × 5 inches. One must, of course, secure the proper negative carrier for the size of film being used. The rotating head permits enlargements to be easily projected onto a wall. The MP-4 XLR's® rotating column permits an image to be projected onto the floor.

The MP-4 stand (base, column and lighting units) is effective also for use with other format cameras, still or motion picture (see Figure 14-9).

Film Adapters

There are a number of medium and large format cameras made by various manufacturers which will accept an adapter permitting the camera to be used with Polaroid films. Many commercial photographers use such an adapter to check lighting and composition before switching to a film holder containing conventional film. One can also use film adapters for the purpose of documenting evidence with conventional film and also use the same camera to obtain Polaroid photographs as back-up.

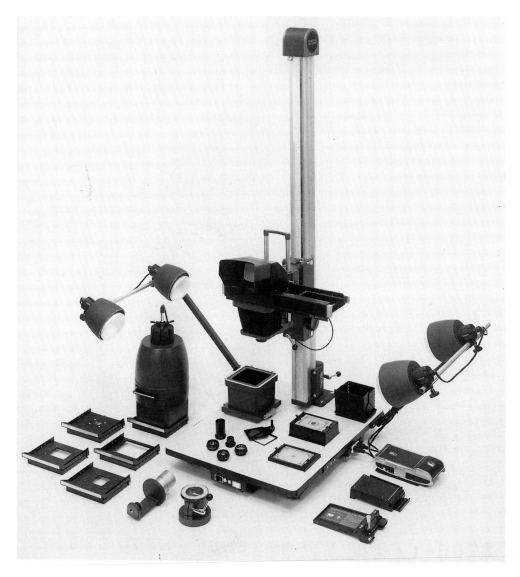

Figure 14-6. **The MP-4 Multipurpose Land camera with its various accessories.** (Courtesy of Polaroid Corporation.)

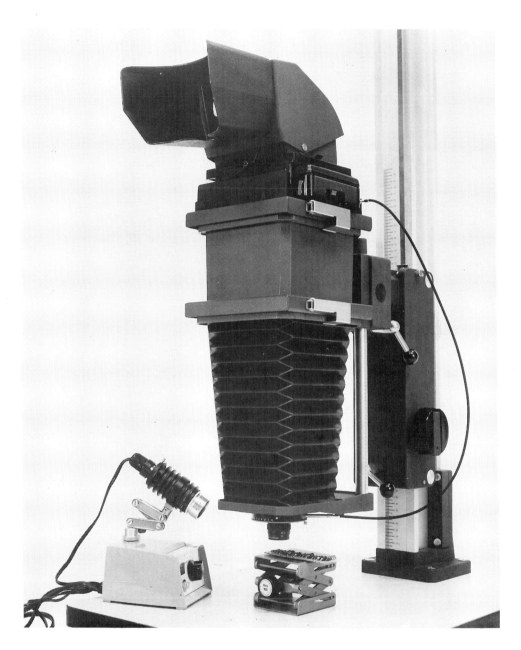

Figure 14-7. The MP-4 Land camera is useful for application of photomacrography. (Courtesy of Polaroid Corporation.)

Figure 14-8. The enlarger head designed to be used upon the MP-4 Land camera accepts negatives from 35mm to 4 × 5 inches. (Courtesy of Polaroid Corporation.)

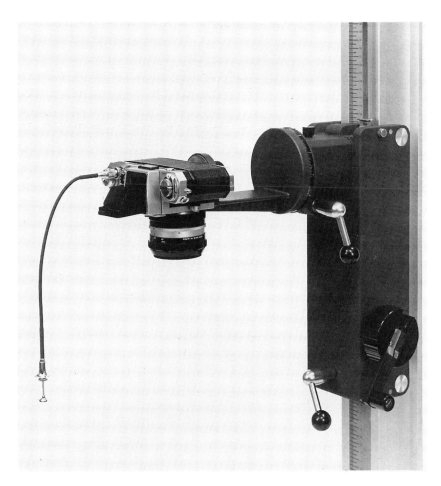

Figure 14-9. The MP-4 stand (base, column and lighting units) is effective also for use with other format cameras, still or motion picture. (Courtesy of Polaroid Corporation.)

Chapter 15

SURVEILLANCE PHOTOGRAPHY

Introduction

Physical surveillance often plays an important role in the investigation of cases such as illegal sales of contraband or establishing and photographically documenting the activities of known and suspected criminals. The camera, both still and motion picture, is often found to be an invaluable tool to one engaged in surveillance. More often than not, however, when one thinks of surveillance photography, it is in reference to a "stake out" rather than to a moving surveillance, whether it be on foot or through the use of a vehicle.

To be effective at surveillance photography, the photographer must know the photographic equipment well and be adept at surveillance. A word of caution is in order. When engaged in covertly photographing a subject, one must exercise extreme care not to violate that subject's right to privacy. To secure photographic evidence at the expense of violating the subject's rights will avail nothing if that violation will make the evidence inadmissible in a court of law.

CAMERA TYPES GENERALLY USED FOR SURVEILLANCE PHOTOGRAPHY

As a general rule, it will be found that the cameras best suited for surveillance photography are 35mm single lens reflex cameras, 16mm motion picture cameras, video cameras, and in some unique situations, subminiature cameras that are about the size of a pack of cigarettes or smaller.

The value of the subminiature cameras lies primarily in their small size and easy concealment. The most notable advantages of 35mm SLR and 16mm motion picture cameras are their fast lenses and the wide variety of film types available for them. The 8mm or Super 8 motion picture cameras offer little in the way of good subject identification

270

because of the limited film selection and the small image format. For that matter, there is even a very notable difference between the degree of subject identification offered by a 35mm camera and a 16mm motion picture camera. The 35mm is better for identification purposes while the obvious benefit of the motion picture camera is the ability to record activity. Video cameras are treated in a chapter devoted to that topic.

35mm Single Lens Reflex Cameras

There is no still camera that enjoys the wide variety of fast lenses that is enjoyed by the 35mm single lens reflex camera. The need for fast lenses arises from the fact that surveillance photography is often under lighting conditions that are less than ideal. Also, because surveillance photography is often under conditions that necessitate the use of moderate to extreme telephoto lenses, a range finder camera is of limited value as there would be no easy way to ensure that the subject is properly framed. Therefore it is the single lens reflex that is the logical choice for surveillance photography. Specific attention is given to telephoto lenses and their use in the chapter devoted to that topic. There is also a wide variety of film types available in the 35mm size. They vary from several types of color film to a number of black-and-white films as well as several specialized types such as infrared and ultrahigh speed films for specialized applications. Many of the film types available in the 35mm size are not available in sizes for many of the larger format cameras. Thirty-five millimeter cameras are small and easily transported, and are much easier to work with surreptitiously than larger format cameras. The design of these cameras makes it easy to make rapid sequence exposures because one sweep of the film advance lever advances the film all the way and cocks the shutter making the camera ready for the next exposure. In addition to this, many of these cameras are available with auto film advance or motor drives, the latter enabling one to make sequence exposures at a rapid rate. Refer to the discussion titled Automatic Film Advance and Motor Drives.

It is possible with many brands of 35mm cameras to attach a special back to the camera that allows one to use more than just thirty-six-exposure rolls of film. Two-hundred-fifty-exposure backs are common, and Nikon offers an 800-exposure back that takes a standard 100-foot roll of film. It is also possible to set up a camera with a motor drive and make exposures by using a radio control device from a distance.

16mm Motion Picture Cameras

General Considerations

As is the case with 35 mm single lens reflex cameras, the 16 mm motion picture cameras have a wide variety of lenses, zoom and telephoto, available to them. In many cases it is possible to use a *C-mount adapter* to enable one to use a 35 mm camera lens system on the 16 mm camera. The C-mount adapter is simply an adapter that is screwed onto the motion picture camera in place of the camera lenses. The adapter then allows the 35 mm camera lenses to be mounted to the motion picture camera in the same manner they would be mounted to the body of the 35 mm camera. The big advantage of this is allowing one to take advantage of the many fast lenses made for 35 mm cameras and also to have a complete lens system for both cameras without having to buy two lens systems.

For those 16 mm motion picture cameras featuring a bayonet mount, one can often obtain an adapter that accommodates the cameras bayonet mount so that a C-mount adapter can be used. Or, if one has lenses with a C-mount, the adapter permits their use.

Motion Picture Cameras for Night Work: Three Basic Designs

Most but not all motion picture cameras are designed similar to the three designs that will be discussed in very general nontechnical terms. This brief discussion is intended to show why some systems are more desirable than others when it comes to work in low light levels.

Most Super 8 reflex movie cameras are intended primarily for amateur use and an effort has been made to make them very automated and simple to use and yet relatively inexpensive. As a result, these cameras tend to waste a lot of light because of the number of optical elements and beam splitter prisms the light encounters before it reaches the film plane. Let us follow a beam of light from the time it enters the primary lens, which in most cases is a zoom lens, until it reaches the film plane. The primary lens will reduce the light value by about 10 to 20 percent. The light, after passing through the primary lens, encounters a beam splitter that will further reduce the light by about 20 percent when taking part of it for the image that will appear in the viewfinder. We have now lost between 30 and 40 percent of our original light value. As the light continues from the beam splitter it passes through a master lens that will absorb about 5 percent of the light. Next it goes through another beam splitter prism to give some light to the cell of the light meter. Our original light value has now been reduced to less than half, or more than one f-stop. For normal daytime photographing this kind of a system is fine, but it has limited usefulness when it comes to night work using available light.

The second system is very effective insofar as maximum light transmission to the film plane goes, but it is also quite expensive. This system is found mostly on 16mm motion picture cameras. It consists of a reciprocating mirror-shutter system. Quite simply, it is a shutter that reciprocates up and down. In the "up" position a hole in the shutter lines up with the lens and film format and allows the light to expose the film. In the "down" position a 45-degree mirror that is mounted to the shutter is positioned in place of the shutter opening and directs the light to the viewfinder and light meter instead of the film. That system offers an image in the viewfinder that, while being bright, flutters. The flutter, however, presents no problem. With that system the only light entering the lens that does not reach the film when an exposure is being made is whatever light the lens elements absorb.

The third basic design is cameras with separate viewfinders. The Bell & Howell camera shown in Figure 15-1 is of this design. The only thing between the lens and the film plane is a shutter; thus, all the light entering the lens reaches the film except for whatever amount is absorbed by the lens elements. Also, with that kind of system the image in the viewfinder is bright. Many of those systems also have a separate window to gather light for the light meter so as not to reduce the amount of light reaching the film.

Except for the reciprocating mirror-shutter that was discussed, most motion picture cameras have a shutter that looks like a disc with a large notch cut out of it. The disc spins and every time the notch passes over the film format, the film is exposed. It used to be that cameras commonly had a notch that was rather narrow. The Bell & Howell Series 70® camera shown in Figures 15-1A and B has a 204-degree shutter (the notch is 204°). A subsequent advancement or improvement was the making of a shutter that had a 230-degree section removed. It can be seen that with the shutter revolving at a given speed, the exposure time will be increased if a wider notch has been made. When this camera is run at eight frames per second (fps) the exposure time is $1/14$ second. While a camera with a 230-degree shutter will probably not be capable of an exposure time longer than this, it can achieve this exposure time while running at a higher number of frames per second. The advantage

Figure 15-1 (A). The Bell & Howell Series 70 camera is a 16mm range finder camera. It is equipped with a three-lens turret but, unlike the Bolex Rex 5, is not self-threading. The range finder is equipped with a parallax adjustment.

Figure 15-1 (B). Bell & Howell motion picture camera with a 135mm lens and a 2X tele-extender.

of this is the fact that the subject's movements, and so forth, will be recorded more smoothly, thus avoiding the "Keystone Cop" effect. The reader should also bear in mind that most projectors will not run at eight frames per second. Filming the subject with an exposure time of less than 1/14 second would not be practical as there would be severe problems with image blur.

In conclusion, when selecting a motion picture camera for work under available light at night, the main points to be taken into consideration and looked for in a camera are fast lenses, slow shutter speeds and the degree of the shutter, and a lack of beam splitter prisms that tend to greatly reduce the amount of light reaching the film. Also worth keeping in mind is how readily one can utilize a C-mount adapter to allow the use of the lens system of a 35mm camera. One should remember also that a large zoom lens with its many elements will tend to rob more light than will a fixed focal length lens with fewer elements. Also, the cost of the camera selected must be in keeping with one's budget. The idea is not to buy the best thing money can buy but to buy the best thing money will buy relative to the purchaser's needs.

Reflex Viewing vs. Range Finder Cameras for Telephoto Work

One of the first differences the reader will notice between these two basic types of motion picture cameras is the cost factor, the reflex cameras being considerably more expensive than the range finder cameras. While it is true that the reflex cameras have many advantages over the latter for telephoto work, the range finder cameras, such as the Bell & Howell in Figures 15-1A and 15-1B are acceptable for this purpose until one begins to get into the area of "extreme" telephoto work. This is where the line is drawn that tends to separate the two. Unless one gets into the area of "extreme" telephoto work, the range finder cameras should offer little in the way of difficulties.

Shown with the Bell & Howell camera in Figure 15-1B is a 135mm lens with a 2X tele-extender giving an effective focal length of 270mm. The range finder is for a 150mm lens. To visualize what portion of the viewfinder would be covered by a lens twice as long would be no trick. A focal length of 270mm on a 16mm camera is about 10½ times as strong as its normal lens of one inch (25.4mm). This will prove to be sufficient for most situations requiring long lenses. Consider this against the fact that a 500mm lens on a 35mm camera offers a magnification ten times over the normal 50mm lens.

An effort has not been made to discuss specific details concerning the many makes and models of motion picture cameras from which one can choose. An effort has been made to provide enough general background data to allow one to make good decisions and a favorable choice when shopping for a motion picture camera to fulfill specific needs in surveillance photography.

Subminiature Still Cameras

While the results that can be achieved by the use of a subminiature camera will in no case equal those possible with a good full frame 35mm camera, it is these little gems that enable investigators, especially undercover agents, to secure photographic evidence that could not be obtained by using a larger and more conspicuous camera or when conditions prohibit working from a distance with telephoto lenses. The cameras being referred to are full working cameras as small, and many smaller, than a pack of cigarettes. Many have in addition to a full shutter speed and aperture range, an internal light meter, several of them being fully automatic. While some have better lenses than others, most of them have multi-element lenses and will perform very well. The price of these cameras vary.

Some models have a spring-wound motor drive that makes it possible to take a series of exposures in rapid succession. The film size of these cameras is quite small and very large blowups are generally not possible. In most cases a five-by-seven-inch enlargement is the maximum. Beyond that point the grain becomes a limiting factor.

The most common film sizes one will encounter when considering subminiatures are 9.5mm used in the Minox and Yashicas, and 16mm used by Minolta. Tessina takes 35mm film but does not accept the standard 35mm cassette. The Tessina has its own special cassette. The image size produced by the Tessina is only about 20 × 14mm, not 36 × 24mm as found in a full frame 35mm camera.

One final point to take into consideration when selecting a subminiature camera: Besides looking for a camera with the features that will suit your needs, consider the system of which it is a part. Does it have accessory filters and lenses? Can one get an adapter for photographing through binoculars? Does the system provide a mini-developing tank, mini-enlarger, mini-tripod, and so forth, thus offering a darkroom and full range of accessories that can be easily transported in an ever-ready case?

TELEPHOTO PHOTOGRAPHY

Introduction

Except for some very distinct problems that are quite characteristic of telephoto photography, much of the art of telephoto photography is simply that of taking pictures. If you have a telephoto lens working at f16, it is very much like any other lens working at f16. There is, however, an exception to this rule that one should be aware of. Lenses employing mirrors to shorten the physical length of the lens by folding the optical (light) path into a zigzag pattern will lose about two thirds of a stop of light value because of the mirrors. If a light meter other than an internal meter in the camera is being used, this factor must be taken into consideration when calculating exposure.

The only distinguishing feature of a telephoto picture is a flat, long perspective. *This is a result of the long camera-to-subject distance and has nothing to do with the lens system being used.* If you take a picture from any given point, the perspective will be the same whether the lens is 50mm or 2000mm in focal length. The flattening of the perspective increases with camera-to-subject distance, not with an increase in lens focal length. The typical squeezed-together effect of long perspective is very much in evidence in television showings of baseball games. The only reason the telephoto lens gives that effect is because with the long lens the photographer can move back and still get a sufficiently large image. Figures 15-2A, 15-2B, and 15-2C help to clarify this point. Figure 15-2A was of that same negative greatly enlarged. Figure 15-2C was taken from the same camera position using a 135mm telephoto lens. Note that the photo taken with the normal lens, and then greatly enlarged, shows the same compressed effect as the photo taken with the telephoto lens. This should serve to illustrate that the compressed effect is a result of the long camera-to-subject distance, not the lens system being used.

Figure 15-2. (A) **View taken using a normal lens.** (B) **Greatly enlarged portion of the scene appearing in that taken using a normal lens.** (C) The three vehicles appearing in the center portion of the view in 15-2A are photographed this time using a mild telephoto lens. Note that by comparing this photo with that in 15-2B, the perspective of the vehicles and buildings is the same.

Telephoto Lenses

In the area of telephoto photography there are basically three types of lenses one will encounter. They are long focus, telephoto and mirror lenses. The long focus and telephoto are both refractive lenses employing no mirrors so the three types of lenses can really be put into two basic groups, refractive and mirror lenses. The simplest of the three types of lenses, and probably the one the reader will encounter the least number of times is the direct objective (long focus) lens (Figure 15-3). All this lens consists of is a direct objective housed in a tube that eliminates extraneous light and positions the lens at the proper distance from the film plane. This lens, with the exception of lack of compactness, is the best for telephoto photography as it offers maximum light transmission and best definition. With the direct objective system the physical length of the lens is the same as the focal length. This can become a matter of concern when getting into the area of extreme telephoto work. The second lens system is a takeoff of the direct objective lens and it is this lens one will encounter the most frequently. It is a true telephoto lens. It has an objective lens in the front of the lens tube just as the long focus lens does, but in addition it has a negative lens in the rear end of the tube that displaces the point of focus further back, thus offering an effective long focal length in a short package (see Figure 15-4). In many cases, lenses of this type have a physical length of one-half to three-quarters the actual focal length, a definite factor in its favor. With the two above-mentioned lens systems, exposure is controlled by the shutter speed of the camera and the position of the diaphragm. The third type of lens the reader is likely to encounter, and a lens that has some outstanding advantages in the area of surveillance photography, is the reflex-mirror lens. This lens uses a system of mirrors and lenses to fold the optical path three times forming a zigzag pattern (see Figures 15-5 and 15-6). The resulting product is a lens of long focal length in a very short package. Take for example a lens with a focal length of 500mm. A direct objective lens of this focal length would physically be about twenty inches long, the true telephoto lens (negative rear element) would be between fifteen and seventeen inches long, while the mirror lens would be between 4³/4 and 7¹/4 inches long depending upon the make of the lens (see Figure 15-7). If one is to be taking photographs while hand holding, the mirror lenses are the best choice. Another factor to be considered is the fact that when working with mirror lenses one is not as conspicuous to onlookers as if using a refractive lens of the same focal length. Mirror lenses are also much more maneuverable than the refractive lenses because of their small size.

Unfortunately, mirror lenses are not generally as fast as refractive

LONG FOCUS LENS

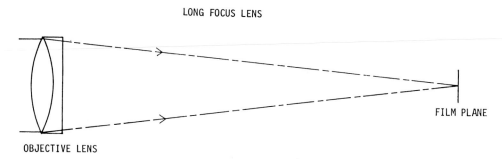

Figure 15-3. Drawing of a *long focus* lens system. With such a lens, physical length is equal to the focal (optical) length.

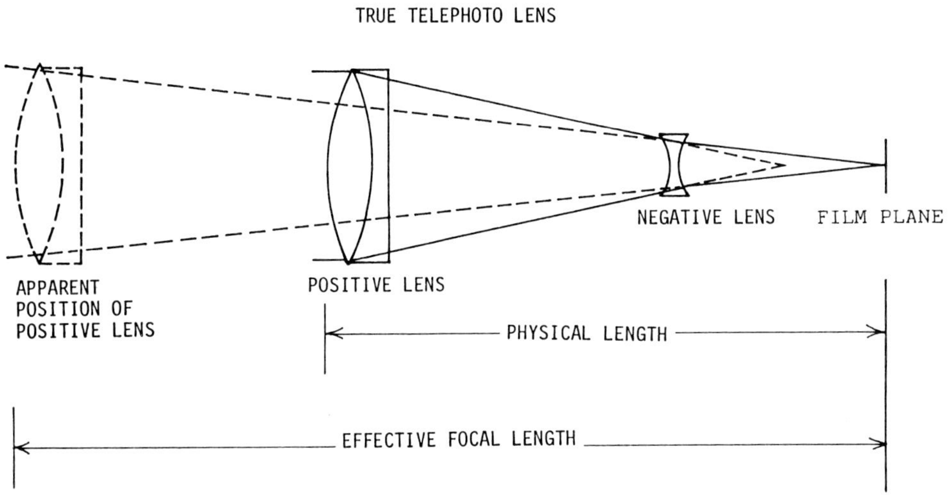

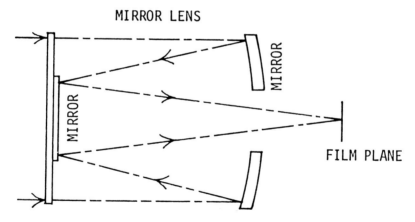

TRUE TELEPHOTO LENS

NEGATIVE LENS   FILM PLANE

APPARENT
POSITION OF
POSITIVE LENS

POSITIVE LENS

PHYSICAL LENGTH

EFFECTIVE FOCAL LENGTH

Figure 15-4. Drawing of a *true telephoto* lens system. The negative rear element displaces the point of focus further back thus giving the lens an effective long focal length, much longer than the actual physical length of the lens.

MIRROR LENS

MIRROR

MIRROR

FILM PLANE

Figure 15-5. Drawing of a *reflex-mirror* lens showing the basic optical path folded to provide a long focal length lens in a small physical package.

lenses (the maximum aperture is not as large). In addition to this, there is a further light loss of about two thirds of an f-stop because the mirrors (there are two of them) are not capable of reflecting more than about 85 percent of the light that strikes their surface. Unlike the refractive lenses, mirror lenses do not have a diaphragm to control the amount of light that reaches the film. In many mirror lenses, neutral density filters are

Figure 15-6. Nikon F2S Photomic mounted on a 2,000 mm f11 Reflex-Nikkor with mounting yoke. While this lens is 80 inches (2,000 m) long optically, it is only 23^7/$_{16}$ inches long physically because of its design. (Courtesy of Ehrenreich Photo-Optical Industries, Inc.)

built into a turret that is mounted in the rear of the lens which can be rotated to position the desired filter to aid in exposure control. Some manufacturers providing this turret with built in filters will provide filters other than those of neutral density. This tends to be the case when the lens happens to be fairly slow, such as Nikon's 1000mm f11 Mirror Lens®. The filters often provided with these lenses are UV haze, yellow, orange and red. Many 500mm mirror lenses which are faster, generally f8, have two neutral density filters to aid in exposure control. Another thing mirror lenses do that refractive lenses do not is cause a vignetting of the image. The vignetting is not a critical problem as its occurrence is not sufficient to be detrimental, and besides, with mirror lenses, so much is gained and so little lost. Mirror lenses also have a very close minimum focus, much more so than is possible with refractive lenses. While a

Figure 15-7. Comparison photo of a true telephoto lens of 500mm focal length and a reflex-mirror lens of 500mm focal length.

mirror lens with a focal length of 500mm can focus down to about ten feet, a refractive lens of 500mm is only capable of focusing down to about thirty-five feet. This question of minimum focus has little effect however on one engaged in long-range telephoto surveillance.

Figures 15-8A–D illustrate the comparative magnification of various telephoto lenses coupled to a 35mm single lens reflex body.

Preset vs. Automatic Lenses

As was stated previously, refractive lenses use a diaphragm to aid in exposure control. Since it is easier to obtain correct focus with the lens diaphragm wide open because the image is then brighter, one finds it is then necessary to stop the diaphragm down the proper amount to coordinate with the shutter speed after focusing. Some lenses do this automatically after the photographer has preselected the f-setting while other lenses leave this to the photographer entirely. There probably would not be too much debate as to which system is more convenient:

A.

B.

Figure 15-8 A–D. Comparison photos of a subject taken from a distance of 400 feet using first a 50mm normal lens (A), a 400mm telephoto lens (B), an 800mm telephoto lens (C), and finally a 2,000mm telephoto lens (D). The 2,000mm lens offers a 40 times magnification over that of the 50mm normal lens.

C.

D.

the automatic, of course. There is, however, a considerable cost difference-between the two types of lenses. The preset (manual) lenses are much less expensive. With the preset lenses, it is simply a matter of adjusting to the idea that after focusing the lens must be stopped down unless the photographer for some reason wants the diaphragm wide open.

Major Camera Brand Lenses vs. Independent Lens Manufacturers

This is another area in which one can save considerable money when purchasing telephoto lenses. While each major camera manufacturer offers an array of lenses for their system which are very good, they are also expensive. There are independent lens manufacturers that do not make cameras but concentrate on accessories with a strong emphasis on lenses that fit the major 35mm camera brands. They make quite a complete system of lenses (except the normal lens) all the way from wide-angle to telephoto, and zoom lenses. While they perform as well optically as those put out by the major camera manufacturers, they will in some cases not meet the same specifications concerning mechanical construction. They are, however, very good lenses and, if treated as any fine piece of optical equipment should be treated, will give many years of satisfactory service.

Tele-Extenders

A tele-extender is an optical device that goes between the camera body and the lens to increase the effective focal length of the prime lens being used. There are four general sizes of tele-extenders. There are extenders that increase the effective focal length by 1.5 times, two times, and three times, and zoom extenders that go from two to three times. When using a tele-extender to double the focal length of a 500mm lens, for example, the effective focal length is 1000mm and can provide good results. It will not, however, in all likelihood provide the results one could expect to obtain with a 1000mm prime lens, but good results nonetheless. Another negative factor of tele-extenders is that they decrease the effective aperture by the same amount they increase the effective focal length. In other words, an extender that doubles the effective focal length of a lens also requires two stops extra exposure. A tripler requires three stops extra exposure.

Tele-extenders will cause a decrease in resolving power of the prime lens with which it is used, as stated. The loss of resolving power is greater towards the edge of the field than in the center. Resolving power in the center, however, can remain close to 80 or 90 percent of the original resolving power. One way to partially overcome the lack of sharpness around the edges is to stop the aperture down thus obtaining better depth of focus. This helps since there is a lack of sharpness around the edges because optically the extender is not capable of focusing the entire image on the exact plane. It is a case of not being able to eliminate spherical aberrations entirely. The problem is greater with a tripler than with a doubler. Another factor concerning tele-extenders that should be mentioned even though it will not generally concern the surveillance photographer is the fact that tele-extenders were designed and intended to be used on the longer telephoto lenses. Because of this, tele-extenders will not work as well on normal lenses and very short telephoto lenses of around 85mm or so. They will start working better on 135mm or 200mm and longer.

Some feel that while there is an advantage to using a doubler, too much is lost when using triplers. The authors disagree inasmuch as there have been numerous instances whereby results have been obtained with a tripler on a prime lens that would not have been possible with a doubler on the same lens. When an 800mm lens with a tripler offers unquestionable subject identification from as far away as one-fourth mile, who can argue with such results? That was accomplished using Vivitar optics (see Figure 15-9). Also worthy of mention is the fact that readable license plate numbers have been photographed on vehicles at distances in excess of two miles using a Questar lens of 1600mm focal length in conjunction with two tele-extenders coupled together. Questar lenses are of extremely high quality (see Figures 15-10 and 15-11).

Air Turbulence and Light Scatter

Telephoto lenses of 1000mm or more will cause problems with atmosphere. Looking at the ground glass with a camera focused at some distant object will prove the fact that air is visible and moves to a great degree. The problems caused by turbulence of the air become greater with increased focal length.

As the sun heats the earth's surface, the air near the ground expands, gets lighter, and then rises, being replaced with cooler air from adjoining

Figure 15-9. Subject photographed at one-quarter mile using a Vivitar 800mm f8 lens with a 3X tele-extender. Photographed with Tri-X film rated at E.I. 1,600 (ISO 1,600).

areas. As a result, the density of the air is not uniform thus causing light rays going from the subject to the camera to refract or bend causing an unsharp and somewhat distorted image.

Air turbulence is not too great in the early morning hours before the sun has had a chance to heat the earth's surface, so if it is possible, photographing should be considered at that time. If there is more than one prospective vantage point from which to choose, there are a number of factors one should take into consideration when making the selection. First, if exposures are made from a high place such as on a hill or a building, looking down onto the subject, much of the air turbulence that is almost always present close to the ground, even on cool days, can be avoided. Secondly, the amount of air turbulence over a field will be much less than over a parking lot or looking down a roadway. The amount of air turbulence over snow and water is even less than one would find over a field.

In long telephoto work, side lighting a bit from the front is preferable to direct front or back lighting. This is because light scattering is quite severe with back lighting, and front lighting tends to reduce contrast.

If working with color film, the use of a skylight filter is desirable as it helps to reduce the blueness of distant subjects. If working with black and white film, one should try using a yellow filter. A red filter will do the job better than a yellow filter but rather than losing $1^1/3$ stops with the yellow filter, the red reduces the light value by three stops.

Problems of Lens Shake, Camera Shake, and Focus

The best optics will not avail if the focus is not accurate and the lens and camera are permitted to shake causing image blur. Generally, lenses as large as 500mm can be hand held if a fast film is used on a bright day that allows a shutter speed of $1/500$ second or more. A mirror lens is much better suited for hand held shots than a refractive lens. In fact a mirror lens as long as 1000mm can be hand held but that is the maximum. A good rule of thumb to remember in hand holding lenses is to use a shutter speed equal to the focal length of the lens being used. That is to say, if one is using a 135mm lens, use a shutter speed of $1/125$ second. With a 200mm lens, one should use a shutter speed of $1/250$ second, and so forth. If this rule of thumb is followed, and if when making the exposure one treats the camera as a rifle (take a deep breath, let part of it out, hold breath and release the shutter gently), a very good percentage of success in obtaining sharp photographs should result. As for the proper method of holding the camera, the lens should be allowed to rest in the palm of the left hand which also focuses the lens; the body of the camera is secured by the right hand which also takes care of the shutter release and film advance lever. Both elbows should be firm against the body for support (see Figure 15-12). Another technique that is helpful for hand held shots is to brace or rest the camera and lens against some solid object such as a pole, tree or door frame while making an exposure (see Figure 15-13). This is also helpful when working under low light levels that require a slow shutter speed.

When using a lens that is too long to hand hold, some other means must be employed to ensure a stable setup. Naturally a good solid tripod is the most desirable route to take. Also worthy of consideration is employing two tripods (see Figure 15-14). Unfortunately, tripods will sometimes be too obtrusive and cumbersome for the conditions under which one must secure the photographs. By studying Figures 15-15 through 15-17 it can be seen that there are several mechanical aids from

Figure 15-10. Visitors at Yellowstone National Park taken from a distance of about 2,000 feet using a Questar Seven Lens. (Courtesy of Questar Corporation.)

Figure 15-11. View of vehicles across Elliott Bay in Seattle, a distance of 2.2 miles, taken with a Questar Seven. Note the clarity of the vehicles' registration numbers. (Courtesy of Questar Corporation.)

Figure 15-12. Hand holding telephoto lens. Both elbows should be firm against the body for support.

which to choose. The belt pod shown in Figure 15-18 is good for short to moderate telephoto lenses, but does not prove effective for long telephoto lenses or for motion pictures employing long lenses of more than moderate focal length. For very long lenses, the stability needed is simply not afforded by the belt pod. When shooting motion pictures, the breathing of the photographer, even though slight, causes the subject to float around in the frame. The longer the lens the more radically the subject will move about. For the motion picture camera a better alternative would be a monopod. The belt pod can be effectively used as a monopod (see Figure 15-19).

When working from an automobile, one might want to consider using a window mount (see Figure 15-20). When using a set-up such as this, one must be sure to shut the engine off as the vibrations caused by it will in all likeliness make one's efforts a waste of time. As can be seen from

Figure 15-13. Bracing telephoto lens against a solid object for added support.

the illustration, a vehicle with a dark interior is preferable to a light interior. The camera is not as noticeable. One may also consider using a gun stock mount (see Figure 15-21). When working from an automobile, if there is not a mount of some sort to use, one may try resting the end of the lens on the steering wheel and photographing through the windshield. A variation of this is to rest the end of the lens on the side window and hold the camera body. The window can be raised or lowered to assist in maintaining a comfortable position while having the correct elevation of the lens. This has an advantage over photographing through the windshield, which does reduce light and resolution. When shooting out the side window, one can try sitting in the back seat, a less conspicuous spot than the front seat (see Figure 15-22). When working from an automobile, a beanbag or sandbag can often prove to be an effective aid. If the bag is fixed with a drawstring or zipper, it can be carried empty as sand or gravel can often be obtained on location.

In the area of *extreme telephoto* photography, say anywhere from 500mm to 2000mm focal length, in many cases it will not be possible to work

Figure 15-14. Utilizing two tripods is often helpful in extreme telephoto work. A cable release is also desirable.

from an automobile and remain at all discreet. In cases such as this it will be necessary to secure a good vantage point within or on top of a building or perhaps to work from a common-looking truck equipped with one-way glass. Also, a sturdy support or mount of some sort will prove to be essential to hold the lens still. When using a tripod, one can try draping a weight such as a sandbag over the lens, or try hanging a gadget bag on the tripod to make fewer vibrations. The use of a cable release is advisable in order to make an exposure without causing camera shake or movement. Often the mirror in a single lens reflex camera, popping up when an exposure is made, will cause some vibration and a loss of image sharpness. There are two simple things one may consider doing to overcome this problem. First is to make use of the self-timer built into many 35mm SLR cameras. When the timer is set (generally one may select a time from three to ten seconds or thereabouts) and the shutter release button depressed, the mirror pops up so as not to cause an obstruction for the light traveling from the lens to the film. The mirror then stays up until after the exposure has been made. If a time of, say,

Figure 15-15. Sandbags (or beanbags) can prove to be useful to rest a lens on for support.

three seconds is selected, when the shutter release button is depressed, the mirror will pop up. Then three seconds later the shutter will be released to make the exposure. The three-second interval between the mirror popping up and the shutter being released allows for any vibrations caused by the mirror to subside. This has a drawback in that it may be necessary to make an exposure *immediately* in order to obtain the necessary evidence being sought. A second technique may then be in order. With the lens on a tripod, one frames the area to be covered, focuses the lens, then secures the tripod. After this has been accomplished, one locks the mirror in the up position. The mirror, being in this position will not move and cause vibrations when the shutter is released. With the mirror up, one will not be able to observe the subject through the camera viewfinder so it will, in many cases, be necessary to use binoculars. It is also advisable to use a cable release for without it one's efforts will probably be defeated. It might not hurt to mount the binoculars on a second tripod with a binocular clamp. There is a second advantage in looking through binoculars. When looking through a camera and lens for several hours one becomes tired. It is easier to look

Figure 15-16. Sandbag placed on lens to dampen vibrations.

for extended periods of time through binoculars than to squint through a camera. Also, the image in the binoculars (7 × 50) is brighter than what is to be seen through the camera. When working in the area of extreme telephoto photography, it will not be possible to observe with the naked eye what is happening; therefore, the use of optical magnification is essential.

Critical focus is of importance in telephoto photography. If one is

Figure 15-17. Weight of gadget bag being used to increase the stability of the tripod against wind and vibrations.

using a preset lens, it is helpful to open the diaphragm of the lens all the way to afford a brighter image to focus. Also, one will do well to use the ground glass collar around the microprism or split image in the center of the viewfinder, as they do not work with long telephoto lenses. A great aid in critical focusing is an eyepiece magnifier. It is a relatively inexpensive item that screws onto the camera in place of the eyepiece and

Figure 15-18. A belt pod is a useful aid when working with short to moderate telephoto lenses, whether with still or motion picture cameras.

magnifies the central portion of the image by about two times. It is made to swing up out of the way after focusing so that proper framing can be accomplished (see Figure 15-23).

One last word about telephoto photography. Nothing is to be gained by using a lens of greater focal length than is necessary to fulfill the needs

Figure 15-19. **Belt pod being used as a mono pod, a technique that often works well with long lenses.** A Vivitar 800mm f8 lens is shown.

of the specific operation at hand. As has already been stated, the longer the lens, the greater the problems of lens vibration, maneuverability, limited depth of field, and so on.

Surveillance Photography at Night Using Ultrahigh Speed Films

Often, the need for surveillance photography arises at night. When this is the case, the surveillance photographer or investigator must decide between using ultrahigh-speed film and working with available light, using infrared materials or using a night viewing device (NVD).

When working with ultrahigh-speed film and available light, there is no easy way to ensure proper exposure. One can, nonetheless, be assured of a very good percentage of success by doing some experimental work taking photographs of a person under various conditions so as to form an

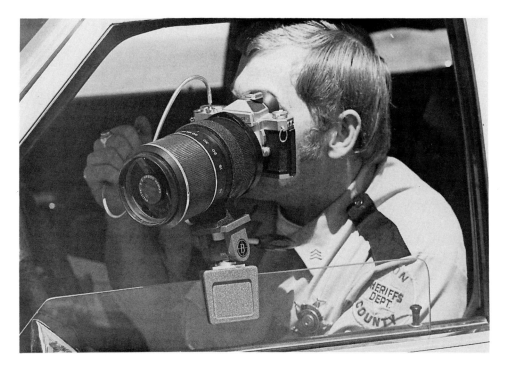

Figure 15-20. Window mounts are very useful when working from an automobile. Be sure to shut off the engine as its vibrations will have a devastating effect on image sharpness.

understanding of how to best approach various situations. Try photographing a subject standing under a streetlight (as shown in Figure 15-24). Also try photographing a subject in a normally lit building from outside. One may also wish to attempt photographing a subject as the lights of a nearby automobile pass over him briefly. Be sure, however, that the light source is a little bit in front of the subject in order to avoid a silhouette that will have little or no value for identification purposes.

Finally, when working at night with ultrahigh-speed film, it will generally be necessary to use as large an f/setting as possible and as slow a shutter speed as conditions will permit. The large f/setting will limit depth of field, and accurate focus is essential. Consider using an eyepiece magnifier; it will help assure good focus. Because the shutter speed will be quite slow, proper support of the camera and lens is essential or there will be image blur.

Figure 15-21. A gun stock mount is very effective when working with telephoto lenses. Here it is being used with a 500mm f8 reflex-mirror lens.

Figure 15-22. Photographer sitting in the back seat and resting the lens on the window for support. Note arrow.

Figure 15-23. Eyepiece magnifier provides a 2X magnification of image for critical focusing. It then swings up so that proper framing can be accomplished. A very useful accessory for telephotography and work under low light conditions.

INFRARED SURVEILLANCE PHOTOGRAPHY

The Light Spectrum

The visible light spectrum is made up of various wavelengths of electromagnetic radiation. The spectrum is made up of violet light on one end with a wavelength of about 400 millimicrons. As the wavelengths get longer we get into blue, then green, yellow, orange and finally deep red which is about 700 millimicrons. Beyond the two extremes at each end of the spectrum is electromagnetic radiation which continues to get shorter in wavelength on the violet end and longer on the red end. Infrared photography takes place in the region just beyond the red end of the spectrum between about 700 and 900 millimicrons. This region is not visible to the human eye. While the spectrum does continue far beyond 900 millimicrons, it has nothing to do with infrared surveillance photography and will not be discussed here.

Figure 15-24. Camera-to-subject distance 200 feet. Illumination one parking lot light 30 feet from subject. Film was T–MAX P3200 push-processed to E.I. 12,500. Exposure ¹/₁₅th second, aperture f6.3, focal length 500mm.

Basic Techniques and Equipment, 35mm Stills

Basically all one needs to surreptitiously take an infrared photo of someone in the dark is any 35mm camera, a roll of Kodak High Speed Infrared® film, a gelatin Kodak Wratten Filter Number 87®, and an electronic strobe unit. The higher the BCPS (candlepower) rating of the strobe the better. The film is a special film that is sensitive to a range of electromagnetic radiation between 700 and 900 millimicrons. Unfortunately this film is also sensitive to the visible region of the spectrum; this is why the filter is needed. Also, the film cassette cannot be taken out of the canister except in total darkness; consequently the camera must be loaded and unloaded in total darkness. It is advisable to take a changing bag into the field for this purpose. The infrared filter allows electromagnetic radiation just beyond 700 millimicrons to pass through but stops the visible light which is less than 700 millimicrons. When a filter-covered strobe is flashed, if one is in the dark looking directly at it he will see a very faint, very brief, dull red glow. There are many fields besides the investigative field that use infrared photography as a scientific tool under daytime conditions. They often put the filter over the lens of the camera to prevent visible light from reaching the film when an exposure is made. The filter does, however, allow the infrared radiation to pass through to the film.

In surveillance photography, however, it is done a little differently. Because it is dark when one is using infrared film, there is no need to worry about visible light interfering with the film when an exposure is made without a filter over the lens. A streetlight or porch light a short distance away will not cause any problems. The filter over the strobe unit is necessary to filter out the visible light; however, if one did not have it, it takes little imagination to guess just how the subject would react immediately following the first exposure made from a carefully selected vantage point. As previously stated, the filter can be obtained in gelatin form. Such a filter can easily be cut to size and taped to the face of the strobe unit. Because gelatin filters are difficult to clean, it is desirable to mount a small piece of glass over the filter to protect it. When dirty, the glass can be easily cleaned.

When focusing for an infrared photograph, one must make an adjustment or a sharp image will not be possible since the infrared rays are longer than the visible light rays, thus focusing at a different point. Most lenses made for 35mm single lens reflex cameras have an infrared, auxiliary focusing mark that allows one to easily make this correction. If a lens has this, after focusing with visible light, one should take the part of the focusing ring that lines up with the infinity mark and rotate the ring until that mark lines up with the infrared focusing mark. No further adjustment should be necessary. If conditions are such that one can stop down, thus having more depth of field, this is to one's advantage. If there is no auxiliary focusing mark, one should make tests. Generally, to get a correct focus with infrared radiation, extending the point of focus (film plane) by one fourth of one percent of the focal length of the lens will result in a sharp image. This is what happens when one uses the auxiliary focusing mark on the lens. If it is known ahead of time what the camera-to-subject distance is going to be, one should just focus on something at that distance, make the correction and tape the focusing ring in position so it does not move. If it is not known what the camera-to-subject distance will be, when the subject appears, the photographer should try focusing on something about as far from him as the subject. He should focus on such things as a streetlight, a porch light, or anything that it is possible to focus upon. Finally, adjust the focus and shoot. If there is nothing to focus upon, one has no alternative but to estimate the distance and hope for the best.

It will also be necessary to establish a guide number for the strobe and filter assembly. That is done just as was described for conventional films in the section discussing electronic strobe units.

The techniques and equipment that have been discussed are those most commonly used by investigative agencies in the United States. A maximum camera-to-subject distance of about fifty feet will be possible if the above instructions are followed (see Figure 15-25).

Advanced Techniques, 35mm Stills

For those who feel that a maximum range of fifty feet is just not sufficient to do the job, there is a very inexpensive way to increase this range by three times or more. A distance of 150 feet or more will certainly enable one to do some good. When working at 150 feet or more, a telephoto lens of 400mm to 500mm will be essential to obtain an image size large enough to have subject identification. Refractive lenses are generally faster than most mirror lenses of the same focal length. While there are available on the market some very fast mirror lenses, they are generally very expensive. Should the photographer, however,

Figure 15-25. Subject photographed at night from a distance of 50 feet using infrared materials and a 135mm lens.

have one of these available, consider using it, as there is no focusing correction or adjustment necessary with mirror lenses when used for infrared photography.

Next, after the telephoto lens, one will need a telephoto strobe unit that throws a narrow, highly concentrated beam of light as opposed to a wide angle of coverage. The photographer needs intensity of radiation. Such devices are available on the market, but they too, just like so many other specialized pieces of equipment, are very expensive. For about ten to fifteen dollars a normal strobe unit can be made to do this job.* This lens is mounted $8^1/2$ inches in front of the strobe unit by using a binocular clamp (tripod mount) or any other means one may wish to devise (see Figure 15-26). The rough side faces the subject. This lens takes the radiation from the strobe that would normally cover a large area and concentrates it into a strong beam, thus greatly increasing the

---

*A Fresnel® lens with a focal length of $8^1/2$ inches (stock no. 40,803; cost, $7.25) can be ordered from Edmund Scientific Company, 620 Edscorp Building, Barrington, New Jersey 08007.

intensity and consequently causing an increase in the effective camera-to-subject distance. By referring to Figure 15-27, it can be seen that hot spots will generally result. If these hot spots do not appear in the area that will be covered by the telephoto lens there is no problem. If they do, one should put a diffusion glass of some sort over the front of the strobe unit along with the infrared filter. Some loss in intensity will result, but that cannot be helped. The setup in Figure 15-25 has no diffusion glass because the hot spots were not causing a problem. One should establish the guide number by using the same method that has already been explained. Once familiar with this setup, the photographer should establish another guide number to be used when the infrared film is going to be push-processed by increasing the development time by 50 percent. With the setup shown in Figure 15-25, a guide number of 900 with normal process gives an effective camera-to-subject distance of 145 feet (see Figure 15-28). By increasing the development time 50 percent, a guide number of 1145 and a range of 182 feet is possible (see Figure 15-29).

Figure 15-26. Illustrated is a typical setup for taking telephoto infrared photographs. The radiation source consists of a Fresnel lens mounted in front of a strobe unit covered with an infrared filter to block visible light.

Figure 15-27. In this photo the pattern of the infrared illumination provided by the equipment shown in Figure 15-26 can be seen. Note the hot spots under the subject.

As is the case with ultra high-speed black and white negative films, one will in many cases find that printing infrared negatives on a high contrast grade of paper will provide the best subject identification.

Finally, if the photographer is in a pinch because he is forced to work at too great a distance for his equipment to handle, there is yet one last maneuver he can try that may put him within range. By removing the Kodak Wratten Filter Number 87 and replacing it with Kodak Wratten Filter Number 88A®, the setup shown in Figure 15-29 had an increase in camera-to-subject distance from 182 feet to 265 feet with a 50 percent increase in development time. An 88A filter is not recommended by Kodak for surreptitious photography at night, but the author sees no reason why it cannot be used effectively for this kind of work in view of the great distance at which it will be used. The 87 filter cuts the electromagnetic radiation off at about 740 millimicrons; the 88A filter cuts it off at about 735 millimicrons. It was stated earlier that we are capable of seeing only up to about 700 millimicrons, but because the cut of these filters is not really sharp, a weak red glow is detectable. It is true

Figure 15-28. Subject photographed from 145 feet in near total *visual darkness* using infrared film and the equipment shown in Figure 15-26.

that the amount of glow given off when the 88A filter is used is greater than when the 87 filter is used. However, the difference is not extreme and the increase in the distance at which it will be used makes up for that difference. Unless the subject looks directly at it, he will not detect it. When Kodak made the filter recommendations for surreptitious infrared photography at night, they were probably thinking in terms of a camera-to-subject distance of only about fifty feet or so, not a distance of or in excess of 200 feet. If they did, it is very probable they too would have included in their recommendations the 88A filter.

One of the big problems encountered in infrared surveillance photography is that of not knowing, because of the darkness, when to make the crucial exposure that will record whatever subject action is of interest. If it is known just where the subject will be (perhaps he always parks in the same spot or meets someone in a certain doorway) the camera and lens can be set up on a tripod to cover that area and the subject can be observed with one of the many World War II sniperscopes that are now

Figure 15-29. Subject photographed from 182 feet in near total *visual darkness* using infrared film and the equipment shown in Figure 15-26. The increased distance was achieved by push-processing; the development time was increased 50 percent. Note porch light about 120 feet beyond the subject that was used as a reference point.

surplus items because of the invention and implementation of the more sophisticated starlight scope. By watching the subject and depressing the cable release at the right time, one can select one's own exposures (see Figure 15-30). Another possibility of the sniperscope is to have a mount for both the camera and the scope. With such a setup, the camera and sniperscope would move together and what the photographer would see through the scope, the film would see through the camera lens. This will not, however, alleviate the problem of focus. If a sniperscope is not available, one will have to guess when the exposures should be made and rely to a great extent on luck. If it is so dark that the subject cannot be seen through the viewfinder, if it is known about where he is in relation to some distant light, and so on, the photographer should use that light as a guide or reference point. The photograph in Figure 15-28 was done in this manner. Note the porch light on the house about 120 feet beyond the subject.

Photographing with infrared along with a telephoto lens and Fresnel

Figure 15-30. Photographer using a Sniperscope to observe a subject and select exposures after setting up infrared equipment to cover a desired area.

lens does result in a setup that is rather bulky. One should consider, however, that working with telephoto lenses in general, with the exception of 500mm and 1000mm mirror lenses, means using equipment that is bulky and less than convenient. This is also true when using a telephoto lens with a starlight scope. In considering whether or not the effort is worth the bother, the photographer simply must ask himself whether or not the evidence that could be obtained is worth the trouble. Generally it would seem that if the case is important enough to warrant surveillance, the trouble should prove to be inconsequential. Finally, bulkiness really should not prove to be too much trouble in cases where a vantage point is selected, the equipment is set up, and then one must sit down and wait.

Honeywell Pentax Nocta for Infrared Photography

In the early 1960's Honeywell Pentax developed a special infrared single lens reflex camera system they call the Honeywell Pentax Nocta®.

A front and rear view of the Nocta is shown in Figures 15-31A and 15-31B. This camera is equipped with a nonchangeable 300mm f3.3 telephoto lens, an image converter system requiring high voltage that operates on the same principal as the infrared snooperscope, and an instantaneous radiation source is used to expose the film while the continuous source is for observing and framing the subject. The Nocta uses a 35mm format.

With the Nocta it is possible for the photographer to view the subject and select exposures. While the system is capable of photographing up to 300 feet, it is questionable what kind of subject identification one can obtain at that distance with the image size afforded with a 300mm lens.

The Nocta is a system that had real potential as a surveillance tool but sales were hurt by the implementation of the starlight scope. Unlike the Nocta, starlight scopes offer the capability of interchanging lenses. Also, because starlight scopes operate on the principal of light intensification rather than infrared radiation, they do not require the use of an infrared radiation source which in the case of the Nocta happen to be infrared flash bulbs which must be changed after each exposure is made. The continuous source on the Nocta is for observation purposes only as it is too weak for exposing the film sufficiently.

The reason the infrared flash bulbs used with the Nocta are capable of such a long range is because a parabolic reflector is used to concentrate the radiation into a strong beam in much the same manner as does the Fresnel lens that was previously discussed.

The Nocta is a good system, but when it is compared with the more sophisticated and modern starlight scopes, feature for feature, and also price, the starlight scopes become the obvious choice.

INFRARED SURVEILLANCE PHOTOGRAPHY, 16MM MOTION PICTURES

In many respects making infrared motion pictures is much the same as making infrared stills. The most notable difference is that one is forced to deal with a continuous radiation source as opposed to the instantaneous radiation source that was discussed for still photographs. It was stated that when looking directly at a strobe filtered with a Kodak Wratten Filter Number 87 one could detect a brief, dull red glow when the strobe was flashed in the dark. The big reason that the telltale glow was fairly difficult to detect was because it was of such short duration,

Figure 15-31 A & B. Front and rear view of the Honeywell Pentax Nocta. This infrared camera is equipped with a 300mm f3.3 lens, an image converter tube, an instantaneous radiation source for film exposures and a continuous radiation source for subject viewing. (Courtesy of Honeywell Pentax.)

only about $1/1000$ second. With a continuous radiation source, however, the dull red glow becomes quite noticeable. Kodak literature states that if a Kodak Wratten Filter Number 87C® is used in place of the 87 filter, this red glow can be eliminated. It is, they claim, eliminated at the expense of about $2^1/2$ f-stops loss in exposure, thus reducing the effective camera-to-subject distance by a considerable degree. The author found that while the 87C filter did reduce the intensity of the red glow a considerable degree, it did not eliminate it entirely.

One should be mindful of ways to disguise the radiation source when examining the area where photographing will take place. It will in some cases be possible to disguise the radiation source as an EXIT sign or put it where the taillight of a car should be. The glow is not by any means as bright as an automobile taillight but a glow there, if set up right, would cause no suspicion. A person will do well to exploit imagination to the maximum. If the radiation source is to be mounted with the camera, a spotlight of some sort will be the best choice. The author tried many spotlights and finally settled on a thirteen-volt General Electric Aircraft Landing Light Number 4537® and used it off a twelve-volt car system. That light has a candlepower rating (BCPS) of 200,000. Using it on a twelve-volt system rather than a thirteen-volt system probably reduces the candlepower some. When using this light with a Kodak Wratten Filter Number 87, a guide number of 400 was established giving a maximum range of 142 feet when using an f2.8 lens and an exposure time of $1/14$ second. If one decides to do some experimenting with continuous radiation sources, he should keep in mind the fact that, as a general rule, low voltage bulbs tend to have a higher infrared output than high voltage bulbs. Also, the more directional and concentrated the beam of a spotlight the harder it will be to ensure that the radiation is on the subject. This is the main reason the author chose the bulb mentioned over other spotlights; it covers a greater area yet is strong enough to give an acceptable guide number and camera-to-subject range. When establishing a guide number for the instantaneous radiation source, shutter speed was important only to the extent that it was set so that proper synchronization was ensured. When determining a guide number for a continuous radiation source, the shutter speed is important. Whatever shutter speed is used when the test exposures are made must always be used with the resulting guide number or improper exposures will result.

The problem of subject identification is a very real problem when making infrared movies with the 16mm motion picture camera, since the area of the frame is less than one-ninth that of a 35mm frame. The frame size of a 16mm motion picture camera is about 10mm × 7½mm while the frame size of a 35mm camera is about 36mm × 24mm. As can be seen, the image size will be very small if the lens used is short enough to give an acceptable degree of coverage. If using a lens with enough focal length to give an image size sufficient to secure good subject identification, the image size of the subject would be so large in comparison to the frame size that it would be very difficult to keep the subject properly framed. If the nature of the case warrants it, a possible solution would be to use two photographers, one to use a motion picture camera to document subject activity while the other uses a 35mm camera to record subject identification. If the activity is such that the subject will be in one spot for the period of time he is to be photographed (drug pusher meeting a user consistently in a certain doorway), it would be possible for one photographer working from a good vantage point to handle both the motion picture and the still camera. By having both cameras mounted on tripods and ready to go when the action starts, the motion picture camera can be activated and left to run itself while the photographer begins taking still shots. These are ideas or points to keep in mind as each situation will be unique.

PHOTOGRAPHY AT NIGHT
USING STARLIGHT SCOPES

Starlight Scopes and How They Differ
from Infrared Sniperscopes

When considering night vision devices (NVD's), there are two basic types of equipment from which to choose. They are infrared scopes and starlight scopes. Starlight scopes, while having a lot in common with the famous World War II Sniperscopes, are much more advanced and sophisticated. Figure 15-32 shows a diagram of a sniperscope system and Figure 15-30 shows a photograph of a sniperscope. Note that the scope utilizes a light source with an infrared filter over it to illuminate the subject with invisible infrared radiation. The electron tube then converts these invisible infrared rays to a visible image after the objective lens has focused them onto the face of the tube. The starlight scope on the other hand does not rely on infrared radiation, but rather takes the photons that are provided by the stars, streetlights, and so forth, and increases their energy, thus relying on light intensification. Depending upon the make of the scope, the usual light energy increase or gain is between 35,000 and something over 65,000 times. In basic simple terms this is done by changing the light energy to electrical energy, amplifying it, and then changing it back to light energy.

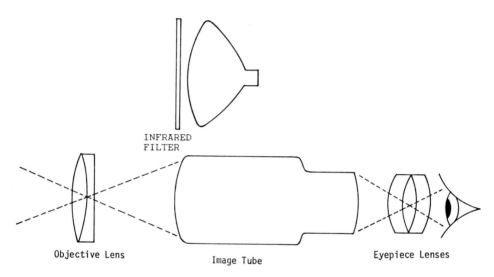

INFRARED FILTER

Objective Lens   Image Tube   Eyepiece Lenses

Figure 15-32. Simple drawing of an infrared sniperscope. Note that a light source and infrared filter are necessary to illuminate the subject. The electron tube then converts the infrared image to a visible image.

Although starlight scopes operate on the principle of light intensification rather than conversion of infrared radiation, many modern starlight scopes feature a built-in *infrared illuminator* which is an auxiliary radiation source to supplement existing light when necessary. Although the gain with these instruments is very impressive, there are conditions where there simply is not enough light. The feasibility of an auxiliary infrared radiation source is possible because although starlight scopes operate on the principle of light intensification, they are also very sensitive to infrared radiation.

Starlight scopes are free from several of the drawbacks that are characteristic of the infrared scopes. With the starlight scopes, unlike infrared scopes, a heavy battery pack for the radiation source is not necessary, thus making it much lighter and easier to carry and manipulate. Also the field of view is better with starlight scopes because the operator is not limited to the small field of view and range provided by the spotlights used in infrared radiation sources. Finally, with starlight scopes, one can use lenses with a wide variety of focal lengths to provide the image size desired at various distances from a subject. Being able to do this is something that the user of sniperscopes does not enjoy.

18mm, 25mm and 40mm Image Intensifier Tubes

There are three standard sizes of starlight scopes available on the civilian market. They are 18mm, 25mm and 40mm sizes. These sizes have to do with the format of the image tubes being used. The 40mm tubes offer the largest image format and consequently they are for that reason the better choice for photographic applications. The 40mm scopes, however, are physically larger and heavier than the 18mm or 25mm scopes, and if size is of great concern, one would not do wrong to invest in the 18mm scopes as they are also very suitable for photographic applications.

First, Second, and Third Generation Image Intensifier Tubes

If one is considering the purchase of a starlight scope system (night vision devices—NVD's), it would be wise to secure promotional literature from the various manufacturers or distributors and carefully study them. And speak with people who have used the various scopes. When so doing, one will notice what is referred to as *first generation, second generation,* and *third generation* intensifier tubes. As with everything, there are compromises one from the other.

The first generation systems, so called because they were the first to be designed and put into production, have the benefit of a higher degree of resolution than do the second generation units, the resolution of the former being about forty lines per millimeter. A fault of the first generation units is a notable degree of distortion around the edge of the field of view.

The second generation systems are considerably smaller and more compact than are the first generation systems and suffer only about one-fifth the distortion that is characteristic of the first generation systems. The resolution, however, is not as good.

Figure 15-33 illustrates a night viewing device, while Figure 15-34 illustrates a photographed observation through a night viewing device.

Figure 15-33. Star-tron electronic light intensifier (night viewing device) that operates on the principle of light intensification. (Courtesy of Smith and Wesson.)

Accessories

Most manufacturers of starlight scopes (NVD's) also offer a variety of accessories such as *telephoto lenses, lens adapters, camera adapters,* and *biocular viewers.* Fast telephoto lenses are important if one is using the instrument for long-range surveillance photography whether it be with a still camera, motion picture camera, or video recorder. Lens adapters are useful if one desires to use the lens system of their 35mm single-lens reflex camera such as a Nikon, Canon, or Minolta. Camera adapters are essential if the instrument is to be used for nighttime surveillance photography. Camera adapters enable one to photograph through the instrument using a 35mm single-lens reflex camera, motion picture camera, or video camera. Figure 15-35 illustrates a Star Tron model MK-880 coupled with both a 35mm camera and video camera. The MK-880 is a very compact pocket scope featuring either an 18mm second or third generation intensifier tube. Available with it are various accessories including camera adapters, a biocular viewer, a built-in infrared illuminator, and a variety of very fast telephoto lenses including a 410mm f/1.5 and 300mm f/1.4, both very impressive.

Biocular viewers enable one to view through a scope using both eyes, a feature that reduces fatigue during long-term surveillance operations.

Figure 15-34. Subject photographed through a Star-tron night vision device at a distance of about 80 feet under lighting conditions that would approximate normal starlight. (Courtesy of Smith and Wesson.)

Figure 15-35. Star-tron MK-880 night vision pocketscopes mounted to a 35mm single-lens-reflex camera and a video camcorder. Various lenses may also be adapted to the MK-880. The MK-880 may also be used for direct viewing. (Courtesy of Star-tron Technology Corporation.)

Figure 15-36 shows a Star Tron Model MK202-A scope with a biocular viewer being used for general night observation.

One innovation that some systems offer is a hinge back. The operator can mount both a biocular viewer and a camera attachment to the scope and use whichever he desires simply by swinging one to the side and the other into place. A setup such as this would make for easy viewing of the subject with both eyes by using the biocular viewer: When the action starts, one can quickly swing the viewer aside and the camera into place. For those who have sat and looked through a camera for eight or more hours, the advantage offered by this innovation should be obvious. It does not take long to develop fuzzy vision when looking through a camera for extended periods.

Photography through Starlight Scopes

When photographing with starlight scopes, fast film must be used. Another point worth noting is that the image in the scope will affect the film differently than it will the light meter in the camera. If the manufacturer does not give specific instructions concerning this, it will be necessary to run exposure tests to determine at what ISO to set the camera's light meter to obtain correct exposures. This is nothing that

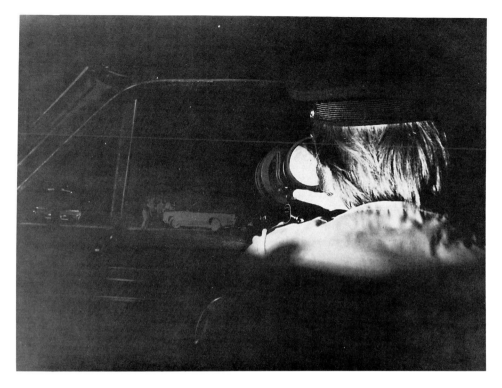

Figure 15-36. Star-tron night viewing device being used for direct viewing.

will cause any difficulty. It is just something that one must be aware of and compensate for.

Conclusion

This discussion of night vision devices (NVD's) was not meant to be all-inclusive, but rather was intended to serve as general familiarization with what NVD's are and what can be done with them. While the many makes of starlight scopes are in general respects the same, they differ in detail and one should write to the various manufacturers or distributors for their promotional literature to make detailed comparisons.

VANTAGE POINTS

There is not much that needs to be said concerning vantage points. The main thing is to secure some form of cover so as not to be *made* or observed by the subject, or to arouse sufficient curiosity or suspicion on the part of anyone else so that a report is made to the local law enforcement authorities. While they would do nothing more than possibly question the cameraman, that act would only serve to draw attention.

Rooftops are generally good but care must be taken to avoid being silhouetted against the sky. Also one should avoid a rooftop directly across from the area to be observed. Another thing of importance, and this holds true for any vantage point, is that a discreet means of coming and going and shift changes must be established. If circumstances permit, a hotel room, apartment, or a business establishment can be secured, and photographing done from that point. If it is summer, the window can often be opened and photographs taken through the opening. If, however, it is winter, make every effort to photograph through not more than one pane of glass and preferably a thick pane as opposed to the thin panes commonly used in private homes. The problem encountered in photographing through glass is that it refracts the light and an unsharp and distorted image can result. The thick glass used on store fronts tends to refract less than the thin panes used in homes as they tend to be more uniform in thickness. It is also extremely important that the glass be very clean, since dirty windows will cause the resulting photographs to be unsharp. If the room is darkened, one will encounter fewer problems with reflections. Finally, if the glass one is photographing through is causing an unsharp image, the problem will become worse as you go to lenses with longer focal lengths. If the windows have curtains, shades, and so forth, one should try to photograph from the top of the curtain rather than through the curtain by parting it a few inches. In some instances a person will be able to work from a darkened room with the curtains partially or fully open. This is possible especially if working from a second- or third-story room. Trucks are very effective as they can be used in more situations than not. A panel truck or pickup truck with a shell can easily be equipped with one-way glass windows or soap can be smeared on the inside of the window with a peephole left. Also worth consideration is a fictitious business name painted on the side or rear windows of such a vehicle with the inside of a letter or letters left unpainted through which observation and/or photographing can be done. If forced to work from a passenger car temporarily, one should sit in the back seat. One should also consider raising the head rests on the front seats and lowering the visors. When working from a passenger car, if cost and circumstances permit it, the photographer ought to work with a female investigator as a couple sitting in a car will generally arouse little suspicion. Also every effort should be made to avoid parking on the same block as the subject, since the chances of being *made* will be greatly reduced if one can work from the next block.

While this discussion of vantage points is not and cannot be all inclusive, it will be found that most vantage points are nothing more than variations of what has been discussed. The reader is referred to the chapter dealing with telephoto photography as it discusses a number of things that should be taken into consideration from a photographic standpoint when selecting a vantage point.

How to Openly Photograph a Person
Without Their Knowledge

Perhaps it will not happen often, but what does one do if there is a need to photographically cover a person's activities but circumstances make it impossible to select a vantage point and work from a distance with telephoto lenses, and it becomes necessary to work within view of the subject? There are a number of simple techniques that make it possible to be quite close to a person, within view, and photograph him without his having any idea of the fact. The following techniques may serve to provide ideas and while the reader may seldom, if ever, have occasion to use them, they may.

It is important that the camera be made ready for action so that, if and when the subject makes a sudden move, one does not lose the opportunity to record it because he was too busy focusing and determining the proper exposure. The camera should be all set so all you have to do is trip the shutter. To do this, one should cock the shutter, establish and set for proper exposure and check it from time to time; finally, one focuses hyperfocally if not knowing exactly where and how far away the subject will be. All one does when focusing hyperfocally is note the f-setting of the lens and then study the depth of field scale on the lens barrel. From this it can be determined what the total range of acceptable focus will be and at what point perfect focus is. This is, however, controlled to a great extent by the f-setting. For example, using a 50mm f1.4 lens on a Nikon camera (35mm) at f11, everything from about thirteen feet to infinity will be in acceptable focus. Whatever happens to be at about twenty-eight feet from the camera will be in perfect focus. With this kind of setting then, if the photographer saw some fast action take place and quickly released the shutter without focusing, he may not get a picture that is in perfect focus but he would, if the subject were not closer than the thirteen feet, get an acceptable photograph. If this technique were not used it is very likely the photographer would have no photograph at all. One should keep this in mind and practice it as it will make the photographer very quick on the draw.

Suppose that the subject and his family or friends should go to the fairgrounds, the zoo or the public picnic grounds and the photographer has seen fit to casually tag along with his *family.* In such settings he will not look conspicuous with his camera hanging around his neck. In some cases, perhaps he can keep his distance and photograph the subject with a 135mm or 200mm lens and the subject will not be aware of him. What does he do, however, if he suddenly finds that circumstances have put him at the picnic table next to his subject, perhaps not more than fifty feet away? The mild telephoto lens is now too long and a normal lens, or perhaps even a mild wide-angle lens, is necessary to get *good coverage of the whole set* because in most of the following techniques he will not use the viewfinder to frame the subject as that would serve to make the latter aware of the cameraman's interest in him. The photographer can try employing some of these techniques. If, for example, the subject is south of him, he can focus on something to the east or west that is about as far from him as the subject. After focusing and setting his exposure, he casually turns around 180° making it appear as though he was done with whatever he was photographing and wants to photograph something else. When he passes over the subject, he should trip the shutter and keep turning; the subject will never know.

Another technique is to have the exposure set and the focus set hyperfocally. One lets the camera hang in front of him with the strap around his neck. It is common that people with a camera in this position hold onto it and fondle it to some degree. Therefore, if one should be casually cocking the shutter and making exposures, someone fifty feet away would very likely have no idea of the fact. There is no need to look through the viewfinder if one has a normal lens on the camera as that offers plenty of coverage to allow for poor framing. If the subject is simply too close and the photographer is not sure of the framing, he should switch to a wide-angle lens. A variation of this is to have exposure and focus set as before, activate the self-timer and then set the camera down facing the subject while one lights a cigarette or whatever. No one would be suspicious of a camera just sitting alone unattended.

The next technique is one that can effectively be applied to a video camera under conditions such as have been described. If using a monopod, one should casually lean on it as it faces in the subject's direction. The photographer should appear to be interested in something else in a different direction, while watching the subject out of the corner of his eye. By using a cable release (it can also be done without one), he can be making a record of all the subject does without his being aware of it. These ideas, with some imagination, should prove to be effective if one is ever in a like situation.

Chapter 16

VIDEO CAMERAS

Introduction

In this section, an overview of video cameras will be provided and their usefulness to the surveillance photographer discussed. In the field of surveillance photography, the 16mm motion picture camera was once used extensively. However, with time, video cameras began to take their place and, today, almost all such filming is done with video. The reason for that change will be found in the many benefits offered by video, not the least of which is ease of operation and instant results, even though better detail can still be realized with the 16mm motion picture camera.

Previously, it was stated that the trend has been to make cameras increasingly user friendly, and that holds true also for video cameras. Most 16mm motion picture cameras require a certain degree of technical (photographic) expertise on the part of the operator, while most video cameras enable the novice to obtain good results. Another benefit of video is the ability to record for a long period of time before a change of tape becomes necessary. For example, one may record activity for 2–3 hours when using a full size VHS format camera (1/2 inch wide tape) at normal tape speed. Conversely, a 100 foot roll of 16mm motion picture film at normal speed will provide approximately 2 3/4 minutes of recording time. The same camera equipped with a 400 foot film magazine enables one to film for only approximately 11 minutes. But, the 16mm motion picture camera can record fine detail better than video, a feature that can be critically important to the surveillance photographer when such things as subject identification and vehicle plate numbers are important. Hence, one cannot arbitrarily say that one system is inherently better or more appropriate than another; it depends upon circumstances and what is needed.

Under some circumstances, accepting the strengths and limitations of video versus 16mm motion picture, one may elect to set up both systems at a selected vantage point. The video may be used for long-term recording of the scene with the 16mm camera activated when it becomes necessary to record critical activity where maximum detail is important. One system can supplement the other.

The person who has some photographic background, but no experience with video cameras, may feel confused when first encountering the array of buzz words and various format options available. But, in reality, that person probably knows more about video than he or she realizes. For example, both video cameras and conventional cameras have a lens that focuses an image onto a light sensitive medium, and the lens features a variable aperture. Both types of cameras feature a shutter speed that governs the duration of time that an image will be projected onto the light sensitive medium. The conventional motion picture camera features a *film transport system* to move the film through the camera at the proper speed, while the video camera features a *tape transport system* to move the tape through the camera at the proper speed. As can be seen, both have much in common one with the other. But while the motion picture camera is largely mechanical, the video camera is largely electronic with the only mechanical functions being the tape transport system and power zoom.

Any photographer, when using a conventional camera for the first time, must study the owner's manual to become familiar with the features unique to the particular camera in question. And so it is with a video camera; the owner's manual must be studied. When so doing, it will be found that there is little mystery involved. But, just as it is advisable to sacrifice some film taking test pictures with an unfamiliar conventional camera, so it is advisable to experiment with a video camera to become familiar with its features and proper operation.

CCD Image Sensor

A conventional camera, whether still or motion picture, produces a picture through a process whereby the lens projects an image onto a light sensitive material (film) which is later developed in a photo lab. A video functions much the same way. The lens projects an image onto a light sensitive surface called an *imaging chip* or *charge-coupled device (CCD)*. The imaging chip contains silicon photodiodes, as many as 400,000, which converts the light energy into electrical impulses which in turn activate the magnetic coating on the videotape via the camera's recording heads.

White-Light Balance

White-light balance is an electronic process utilized in video cameras to retain true color rendition. Visible light consists of many colors, but the manner in which people view them is not always the way a camera will see them. Refer to Chapter 2 on *Filters*. Natural light has a value different from artificial light, and there are many kinds of artificial light such as more than one kind of tungsten, and two basic kinds of fluorescent. Hence, video cameras have a feature called a *white-light balance correction* that automatically adjusts for varying light conditions that works well under most circumstances. That feature enables the camera to record colors that appear natural. For conditions that the camera cannot automatically compensate for, there is a feature for controlling it manually.

The Viewfinder

When looking through a conventional camera, one is either looking through an optical viewfinder or through the camera's lens as is the case with a single-lens-reflex (SLR) camera. When looking into the viewfinder of a video camera, however, what one is actually viewing is an image on a screen much as if looking at a miniature TV monitor. Everything except the focusing and zooming of the lens, and tape transport, is electrical not mechanical.

The Lens

Most video cameras feature glass lens elements, and that is preferred. Avoid cameras featuring plastic lenses because the quality is not comparable. Further, when considering quality video cameras, it would be unlikely to encounter lenses that were not properly *coated* to enhance their performance by maximizing light transmission and minimizing flare and ghost images.

Today, almost all video cameras feature a zoom lens that commonly goes from mild wide-angle to telephoto. Because video cameras are generally available only with a mild wide-angle capability, many manufacturers offer a *wide-angle converter attachment.* Similarly, many manufacturers offer a *telephoto attachment* to increase the effective focal length of the lens.

Somewhere on the camera or lens will be printed the focal length range of the lens, and the maximum aperture. It might read, for example, 8–120mm f/1:1.4. And it may also indicate, as in this case for example, the lens as being a 15x. It may also indicate *power zoom.* The term *power zoom* indicates that the lens can be zoomed throughout its range by pressing buttons with the zooming action being powered.

When the range of a zoom lens is indicated as being, for example, fifteen times (15×), that does not mean that it provides a magnification of 15 times over the normal focal length lens. It is actually a reflection of the range of the lens when the longest focal length of the zoom range is divided by the shortest. Looking at the example that was given, the 8–120mm lens, 120 divided by 8 gives us 15 which is the range of that lens. Another lens indicated as being 15× has a focal length range of 16–240. The larger divided by the smaller gives us 15, but its power at the longest setting is far greater. Hence, a 15× lens may have a strong telephoto capability, but not necessarily. One needs to consider the maximum focal length in millimeters. A focal length of 240mm is twice as powerful as a focal length of 120mm, the former being capable of producing an image of the subject twice as large. Naturally, for surveillance photography from a distance, the 240mm lens would be the logical choice.

For surveillance photography, maximum focal length is important, as is the maximum aperture. All things being equal, a lens with a maximum aperture of f1.4 will transmit more light than will a lens with a maximum aperture of f1.8.

Format Options

There are, at the time of this writing, *six* video camera formats available. The six formats can be broken down into two groups called *low-band* and *high-band.* Low-band offers good picture quality but is not equal to the high-band image which is noticeably sharper with colors that bleed into each other less. The high-band systems, being better, tend to be the more expensive of the two. The six systems will be briefly discussed in the following order:

Low-band: Standard VHS
                                       VHS-C
                                       Video 8
High-band: Super VHS (S–VHS)
                                       Super VHS–C
                                       Hi-8

Standard VHS, a low-band format, uses ½ inch tape and offers up to three hours of recording time when operated at normal speed. The standard VHS cassette is large, so the camera is also bulky. But, although some don't like a bulky camera, the size and weight can aid in camera stability. Picture quality tends to be good and the tape can be played on standard VHS equipment.

VHS–C is a compact version of the standard VHS and is also a low-band format. The *"C"* stands for *compact.* The cassette is smaller because the film is shorter, not narrower, because it also is ½ inch wide. Because the film is shorter, the maximum recording time is considerably reduced: 20–30 minutes at normal speed and about 60 minutes when set on *extended play.* Extended play, because the film is traveling at a slower speed, results in a lower quality image. At normal speed the picture quality is the same as with the standard VHS. The compact format was created to offer a camera that is smaller and easier to handle. The tape, to be played on standard VHS equipment, must first be inserted into a *VHS–C Adaptor.* Some machines will accept both size cassettes.

Video 8, a low-band format, is small in comparison to the VHS, measuring only 8mm (¼ inch), but results in good picture quality and sound reproduction in a small size camera. Picture quality rivals that of the VHS and VHS–C. Recording time is about 1 and 2 hours, normal and extended play respectively. The tapes cannot be played in standard VHS equipment. One must purchase equipment specifically for that system or play directly into the TV from the camera.

Super VHS, high-band, is the same size as standard VHS but with significantly improved picture quality. While standard VHS features resolution in the range of 150–300 horizontal lines, Super VHS features approximately 400 lines, which is approaching commercial broadcast quality. And the color rendition is better.

Standard VHS tapes can be played in Super VHS playback equipment, but Super VHS tapes cannot be played in standard VHS machines. Super VHS, which is high-band, can be copied to low-band without objectionable loss of image quality.

Super VHS–C is the same as the Super VHS but with a smaller cassette containing shorter film. Like the standard VHS–C, the recording time is short.

Hi-8 is the same size as Video 8, 8mm or 1/4 inch, but offers picture quality comparable to Super VHS. The cameras are small and light weight. Hi-8 cassettes cannot be played in standard 8mm equipment, but the latter can be played in equipment intended for the former. In Figure 16-1 is illustrated the Canon 8mm Video Camcorder. It is a high quality Hi-8 camera.

Figure 16-1. Canon Hi-8 video camcorder L2 with CL 8-120mm f/1.4-2 zoom lens. (Courtesy of Canon USA, Inc.)

Light Levels

Just as the maximum aperture of a lens is important to the surveillance photographer working at night using only available light, so is the camera's low light level ability. The two work together. Some video cameras perform better than others in that respect. The technical data will often indicate the minimum illumination requirement of a given camera. The Minolta Series-C 3400, for example, has a minimum illumination requirement of 10 lux. The Cannon L2 Hi-8 camcorder will record under light levels as low as 0.5 lux using a slow shutter speed (1/8th second). Many video cameras feature a minimum illumination requirement of 3 lux.

Lux is a standard scale for the measurement of light that has largely replaced candle power as a measure of illumination. One lux is equal to .09 footcandles, and one footcandle is the intensity of light measured at a distance of one foot from the candle. The technical specifications for a particular camera lets one know how much light that camera needs to operate. But one needs to know what that means in terms of the environment at night so that an appropriate camera can be selected. Will a minimum illumination requirement of 10 lux be sufficient, or does one need a camera that will work with only 3 lux, or perhaps 1 lux? Bright sun typically features a value of 50,000–100,000 lux. An overcast day will feature 2,000–10,000 lux. A typical office will feature 200–300 lux. A well-lit street scene at night will typically feature 10–20 lux, while a dimly-lit rural street will be under 1 lux.

Some video cameras have a feature called a *gain-up* that, when activated, amplifies the voltage produced by the light striking the image sensor, thus increasing the apparent brightness of the image. And while such a feature enables one to film under conditions that would otherwise render filming impossible, the quality of the resultant picture suffers notable grain and lack of contrast. For the surveillance photographer, that fact is secondary to being able to document the activity of interest.

From this it can be seen that a camera that will record in the 3–5 lux range will handle most nighttime surveillance requirements in an urban setting, but may not be adequate in a rural environment. For the latter a camera with a minimum illumination requirement of 0.5 lux would be the better choice. The Minolta camera with a minimum illumination requirement of 10 lux would no doubt work well if photographing, from across the street, people in a convenience market.

Power Source

Modern video cameras exhibit a wide range of features from power zoom, automatic exposure control, auto focus, sound recording, and the tape transport system. All those things require power to operate. Hence, a power source is necessary. Commonly, video cameras contain rechargeable *nickel-cadmium* batteries, more simply called *nicads.* Nicads, although good, are expensive. But they can be recharged, with each charge offering about two hours of recording time. It is good to carry spares. Power may also be obtained from a vehicle's 12 volt DC electrical system, and one can use a vehicle's electrical system to recharge nicad batteries. Further, one may use a battery pack of various sizes.

Today's nicad batteries are much better than they once were. They no longer have a *memory* limiting their ability to store a full charge, yet it is advisable to not fully discharge a battery before recharging it. And before recharging a battery, it is best to let it cool; a hot battery does not accept a full charge well. When not using nicad batteries for a period of time, it is advisable to periodically charge them.

Sound Recording

All video cameras record audibly as well as visually by means of a built-in microphone that is mounted on the camera as far forward as conditions will permit. Quality varies one from another. A feature to look for on any video camera is an external microphone jack in addition to the built-in microphone that allows one to make multiple sound recordings. Another feature available is a radio microphone. A speaker can attach a microphone to his or her lapel and place a transmitter in his or her pocket so that the sound can be transmitted to the video camera. That enables one to record from a distance and still be able to realize quality sound reproduction.

Videotapes

Quality grades vary from very good to poor when considering video tapes. A good indication of the quality of any tape is the *signal-to-noise ratio,* something that determines the clarity of the image. *Audio noise* can be described as background hiss while *video noise* exhibits itself in the form of interference in the picture; one writer referred to it as electronic dirt. The signal-to-noise ratio is determined by dividing the value of the signal by the value of the noise with the resultant figure being the ratio of good signal to bad noise. It is expressed in decibels (dB) with higher ratio numbers being better.

Length of play is the duration that one may record on a given cassette, and is determined by two factors. One factor is the length of the tape with the other being the speed at which the tape is traveling, expressed in inches-per-second (ips). A long tape is thinner than a shorter tape. Hence, while one receives the benefit of longer recording time with a thin tape, the disadvantage lies in the fact that a thin tape is physically weaker and may stretch or break. The extended play setting, which results in the tape traveling at a slower speed, does provide more recording time, but the image quality suffers as a result.

Durability refers to how long an image will remain on a tape after it is recorded. Unfortunately no one knows for sure because video technology is new. However, some degree of picture deterioration can be expected after perhaps ten years. If the tapes are important, it is advisable to have electronically enhanced copies made every 8–10 years.

Low light capabilities of modern video tapes exceeds that of high-speed photographic film enabling one, with the proper video camera and lens combination, to film under very subdued lighting.

Accessories

Just as there are a number of accessories available to the photographer using conventional photographic equipment for either still or motion picture photography, so there is much available to the videographer. And, most of the accessories applicable to the conventional photographer are applicable to the videographer. Useful are such things as tripods, mono-pods, or a shoulder brace for camera stability; gadget bags for carrying miscellaneous items that one anticipates may be needed; extra tapes; extra batteries; a rain cover to protect the camera if necessary; wide-angle and telephoto adaptors; filters; lights; and microphones.

Video vs. 16mm Motion Picture Relative to Image Detail and Cost

With little doubt, perhaps 99 percent of the surveillance photography, wherein documentation of motion is important, is today being done using video rather than 16mm motion picture. As stated previously, the benefits of video are many with some being a recording time of hours rather than minutes, the low cost per minute of filming, and instant results; it is not necessary to wait for film to be developed. Desirable also is the automated nature of video cameras, making them easy to use. But, for all the benefits afforded by the video camera, the ultimate quality of the image cannot compare with that possible when using a 16mm motion picture camera. Figures 16-2 and 16-3 illustrate that fact. The photo in Figure 16-2 is the result that was obtained using a S–VHS camera, while the picture in Figure 16-3 is the result obtained with a 16mm motion picture camera using ISO 50 color negative film. Both were filmed at the same time to eliminate variables.

Figure 16-2. Print of a frame taken from a video film created using a Canon Hi-8 camcorder with 120mm lens from a distance of about 150 feet. Although video detail quality cannot compare with that possible using a 16mm motion picture camera, the Hi-8 and Super VHS systems do provide admirable quality. A color print tends to produce better detail quality than a black and white print.

When using a 16mm motion picture camera for surveillance purposes because maximum detail is important, one should also understand that significantly better results will be realized by filming with a negative film and then having that film printed onto a second film to obtain a positive image for viewing. And, if necessary, good quality paper prints can be made from the original negative film. A negative motion picture film will provide notably better results in terms of image sharpness when compared with a reversal film of comparable speed (ISO rating).

The cost difference between video versus motion picture film was

Figure 16-3. Print of a frame taken using color 16mm motion picture negative film, ISO 50, from a distance of about 150 feet using a 120mm telephoto lens. Camera, subject, and lighting position is the same as that illustrated in Figure 16-2.

mentioned, and it is tremendous! Hence, that factor must be considered if budgetary constraints exist. At the time of this writing, the film used to record the image appearing in Figure 16-3 cost approximately $35.00 for a 100 foot roll which records for approximately 2¾ minutes. In addition to that cost is a development cost of $22.00. If that film were to be printed onto a second film so as to obtain a positive image, that would cost an additional $30.00. Hence, the total cost for the 100 foot roll of film is $87.00. That works out to be a cost of $30.90 per minute of filming.

When using a reversal motion picture film, one does not suffer the cost associated with printing onto a second film, which brings the overall cost down considerably. But, regardless, the cost remains significant. A 100 foot roll of reversal motion picture film and processing works out to be approximately $53.50, or $19.45 per minute of filming. By comparison, a 120 minute S–VHS tape costs approximately $13.00. That works out to be $.11 per minute of filming.

Is the increased cost of 16mm film over video worth it? Only circumstances can answer that question. If the case is critically important, and maximum detail is essential, then in all probability the cost is justified. Governmental surveillance of a suspected terrorist group would likely justify such a cost. Conversely, a private investigator filming a worker compensation recipient engaged in physical activity that is inconsistent with his or her alleged injuries would likely choose video.

Chapter 17

PHOTOGRAPHIC COURT EXHIBITS

In many cases, photographs are used to create a record of evidence and these are used in court rather than the actual piece of evidence. This is often the case, for example, with bullets, cartridge cases, tool impressions, footwear impressions, fingerprints, photographs of the overall scene, and other forms of evidence that cannot be conveniently brought into the courtroom. In other instances, the photographs themselves are the evidence, as they may document an event or happening rather than a piece of physical evidence. Consider, for example, the case of an illegal drug transaction between two people that was photographed with either a still or a motion picture camera. The resulting film photographer and any other persons present, would serve as the evidence that the two individuals met and conducted a transaction.

The reader should clearly understand that when a photograph is introduced as evidence in a court of law, the photograph will not stand alone upon its own merits, but must be authenticated by someone who personally observed whatever is portrayed in the photograph. This person must attest to the fact that the photograph accurately and fairly depicts the scene as he or she saw it, and that the photograph is relevant to the case and in no way misleading or sensational. It is not essential, however, that this person be the one who actually took the photograph or processed it.

For these reasons, no evidential photograph may be altered or retouched in any manner. This is not to say, however, that a photograph may not bear certain types of markings to aid the viewer in understanding and accurately interpreting what is significant in the photograph. This is commonly done, for example, when a fingerprint or footprint found at a crime scene is shown to be the defendant's. When in doubt as to whether or not the marking may be objectionable to the court for some particular reason, it is advisable to prepare two sets of photographs, one with markings and one without. An overlay is advisable. The reader should refer to the section concerning markings in the field of view in Chapter 5, "Crime Scene Photography."

When preparing prints for use in court, the photographer should realize that the proper degree of enlargement will ensure that the viewer will see a fair and accurate reproduction of the scene insofar as angular relationships are concerned. This is determined by the normal viewing distance of photographs and the focal length of the lens that was used. This is discussed in detail in the section concerning the viewing distance of photographs at the end of this chapter.

Projection Method

It is not essential that photographic evidence being introduced into a court of law be in the form of paper prints. Slides (transparencies) and motion picture films may be introduced to the court by means of a projector, the only real stipulation being, as always, that the slides or films be relevant to the case and in no way misleading. The projection method is useful and prevents having to pass photographs among the jurors. The projection method is essential in cases involving motion picture evidence such as is often the case involving surveillance photography.

Matching Transparencies

Matching transparencies is not a difficult technique and is useful in a number of situations, especially where a signature has been forged. All that is necessary in such a case is to photograph the authentic and the forged signatures using a reversal (slide) film. One transparency is then placed over the other. Remember, no two signatures are identical; if they are, one is a forgery. When producing transparencies for the purpose of creating a matching overlay, it is essential that both photographs be taken at the exact same reproduction ratio.

Matching Photographs

This technique will serve to illustrate, in much the same manner as does the comparison microscope, similarities of items such as cartridge cases, firing pin impressions and tool impressions. As Figure 17-1 shows, one photograph is aligned over a second. If, for example, one had recovered a bolt cutter and a padlock that was believed to have been cut with the bolt cutter, a photograph could be made of the cut ends of the shackle of the lock and a second photograph made of a metal that is known to have been cut with the bolt cutter in question. The second photograph would then be carefully placed over the first to illustrate the similar striations. Again, as was the case with matching transparencies, the reproduction ratio and degree of enlargement must be the same.

Figure 17-1. A matching photograph exhibit is made by aligning one photograph over another to show similarities in much the same manner as does a comparison microscope.

Composite Exhibit

A composite exhibit is simply two photographs placed side by side to show the existence of certain similarities. The composite exhibit can be said to be the most common and widely used technique to show that a given impression found at a crime scene was made by a known source. This technique is very commonly used with such evidence as footwear impressions, tire impressions and fingerprints (see Figure 17-2A, B).

In the preparation of photographs for the purpose of composite exhibits, the lighting should be the same on both, and they should be printed at the same size. It is often desirable to have a scale included for this purpose. When markings are made to aid the viewer in accurately interpreting the prints, such as is the case with the two fingerprints in Figure 17-2, it is desirable to work in a systematic manner. More often than not the markings are made in a clockwise direction.

When making a composite exhibit, if a paper surface "N" is used, the markings can be made with a pencil without any trouble. If it is for some reason deemed desirable to use a glossy surface paper, India ink or graphic tape will work well. Remember, however, that a glossy surface will reflect light and create greater difficulty on the part of the viewer.

Size and Viewing Distance of Photographs

Natural perspective, or lack of it, is often the determining factor concerning whether a photograph will be accepted or rejected as evidence in a court of law. This section will examine how a photograph may be prepared and presented so that it will be properly viewed and the subject matter thus perceived in its proper or natural perspective.

The angular relationship of any scene will change as the person viewing that scene alters the viewing distance and/or angle. If a person who is very close to a given scene makes a geometrically accurate sketch of the scene, and a second person who is at a greater distance from the same scene also makes a geometrically accurate sketch of the scene, the two sketches, when examined side by side, will possess angular relationships that do not agree with each other. Both sketches will, however, be geometrically accurate insofar as angular relationship is concerned, providing that they are viewed at the proper viewing distance. The angular relationship of a given scene will depend to a large degree upon the focal length of the lens used to take the photograph and the distance and angle at which the photograph is taken. Assuming now that the photograph has been properly taken, the resulting photograph, in natural perspective, must be viewed at the proper size and distance in accordance with the focal length of the lens that was used to take the picture.

The section that deals with wide angle and telephoto lens distortion explains that although such lenses are very commonly thought to provide a distorted angular view of the subject matter, this is only because incorrect size and distance.

LATENT PRINT

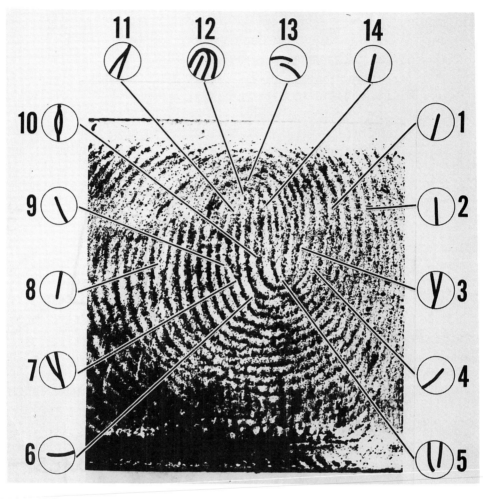

A

Figure 17-2. Composite exhibit is perhaps the most commonly used type of exhibit for illustrating similarities between known and unknown impressions. (Courtesy of Frayne B. Johnson.)

Any photograph, in order to portray a given scene in its natural perspective, must be viewed at the proper size and distance. If a scene is photographed using a normal lens, and the resulting photograph is viewed at the incorrect size and distance, the viewer will not perceive an accurate angular relationship. In other words, the scene will be seen as

INKED PRINT

B

being a bit out of perspective just as will be the case with any photograph taken with a wide angle or telephoto lens and viewed at the incorrect size and distance.

People have become accustomed to viewing photographs taken with a normal lens at such a wide variety of sizes and distances that they have become accustomed to seeing them in this manner and no longer perceive them as being distorted. This is true, even though technically the angular relationship is distorted. A scene photographed using a wide-angle or telephoto lens, however, is not as common and people have a tendency to view them as being out of perspective insofar as angular relationships are concerned, even though the degree of angular distortion is no more or less severe than the scene taken with the normal lens and then improperly viewed.

It is interesting to note that adults will experience a great degree of difficulty in accurately interpreting a photograph if viewed in the upside-down position. Moreover, any attempt by an adult to sketch a picture in an upside-down position will be disastrous. A child, however, will often view and interpret pictures sideways and upside-down, and also draw them this way. The child finds this possible because he has not yet learned to view things only within a given context. As the child grows older and learns to do so, however, he loses this ability.

Actually, to present a photograph that will be seen in its natural or proper perspective is not difficult. Fifteen inches has been established as the universal viewing distance since most people tend to hold photographs and reading material at approximately that distance. Any photograph which will be shown to a jury will be viewed by each member from a distance of about fifteen inches; the negative should be enlarged accordingly. To establish how much enlargement will provide proper perspective, divide the viewing distance which, as stated, in fifteen inches, by the focal length of the lens. For example, if a photograph is taken using a two-inch lens, the proper degree of enlargement of the negative is $7\frac{1}{2}$ times, since fifteen divided by two equals $7\frac{1}{2}$. If a photograph was taken using a telephoto lens, however, it will be impossible to prepare a print that will be properly viewed according to distance and size. Furthermore, when preparing photographs of flat subject matter such as fingerprints, footprints, tire impressions and so forth, no attention need be given to proper degree of enlargement for proper angular perspective because there is none.

Finally, as was stated in the preceding section, crime scene photographs should be taken from a normal eye level, keeping the back of the camera (film plane) parallel to the walls in order to avoid lines that are not parallel and natural. If difficulty in this respect is experienced, a small level may be helpful. One should be especially careful in this way when photographing stairways, inclines or declines.

Commercial Photo Lab Services and Affidavits

In situations where the services of a commercial laboratory are utilized for the processing of photographic film, it is desirable to obtain from the laboratory an affidavit showing who received the film, who supervised its processing and, in general, who can account for the materials from the time they were received at the laboratory until they were picked up. If the laboratory in question provides no affidavit form for this purpose, one can be drawn up by the photographer himself. The affidavit form shown in Figure 17-3 is that used by Sly-Fox Films, Inc. The form shown in Figure 17-4 is that used by Kodak. While the two forms are different in their format and wording, they both say basically the same thing.

Legal Aspects of Investigative Photography

This book, dealing with police and fire photography, or simply stated, investigative photography, raises the question of whether various legal issues should be discussed. At the risk of being guilty of omission, the authors have decided that because the legal requirements for the admissibility of photographic evidence into court will vary somewhat by jurisdiction, and will also vary with time, a chapter on the legality of photographic evidence would not be included. Only a few passing thoughts would be included. Indeed, that topic would justify a book devoted specifically to that topic. The reader is encouraged to consult a department's legal council, or the prosecuting office, relative to such concerns. But, the one major concern relative to fire and crime scene photography that does not seem to vary by jurisdiction is whether the photographs introduced into evidence accurately portray the scene as viewed by the investigator. And chain-of-evidence must remain intact.

AFFIDAVIT

STATE OF MINNESOTA)
) ss.
COUNTY OF HENNEPIN)

I, _____ , having been duly sworn, on oath depose and say that I am the _____ of Sly-Fox Films, Inc., 1025 Currie Avenue, Minneapolis, Minnesota 55403.

That on the _____ day of _____ , 19__, at _____ o'clock

M. I received from _____ at the office of Sly-Fox Films, Inc., as shown above,

of film for development or printing.

That the films in the said containers were processed under my supervision and control and they were processed in the normal and customary manner for development of film of the particular type.

That these films were not cut, edited, changed, negatives were not reversed, superimposed by other film, retouched, over or under developed or was other thing done which could alter or change the film in any manner or what the film attempts to portray.

That after processing the films and/or prints were returned to _____ at _____ o'clock _____ M. on the _____ day of _____ , 19_____.

_____

Subscribed and sworn before me this _____ day of _____ , 19_____.

_____

Figure 17-3. **Affidavit form used by Sly-Fox Films, Inc., in Minneapolis, Minnesota.** (Courtesy of Sly-Fox Films, Inc.)

AFFIDAVIT OF KODAK PROCESSING LABORATORY

State of Illinois :
: SS
County of Cook :

John M. Kogler, being duly sworn deposes and says that he is employed by the Color Print and Processing Services Division of Eastman Kodak Company, 1712 S. Prairie Avenue, Chicago, Illinois 60616.

That his division received on November 14, 1974, one C135-20 Film from Pako Photo, 9 West 14th Street, Minneapolis, Minnesota 55403 under Envelope 9834.

That the film was developed and printed. That the film was not mutilated or altered in any way except for the standard procedure of printing and cutting to size. That while the film was in the possession of Eastman Kodak Company it was not shown to any person other than employees of said laboratory of known integrity in the ordinary course of handling the same.

And that the original film, prints and this affidavit were returned under KODAK seal to Pako Photo for Marshall Police Department.

John M Kogler

Sworn to before me this
18th day of November, 1974

William E. Gray
Notary Public

Figure 17-4. **Affidavit form used by Kodak Processing Laboratory.** (Courtesy of Eastman Kodak Company.)

INDEX